S0-BSM-622

WITHDRAWN

MARSH'S DINOSAURS

The Collections from Como Bluff

Frontispiece. Como Bluff, site of Yale's famous Jurassic dinosaur and mammal quarries which were worked from 1877 to 1889, as painted by Arthur Lakes during the height of excavating activities. The view is looking south at the main bluff and the principal exposures of the *"Atlantosaurus* Beds" or Morrison formation, the strata that produced most of the Como Bluff fossils. The "Indian Fort" is atop the low mound on the far left horizon. The famous Mammal Quarry (No. 9) and the *"Brontosaurus"* Quarry (No. 10) are to the immediate right of the "Indian Fort." Big Canyon Quarry (No. 1A) lies in the prominent ravine directly behind Como Station on the far side of Lake Como, and the Three Trees Quarry (No. 7) is at the right end of the main bluff. Elk Mountain is on the distant horizon at the right. Upon his arrival here, Samuel Williston wrote Professor Marsh that this locale was far superior to Morrison and Garden Park and that the bones were "magnificently preserved and scattered for six or seven miles."

MARSH'S DINOSAURS

THE COLLECTIONS FROM COMO BLUFF

---

by

JOHN H. OSTROM

and

JOHN S. McINTOSH

New Haven and London, Yale University Press, 1966

Copyright © 1966 by Yale University.
Designed by John O. C. McCrillis,
set in Garamond type,
and printed in the United States of America by
the Carl Purington Rollins Printing-Office of
the Yale University Press, New Haven, Connecticut.
Distributed in Canada by McGill University Press.
All rights reserved. This book may not be
reproduced, in whole or in part, in any form
(except by reviewers for the public press),
without written permission from the publishers.

Library of Congress catalog card number: 66–23762

568.19
057m

O
QE
862
.D5
0817

QE 862.
D5
0817

PREFACE

Publication in 1859 of *The Origin of Species* stands as one of the great moments in the history of science; it marks the beginning of the era of modern biology. A comparable moment in the history of paleontology occurred in 1877. The discoveries in the spring of that year at an obscure little hill called Como Bluff in southeastern Wyoming, probably had greater impact on the study of paleontology than any other event save publication of Darwin's theory. The finds at Como Bluff revolutionized field and collecting procedures, generated a startling growth in paleontologic studies, stimulated great public interest, and left a permanent mark on the major museums of the world. For the next sixty years paleontologic expeditions were planned and undertaken with the fervent hope that another "Como Bluff" might be discovered.

Como Bluff was the site of one of the greatest assemblages of giant and small dinosaurs and of minute and extremely precious Jurassic mammals ever to be found. These collections now form the prized nuclei of the world-famous paleontologic collections in Yale's Peabody Museum and the National Museum in Washington, D.C.

Publication of this volume on Marsh's finds at Como marks the occasion of the Centennial Celebration of the Peabody Museum of Natural History, Yale University. Although the subject matter represents only one of many scholarly disciplines pursued within the Peabody Museum, the previously unpublished lithographs of Como dinosaurs represent a particularly appropriate tribute to George Peabody and Othniel Charles Marsh, the two men who, more than any other individuals, were responsible for the founding and rapid growth of this institution into a renowned research center in the natural sciences.

O. C. Marsh received much of his education at Yale, largely through the generosity of his uncle, George Peabody; he was graduated from Yale College in the class of 1860 and from the Sheffield Scientific School in 1862. From Yale, Marsh went to Europe for further study, returning in the fall of 1865 to assume a professorship of paleontology in Yale College. This appointment, approved by the Corporation on July 24, 1866, was the first such post in the New World. The following October, George Peabody presented his gift of $150,000 for "the foundation and maintenance of a Museum of Natural History, especially for the departments of Zoology, Geology and Mineralogy, in connection with Yale College." The first trustees were Professors Benjamin Silliman, Sr., James Dwight Dana, O. C. Marsh, and Senator James Dixon.

During the years that followed, until Peabody's death in 1869 and that of Marsh in 1899, George Peabody and O. C. Marsh were the dominant figures behind the planning and development of the new Peabody Museum. Peabody's great fortune not only provided Marsh with his education and Yale College with its first museum building—it also provided Marsh's salary and considerable funds for paleontologic, zoologic, and mineralogic collecting and research. Between 1868 and 1882, when he was appointed Vertebrate Paleontologist of the United States Geological Survey, Marsh expended some $200,000 of his own resources in exploration for and collection of fossils. Included among these were nearly all of the great sauropods and stegosaurs collected by Yale parties from Cañon City and Morrison, Colorado, and Como Bluff, Wyoming. This volume illustrates a fraction of the Como finds. The sauropod and stegosaur specimens that are so superbly illustrated in the lithographs are the direct result of the generosity of George Peabody and the industry and scientific genius of Professor Marsh.

The one hundred and fifty lithographs published here were originally intended to be part of monographic studies by Marsh of the sauropod and stegosaurian dinosaurs. They were prepared under Marsh's direction by illustrator F. Berger and lithographer E. Crisand, and financed by the United States Geological Survey; their total cost of preparation during the 1880s exceeded $45,000. Only a few have been previously published, chiefly in Marsh's *Dinosaurs of North America*. The majority are published here for the first time by permission of the Director of the United States Geological Survey and the Director of the Peabody Museum of Natural History, to commemorate the founding of the Peabody Museum.

The authors are indebted to Dr. E. H. Colbert of the American Museum of Natural History and to Drs. C. L. Gazin, D. H. Dunkle, and N. Hotton III of the United States National Museum for providing data pertaining to Como Bluff specimens in their care.

J. H. O.
J. S. M.

New Haven, Connecticut
January 1966

ABBREVIATIONS

Institutions referred to throughout this volume are abbreviated as follows:

AMNH	American Museum of Natural History
CM	Carnegie Museum
USNM	United States National Museum
YPM	Yale Peabody Museum of Natural History

CONTENTS

TEXT FIGURES

LIST OF PLATES

SAUROPODA

STEGOSAURIA

A HISTORICAL SKETCH OF COMO BLUFF

INTRODUCTION

In a very real sense, a rather ordinary looking locale in southern Wyoming, commonly known as Como Bluff, had an extraordinary influence on the development, both philosophical and architectural, of many of the great museums of the New World, and probably on the principal museums in Europe as well. Short of the original gift by George Peabody to Yale College in 1866, it would be difficult to cite a more significant event in the hundred years of Peabody Museum's history than the discovery of this particular ridge. Como Bluff was the site of the first major discovery of dinosaur remains anywhere in the world. From this place were collected many of the fine skeletons now displayed in the Peabody Museum at Yale, the National Museum of the Smithsonian Institution in Washington, D.C., and the American Museum of Natural History in New York. Discoveries by Yale parties at Como Bluff during the late 1870s and 1880s precipitated a number of expeditions by the Philadelphia Academy of Sciences, Harvard College, the American Museum of Natural History, the Carnegie Museum in Pittsburgh, the University of Wyoming, the Royal Ontario Museum in Toronto, and the National Museum of Canada at Ottawa, all in search of comparable specimens for display in their public galleries. Today, there is scarcely a major museum of natural science in the New World—or anywhere else—that does not count at least one dinosaur among its prize exhibits. And there is little dispute about the great public appeal of such displays.

By the 1900s it was fashionable to design museum buildings around the prospect or specific plan that such structures would in due time shelter an assortment of giant saurians of past eras. And it was not long before there was a brisk trade in dinosaur skeletons to many of the smaller museums being founded all over North America and to many of the well-established and famous museums of Europe. Dinosaur skeletons became status symbols and soon every museum had to have its own; today they are still very much in fashion. All of this can be attributed directly to Como Bluff and the great variety, the unbelievable numbers, and the exceptional preservation of dinosaurian skeletons uncovered there. Never before had such spectacular fossil remains been found.

Fossil bones of large extinct reptiles had been known from several localities in England and western Europe for fifty years or more prior to the discoveries at Como Bluff. Fragmentary dinosaur remains had also been collected in central Montana by the Hayden Surveys more than twenty years before, and a moderately complete skeleton of an advanced ornithischian dinosaur (*Hadrosaurus foulkii*) had been excavated in southern New Jersey during 1858 and placed on public display some ten years later at the Philadelphia Academy of Sciences. Thus the Como discoveries were not the earliest even in North America, but they were the first of truly spectacular magnitude, and they were the first complete or near-complete dinosaurian skeletons of a variety of kinds that were suitable for free-mount display.

Stimulated by the amazing abundance and preservation of fossil animals at Como Bluff, other institutions sought and soon discovered other similar caches of ancient saurian trophies. Notable among these were the Bone Cabin locality, discovered a few years later in the nearby Medicine Anticline to the north, which was worked by the American Museum, the Dinosaur National Monument site discovered by the Carnegie Museum near Vernal, Utah, the fabulous Red Deer River region of central Alberta, and the Lance Creek area of eastern Wyoming. Abroad, there were the spectacular discoveries in Bernissart, Belgium, in 1878, those of German expeditions to East Africa in 1910, and the discoveries in Mongolia by the American Museum expeditions of the 1920s. The impact of Como Bluff was long-lasting and far-reaching.

PREVIEW TO COMO BLUFF

In early April of 1877, Professor O. C. Marsh, trustee and paleontologist of the newly completed Yale College Museum, received a letter from Professor Arthur Lakes, a Colorado schoolmaster and part-time collector and geologist, about his discovery of giant bones in the sandstone hogbacks near Denver, Colorado. Lakes wrote:

> A few days ago whilst taking a geological section and measurements and examining the rocks on the banks of Bear Creek near the little town of Morrison about 15 miles west of Denver, I discovered in company with a friend a Mr. Beckwith of Connecticut some enormous bones apparently a vertebra and a humerus bone of some gigantic saurian in the upper Jurassic or lower Cretaceous at the base of (Hayden's) Cret. No. 1 Dakotah group.

Enclosed with this announcement were two small sketches of the bones and a rather detailed cross-sectional diagram of the Mesozoic hogbacks in the vicinity of Morrison, showing the approximate stratigraphic position where the bones were discovered. Several days later, two additional larger drawings of the same bones were received by Marsh. These should have removed any doubts about the nature of Lakes' find but, in spite of the evidence of the drawings and the

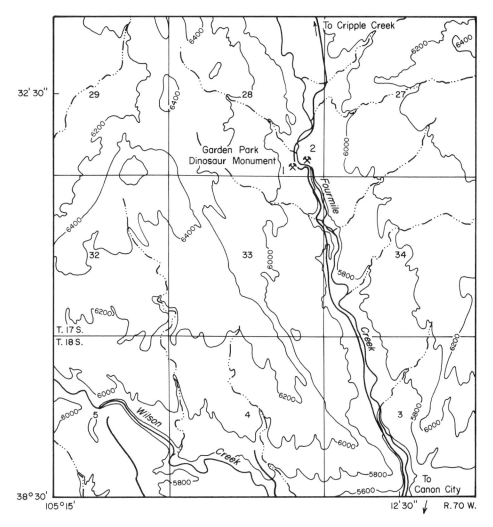

32' 30"   29

28   To Cripple Creek

27

Garden Park
Dinosaur Monument

2

1

32

33

34

T. 17 S.
T. 18 S.

5

Wilson

4

3

Creek

To
Canon City

38° 30'
105° 15'   12' 30" ↓   R. 70 W.

YALE FOSSIL VERTEBRATE LOCALITIES, GARDEN PARK, COLORADO
1877 - 1879

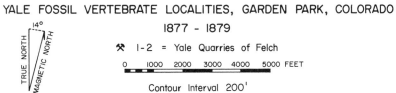

TRUE NORTH / MAGNETIC NORTH   14°

⚒ 1-2 = Yale Quarries of Felch

0   1000   2000   3000   4000   5000 FEET

Contour Interval 200'

Fig. 1. Map of the Garden Park (Cañon City), Colorado, region and the Yale fossil vertebrate localities.

fact that such bones would represent some of the first such fossil remains to be
found in this part of the Mesozoic section of North America, Marsh seems to have
had only a passing interest in the new discoveries. A fourth letter from Lakes
dated April 26, 1877, reported additional discoveries of other "colossal" bones
of "no less than six different animals if not different species."

In this letter, Lakes indicated that he was prepared to ship a total of ten boxes
of these gigantic bones (they were in fact already packed) weighing about 1,500
pounds (they actually weighed more than 2,100 pounds) to Marsh as soon as he
received such instructions. After several weeks with no response of any kind
from New Haven, Lakes dispatched the specimens to Marsh for identification.
But, not confident that a response from Marsh would be forthcoming, Lakes
wrote to Professor E. D. Cope, paleontologist and naturalist at the Philadelphia
Academy of Sciences, about his discoveries near Morrison. He followed this up
by shipping some of the specimens to Cope. In late June, only a few days after
the arrival of Lakes' ten boxes of bones, Marsh learned of the correspondence
between Lakes and Professor Cope and decided that the Morrison region should
be investigated and evaluated more thoroughly, whereupon he wired to his chief
collector Benjamin Mudge, who was then in Kansas collecting from the Niobrara
chalk, to proceed directly to Morrison and take charge of the operations there.
The first published announcement of Lakes' finds appeared a few weeks later in
the July 1 issue of the *American Journal of Science*.[1]

Almost precisely at this same time O. W. Lucas, an amateur naturalist and
coincidentally also a schoolmaster, was making similar discoveries of large fossil
bones some hundred miles to the south near Cañon City, Colorado. Like
Lakes, Lucas marveled at the incredible size of the fossil vertebrae he had found
and rushed off an inquiry, together with several specimens, to Professor Cope at
Philadelphia. Of course it was not long before word of the Cañon City finds
reached Professor Marsh in New Haven, and as soon as Marsh realized that "rival
parties" were onto something new, he once again wired to Mudge—this time
instructing him to leave Morrison at once for Cañon City to investigate the
situation there. Mudge's reports in August 1877 indicated that Cope's collectors
were obtaining excellent material at very cheap cost and many of the bones were
considerably larger than those discovered by Arthur Lakes at Morrison. Mudge's
reports decided the matter for Marsh, and he ordered Mudge to initiate operations
at Cañon City (actually Garden Park, several miles north of Cañon City). In
early September, after further examination of the prospects in the Garden Park
area, Mudge requested that Samuel Williston be brought from Kansas to take
charge of the excavations. Within a few weeks after Williston's arrival, however,

1. O. C. Marsh, "Notice of a new and gigantic dinosaur," *14* (July 1, 1877), 87–88.

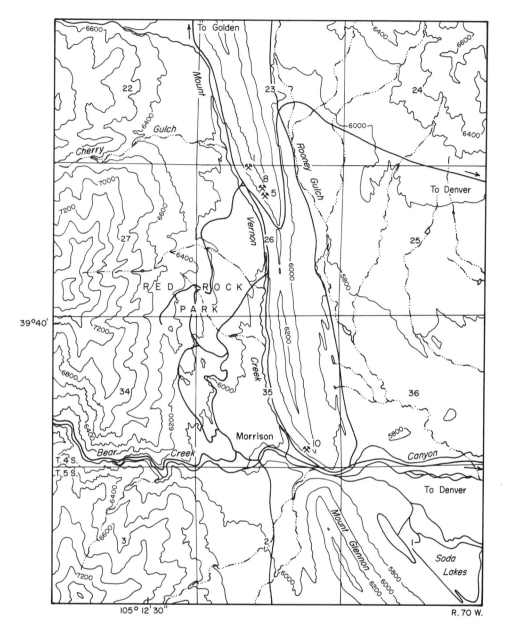

To Golden

22

23

24

6600

6400

Cherry

Gulch

Rooney Gulch

To Denver

6000

8
5

7000

7200

7200

6600

27

Vernon

26

25

6400

6000

5800

RED ROCK

PARK

39°40'

7200

6200

Creek

6800

34

35

36

6600

6400

6200

Morrison

5800

10

Bear

Creek

Canyon

T. 4 S.

T. 5 S.

To Denver

6400

Mount Glennon

3

2

Soda Lakes

6600

6000

5800

6200

7200

6000

105° 12' 30"

R. 70 W.

YALE FOSSIL VERTEBRATE LOCALITIES, MORRISON, COLORADO

1877 - 1879

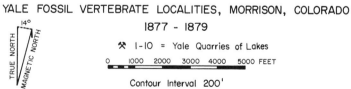

⚒ 1-10 = Yale Quarries of Lakes

0   1000   2000   3000   4000   5000 FEET

Contour Interval 200'

14°

TRUE NORTH

MAGNETIC NORTH

Fig. 2. Map of the Morrison, Colorado, area and the Yale fossil vertebrate localities.

Marsh decided to abandon the Yale quarries at Garden Park, apparently because of Williston's report that Cope was getting the best of the material and there appeared to be little prospect of obtaining the services of Lucas and his brother. Marsh ordered his collectors to return and concentrate their efforts on the operations at Morrison. At Marsh's instruction, Williston left Garden Park and joined Arthur Lakes at Morrison while Mudge departed for the east. Lakes had been excavating and collecting in a series of quarries north of Morrison (see Fig. 2) throughout the summer of 1877, shipping large quantities of fossil bones back to Yale College. However, operations came to a sudden but temporary halt at Morrison after a huge rockfall late in October nearly killed the entire party at work in the main quarry.

The six-month interval from early April to late September of 1877 had revealed to the rival camps at New Haven and Philadelphia the unsuspected existence of fossil remains of giant reptiles of unprecedented size. Initial skepticism on both sides was quickly offset by knowledge that the other party was deeply involved. Both camps then intensified their efforts and, within the span of two months, and less than five months after the original discovery, both Marsh and Cope had published announcements of the discovery of gigantic ancient reptiles.[2] Into this atmosphere of intense competition for new discoveries of dinosaurian remains came word of Como Bluff and its spectacular treasures.

DISCOVERY OF COMO BLUFF (1877)

In late July 1877, while Benjamin Mudge and Arthur Lakes were collecting at Morrison, Colorado, Professor Marsh received the now famous letter[3] from "Harlow and Edwards" of Laramie, reporting their discovery of large fossil bones in Wyoming Territory. Their letter read:

UNION PACIFIC RAILROAD COMPANY
AGENT'S OFFICE, LARAMIE STATION

July 19, 1877

Prof. C. Marsh, Geologist.
Yale College.

Dear Sir:

I write to announce to you the discovery not far from this place, of a large number of fossils, supposed to be those of the Megatherium, although

---

2. O. C. Marsh, "Notice of a new and gigantic dinosaur," *Amer. Jour. Sci., 14* (July 1, 1877), 87–88. E. D. Cope, "On a gigantic saurian from the Dakota epoch of Colorado," *Paleont. Bull. No. 25* (Aug. 23, 1877), pp. 5–10.

3. Charles Schuchert and C. M. LeVene, *O. C. Marsh, Pioneer in paleontology*, p. 196.

there is no one here sufficient of a geologist to state for a certainty. We have excavated one (1) partly, and know where there is several others that we have not, as yet, done any work upon. The formation in which they are found is that of the Tertiary Period.

We are desirous of disposing of what fossils we have, and also, the secret of the others. We are working men and are not able to present them as a gift, and if we can sell the secret of the fossil bed, and procure work in excavating others we would like to do so.

We have said nothing to any-one as yet.

We measured one shoulder blade and found it to measure four feet eight inches 4 ft. 8 in. in length.

One joint of the vertebrae measures two feet and one half 2½ in circumference and ten inches (10) in length

As a proof of our sincerity and truth, we will send you a few fossils, at what they cost us in time and money in unearthing.

We would be pleased to hear from you, as you are well known as an enthusiastic geologist, and a man of means, both of which we are desirous of finding—more especially the latter.

Hoping to hear from you very soon, before the snows of winter set in,

We remain,

Very respectfully

Your Obedient Servants

[Signed] Harlow and Edwards

Although the letter from "Harlow and Edwards" was mailed from Laramie to conceal the location of their find, the discovery was of course at Como Bluff, a prominent ridge near Como Station on the Union Pacific Railroad, a place where, coincidentally, Marsh had stopped briefly nearly ten years earlier. In fact, Williston has reported that one of these men had shown a dinosaur bone to Marsh on that first visit in 1868, but it apparently made no impression on him at the time. Upon receipt of this letter, Marsh may have been misled by Harlow and Edwards' reference to the horizon as being of Tertiary age, and thus of no interest to him in his quest of giant reptiles. Yet he apparently did urge them to ship the bones they had collected.

As of the middle of August, however, the shipment had not been sent, but Harlow and Edwards indicated in a letter of August 16th that it would leave Como Station about the 20th or 21st. For some reason that is not clear, the shipment was not dispatched until the 17th of September, nearly two months after the original letter to Marsh. The long delay probably occurred because

Harlow and Edwards did not have sufficient funds to cover the freight charges ($26.95, an amount equal to about half a month's wages), or because they expected payment in advance.

In mid-October, Marsh finally received the two boxes, which contained twelve or thirteen vertebrae, "pieces of teeth and claws and a few other specimens of petrifications and stone," "two leg bones" (two femora, one of which was later described by Marsh as the type of *Apatosaurus grandis*), pieces of "shoulder blade" (a left humerus), and part of a large vertebra. Preceding this shipment was another letter from Harlow and Edwards reporting that they had excavated an additional 1,500 pounds of bones of all shapes and sizes:

> Besides this, we have discovered the bed of two more animals which we judge to be of the same kind. But, which we have not done any work upon yet, and shall not until we hear from you and learn whether they will pay us for the labor and time which will be necessary to get them out in good shape.

Upon receipt of this letter and the two boxes of specimens, Marsh lost no time in replying by telegraph: "Bones came today. Send rest with all small pieces."

He then wrote a long letter with complete, detailed instructions and a series of questions about the locations and associations of the various bones. He also included a check for $75 payable to "Harlow and Edwards" which, for reasons that will become obvious later, could not be cashed. The responses to his questions about the specimens and their associations apparently satisfied Marsh that this new locality was indeed a valuable discovery that should be investigated at once. But it took the next communication from Harlow and Edwards to stir Marsh to immediate action.

> We are keeping our shipments of fossils to you as secret as possible as there are plenty of men looking for such things and if they could trace us they could find discoveries which we have already made and which we do not desire to have known.

Upon receiving this disturbing warning, Marsh wired to Samuel Williston at Morrison to leave immediately for Como, Wyoming. Marsh assumed that Williston was still at the Morrison quarries, but Williston, suffering from poor health, had left a few days before for his home in Manhattan, Kansas, shortly after the big rockfall in the main quarry. Consequently, Williston did not learn of the Como discovery until November 7th and thus was unable to reach Como

Station until the 14th. Williston acknowledged Marsh's instructions to go to Como:

> It is impossible almost to keep my movements here unknown so that I shall give it out that I am going from here to Oregon! and nobody will know where I am.

The first significant indication of the importance and magnitude of the discoveries of Harlow and Edwards reached Marsh in a letter from Williston dated November 14, 1877, apparently written just hours after his arrival at Como Station. It is not difficult to visualize Marsh's elation and anxiety as he read:

Dear Professor:

I arrived here a few hours ago and on the same train found your letter with the $75. I found Messrs. "Harlow and ~~Reed~~ Edwards" (~~Collins~~ Reed and Collins). Mr. Collins is the station agent and Mr. Reed the section foreman. They used those names to conceal their identity with the fossils and you had better address them thus still. They have so far succeeded in keeping the matter very quiet, although it is going to be hard to still contrive it. I have seen a lot of bones that they have ready to ship and they tell me the bones extend for *seven* miles and are by the ton. . . . I go out in the morning to find out all I can and will write you tomorrow.

Very truly yours
[Signed] S. W. Williston

Marsh's anxiety and impatience for "tomorrow" were cheap prices indeed for the letter that followed:

November 16, 1877

Dear Professor:

I have gotten everything ready to go to work tomorrow on the bones and will send them fast. . . . Will have to employ Carlin (not Collins) and Reed probably at $75 but they prefer to leave that open till Carlin sees you at N.H. . . . There will be great danger next summer of competition. At present but *seven* persons here have seen or know about the fossils but it will be almost absolutely impossible to prevent others to know in the spring. Cañon City and Morrison are simply nowhere in comparison with this locality both as regards perfection, accessibility and quantity.[4] . . . [The

4. Subsequent work by M. P. Felch at Cañon City (Garden Park) proved this judgment to be premature. Felch worked Quarry 1, Garden Park, for five years and others worked it subsequently. The total yield of this quarry rivaled any single quarry at Como and included most of Marsh's Jurassic dinosaur skulls.

bones are] magnificently preserved and scattered for 6 or seven miles. The shales are clean and exposed and it will be the grandest place immaginable to hunt for small specimens. . . .

Very truly yours
[Signed] S. W. Williston

Thus was Como Bluff and its unbelievable treasures discovered—amidst the furor and controversy over George Custer and the Battle of the Little Big Horn —barely eleven years after the founding of Yale College Museum.

The Early Years (1877–1879)

Williston's first letter from Como evoked an immediate reaction from Professor Marsh. Among the rare preserved letters written by Marsh is the original agreement in Marsh's own handwriting between him and Carlin and Reed dated November 17, 1877—only three days after Williston had arrived at Como! As a matter of fact, it appears that Williston thought the situation at Como was so urgent that he wired Marsh, urging him to draw up an agreement as soon as possible. Although no record of any such telegram exists today, it is quite evident that Williston was in close contact with Marsh, for the agreement drawn up, ostensibly on November 17th, named William E. Carlin and William H. Reed as "parties of the first part." At that time, Williston was the only person other than Carlin and Reed themselves who knew that they, and not "Harlow and Edwards," were the parties involved. Furthermore, none of Williston's letters from Como, prior to November 17th, mentioned either Reed's or Carlin's first name. Thus it is clear that Williston must have communicated by telegraph the urgent necessity of drawing up such a contract of employment with the discoverers of the Como bone fields.

Although this is highly speculative, in view of the skeptical, even pessimistic, tone of many of Samuel Williston's letters, it seems not unlikely that he feared Carlin and Reed might be lured away by other parties. He had already warned Marsh that it would be virtually impossible to keep the secret of Como much longer. Whatever the details and reasons, Marsh promptly attempted to contract that Carlin and Reed:

> work for Prof. Marsh for one year from date collecting and shipping vertebrate fossils in the region around Como, Wyoming and vicinity, to take all reasonable precautions to keep all other collectors not authorized by Prof. Marsh out of the region and to use their best efforts in every way to promote Prof. Marsh's interests for the sum of ninety dollars per month each.

To

In this contract Marsh anticipated the prospect that Reed and Carlin might refuse to sign if there was any likelihood that they would be overseen or supervised by any of Marsh's professional collectors. Consequently, he included a provision whereby he had the privilege of keeping one or more "superintendents" on the scene to direct the work. Carlin and Reed did object, but apparently both men finally accepted these terms and signed the agreement. In the years that followed, the presence first of "superintendent Williston" and later, more particularly, of Arthur Lakes, was the source of much friction and ill will.

About a week after the agreement had been drawn up by Marsh, the first progress report by Harlow and Edwards was received. Included with it was the very first (and very crude) quarry sketch from Como Bluff. It proved to be the first of hundreds, most of which are preserved in the archives of the Peabody Museum at Yale or at the National Museum of the Smithsonian Institution in Washington. The site sketched was to become known as Quarry 1, the first of perhaps a hundred or more excavations opened by various parties at Como Bluff during the next decade. This quarry was in the southwest quarter of Section 10 approximately one and a quarter miles east and south of Como Station (see Fig. 3, map of the Como Bluff region). An excavation believed to have been Quarry 1 was relocated in this area by a Peabody Museum field party in 1965. Reed and Carlin opened Quarry 1 before April 1877—perhaps as early as the summer of 1868—but the precise date is not recorded.

During the summer of 1877, before Yale College was involved, Reed and Carlin removed many tons of rock and collected several thousand pounds of fossil bones. When Williston arrived in November, he was startled at the quantity of fossil bones that had already been removed and were ready to be packed and shipped to New Haven. At that point, a systematic program of quarrying and collecting was established, and during the next seven months an orderly and continuous stream of materials flowed from this site to Marsh's laboratory at Yale. With winter hard upon them, and several severe snowstorms already behind them, Williston quite naturally was anxious to unearth the fossils as rapidly as possible. He had Reed and Carlin erect a large tent over the quarry so the work area would be protected from snow and the three men would be able to work except during the worst storms. As quarry work was extended, the tent was moved along the quarry floor to cover the new areas. This provided some protection for the men against the cold and the near-hurricane winds that are so typical of the Como area, but as the winter of 1877–78 progressed, the elements increasingly interfered with the excavations. At times it was impossible for the men even to reach the quarry site from their quarters at Como Station because of high winds or blizzards.

The desires of Carlin and Reed to be employed, but independent, soon led to difficulties. Although they appreciated the instructions and tutoring of Williston regarding quarrying procedures, record-keeping, and packing techniques, they clearly resented his role of supervisor. Marsh's attempts to guarantee their services at Como met with complete failure until his meeting in New Haven with Carlin during January 1878. Williston, meanwhile, continued to push the excavations in Quarry 1, probably with appropriate complaints from Reed. Williston also devoted much time to careful exploration of the exposures along the north slope of Como Bluff. One of the earliest discoveries was noted in his letter of November 24th, ten days after his arrival. He wrote Marsh that he was shipping portions of a small saurian, the vertebrae of which were less than an inch long, that he had discovered approximately two miles east of Quarry 1. This may be the first fossil material from the area that ultimately was to become the site of the most famous fossil quarry in the world—Quarry 9—still the most important site of Jurassic mammals in the New World. The small saurian specimen became the type of *Laosaurus gracilis* (YPM 1875), a small bipedal ornithischian dinosaur. Considerable difficulty was encountered in salvaging this specimen because of heavy snows, as noted by Williston in letters posted November 30th and later:

> The small saurian I have not yet sent and cannot for a few days till the snow blows off so that *we can find it.*

By this time, Carlin had departed on his business trip to Michigan and Washington, D.C., and ultimately New Haven, where he conferred with Marsh. Reed and Williston continued the excavation at Quarry 1 and in spite of severe weather succeeded in removing numerous bones. Most of the bones proved to be of at least four different sauropod skeletons that were so badly intermingled that they could not be separated with absolute certainty even in the quarry. These remains included the types of *Morosaurus impar* (YPM 1900), *Apatosaurus grandis* (YPM 1901), and *Morosaurus robustus* (YPM 1902)—all of which by modern standards probably are assignable to *Camarasaurus grandis.* Fragmentary remains of a juvenile sauropod were also recovered from Quarry 1. Marsh designated the latter as the type of another new species, *Pleurocoelus montanus* (YPM 1908).

As mid-December and winter arrived, shipments of fossils from Como began to arrive in New Haven at frequent and regular intervals. Williston and Reed were uncovering great quantities of bone and the world must have seemed bright and beautiful to Professor Marsh. Como appeared to be a source of almost unlimited new material. Then Marsh received the first disquieting note from Como via Williston's letter of December 9th:

> I am sorry to say that Cope knows of this locality and the general nature
> of the fossils. A miner found some vertebrae here last spring and wrote to

the Smithsonian describing them. Baird [Secretary of the Smithsonian] sent the letter to Cope and both replied. He (Brown the miner) was here last week and I read Cope's letter who seemed very anxious to get "some teeth" or "joints of the back bones"!

No positive evidence has been turned up as yet to verify this, but there are indications[5] that the "miner Brown" may have been Fred Brown, later one of Marsh's most trusted and effective collectors, who supervised Marsh's collecting program in the Como area from 1885 to 1889.

This depressing news arrived in New Haven about the time that Marsh and Carlin were preparing to meet. There can be little doubt that Williston's letter was a major factor in Marsh's mind as he and Carlin argued and haggled, first by telegraph and correspondence and then face to face, over the details of the contract between Reed and Carlin and himself. It may be that Carlin was quite aware of Cope's knowledge of the Como discoveries—either directly from Brown's first visit the preceding spring or by telegram from Reed. Whether he was or not, the immediate threat of Cope's collectors descending on Como surely lessened Marsh's bargaining power and resulted in quick agreement on terms that seem to have been dictated largely by Carlin.

But before agreement was reached between Marsh and Carlin, another setback occurred. Samuel Williston, who had never been particularly healthy, fell very ill and decided to leave Como for his home in Kansas. This left Reed, a man Marsh had never set eyes upon, and a hired man (Vincent) entirely responsible for Marsh's interests at Como. Before he left, Williston tried to assure Marsh of Reed's abilities and integrity and of the value of Reed's extensive knowledge of the region. Nevertheless, late December and early January must have been depressing times for Marsh. His greatest discovery to date was at that moment in the hands of men he did not know and had never even met.

Reed and his helper Vincent continued to work Quarry 1 after Williston's departure, recovering more of the original four skeletons plus fragments of *Diplodocus* and a large carnivorous saurian. The latter became the type of *Creosaurus atrox* (=*Antrodemus*) (YPM 1890). Late in January 1878, Reed wrote Marsh of the completion of Quarry 1 and that a new quarry had been opened three quarters of a mile west of it. This was to become known as Quarry 2, a lesser site that was worked almost exclusively by Reed alone until early in February when it was abandoned. (Reed actually reopened it briefly during December 1880, but nothing new was found.) Parts of a large but very poorly preserved

5. See correspondence of Fred Brown to Prof. Marsh dated Nov. 30, 1883. In this letter, Fred Brown claims it was he who informed the Smithsonian Institution.

skeleton, probably of *Apatosaurus,* were the only fossil remains to be collected from this site before work was shifted to Quarry 3.

The new quarry, No. 3, which was located more than a mile east of Quarry 1 and about three miles east of Como Station, proved to be a very rich site. Excavation was carried on here intermittently until the summer of 1879 by Reed, Carlin, Frank and Samuel Williston, and Arthur Lakes. Shortly after Reed initiated work here, Carlin returned from his trip east, but indications are that he was very lazy and contributed little effort in the quarry. Reed seems to have done most of the work in Quarry 3 and, during the early stages of its excavation, he wrote to Marsh almost daily about the progress and the latest bones unearthed. He succeeded in removing portions of a number of young sauropod skeletons, all of which probably are assignable to *Camarasaurus.* At least five or six individuals were represented. In addition, several individuals of carnivorous dinosaurs were found, including the type of *Labrosaurus lucaris* (=*Antrodemus*) (YPM 1931), as well as another specimen of *Laosaurus.*

Although it is not specifically identified as such until much later, Quarry 4 seems to have been discovered about the middle of March 1878. In a letter dated the 18th, Reed reports that they were still prospecting and had found lots of beds of small bones, but until that day had found no large bones worth shipping. Reed notes that there were large vertebrae that were different from any he had seen before and that this quarry was farther from the station than any of the previous ones. Unless the site described here was an unsuccessful locality that was abandoned as soon as it was opened (there evidently were many unsuccessful excavations all over the Como area that were never reported or assigned specific designations), Reed's comments must refer to Quarry 4. This quarry was being mentioned regularly in correspondence of the next month. It was more than five miles east of the station on the opposite side of Rock Creek in Section 6 of Township 22 north and Range 76 west. Reed wrote to Williston in mid-March exclaiming about his new find:

> I have had the worst time finding a good quary that a man ever had but now I wish you wer here to see the bones roll out and they are beauties to I think this quary eaqual no. 1 for good bones and quanity it outcrops for X80 feet length there is more than one animal it would astonish you to see the holes we have dug since we left no. 3. I think I took up ten ton of bones.

Quarry 4 did indeed prove equal to No. 1 in diversity, but not in quantity, of fossil specimens. From mid-March until late May of 1878, and again during February of the following year, Quarry 4 produced large portions of skeletons of *Diplodocus, Apatosaurus,* and *Camarasaurus,* plus some *Barosaurus* material,

Fig. 4. Como Bluff as seen looking almost due west from the site of the old "Indian Fort." In the lowland to the right (north) of the bluff are Lake Como (now Aurora Lake), Como Station, and the former tracks of the Union Pacific Railroad. The famous Mammal Quarry (No. 9) and the *"Brontosaurus"* Quarry (No. 10) are in the low section of the ridge just behind and to the left of the figure (William Reed) standing in the Indian rifle pit. Elk Mountain is on the horizon to the left and the Freeze Out Hills on the horizon to the right. From a watercolor painted by Arthur Lakes in 1879.

Fig. 5. Como Bluff as seen from the west in the vicinity of Robber's Roost near Quarry 12. The Three Trees Quarry (No. 7) is high up in the notch in the face of the bluff. The *"Atlantosaurus* Beds" (Morrison formation) form the upper part of the Bluff from the thin dark band near the base of the section up to the cap rock "Dakota sandstone" (Lakota or Cloverly formation) at the cliff top. The lower slopes are formed of the *"Sauranodon* Beds" (Sundance formation). Arthur Lakes is shown at his sketch board while William Reed on horseback directs their "hired men" on to the *Stegosaurus* Quarry (No. 12). From a watercolor painted by Arthur Lakes in 1879.

plates and spines of *Stegosaurus,* and the pelvic bones of several large *Antrodemus* specimens. The productivity of this quarry is all the more impressive when it is realized that not only was Quarry 4 more than five miles from Como Station and on the opposite side of Rock Creek, but also all the fossils that were removed from this quarry during the first month were packed out on Reed's and Vincent's backs over the entire distance to the station. This unpleasant task may well have been the "straw" that precipitated Vincent's sudden resignation toward the end of March. Reed repeatedly requested additional funds from Marsh to purchase a horse with which to pack out the fossil bones, but Marsh seems to have been inattentive to these requests. During March, Rock Creek presumably was still frozen and thus probably presented no great difficulty, but with the coming of spring thaws, crossing the swollen creek became a hazardous matter, as is so often noted by several of Marsh's collectors at various later times. By April, however, Carlin had arranged to have the fossils brought to the station, apparently by handcar over the Union Pacific tracks, but it was still necessary to back-pack everything more than a mile from the quarry across Rock Creek to the railroad tracks. The size and weight of many of the specimens considered, it is surprising that anything was successfully collected from Quarry 4.

Although Marsh appears to have been quite insensitive to the arduous labors of Reed and Vincent, and of Vincent's successor Pat Donelly, before he was able to respond to Reed's pleas, he received a severe jolt in a letter from Carlin dated April 1st.

> Dear Sir:
>
> I inclose you an item clipped from the "Daily Sentinel" a paper published in Laramie City in regard to our discoveries.
>
> I think that it would be well to hasten operations as much as possible as it will probably be included in the Associated Press Repts from that City and it may be difficult to keep other parties out.
>
> We will make another shipment in a day or two.
>
> Yours Truly,
>
> [signed] Wm. E. Carlin

Reed, who at that time was camped at Quarry 4 with Donelly, apparently knew nothing of the published announcement of the Como discoveries, or of Carlin's letter to Marsh, for he made no mention of either in any of his subsequent letters to Marsh. The news article although carefully concealing the identity of the informant, leaves one wondering if it may not have been Carlin himself:

The Como Crocodile

Full Statement of the Facts Concerning the Great Find

Yesterday we briefly alluded to the operations of the discoverers of the remains of a mammoth beast of some sort near Como, about sixty miles west of this place. As intimated in that item, we had heard frequent rumors of this discovery, but the affair was kept so darkly secret that we could obtain nothing definite or authentic upon the subject. Our information yesterday was deemed reliable, but it, too, was somewhat faulty. This morning we found a man who is familiar with the discovery, and every detail of the subsequent operations, but who does not wish to have his name published in connection with the matter. From him we learn the following particulars, which we deem perfectly reliable:

Several months ago, two railroad employes at Como, Mr. Carlin, the agent, and Mr. Reed, a section boss, while out antelope hunting, discovered the fossil, and extracted small portions of the tail, which they at once forwarded to Professor Marsh, with an inquiry as to their value. A reply was shortly received that the specimens were very valuable, and the discoverers were at once authorized by the learned gentleman to begin exhuming the remains at the expense of Yale College.

The two men above named at once resigned their positions on the road and set about the work of taking out the fossil, which proved to be the carcass of a huge animal of the crocodile species, and instead of being bones, as asserted by our informant yesterday, is a petrifaction of the hardest character, resembling flint.

In taking out the body, which was found to be forty-six feet in length, of course it was necessary to break it into sections. Lumber was procured here by Mr. Carlin and the remains, weighing 8000 pounds, boxed and forwarded to Yale College, where men are now employed in reuniting the sections and putting them into proper shape.

At the instance of Professor Marsh, who was fearful that some rival institution should obtain possession of the wonder, the strictest secrecy was maintained concerning the discovery.

The two discoverers have already realized the handsome sum of $2500 for their labors; and besides this immense crocodile, have discovered the petrifactions of two other smaller ones, which have been shipped to Professor Marsh.

In appreciation of their services in this valuable discovery, these two gentlemen, Messrs. Carlin and Reed, have been placed on a salary of $130 per

month and commissioned to lead two parties this summer on a search for
fossils through the National Park and the Big Horn country, under the direction of the authorities of Yale College.

Is it possible that this public announcement may have been a deliberate attempt
on the part of Carlin to attract the interest of others to the Como bone field and
thereby increase the value of his knowledge of the Como area and the location of
fossil specimens? It is perhaps significant that the monthly salaries cited in the
article are $40 more than he and Reed were actually receiving and the "handsome
sum" is more than twice what they had received by that date. Was this merely
exaggerative journalism? Or was this an intentional inflation of their monetary
returns in order to jack up the pay from future bidders?

Receipt of this catastrophic news—precisely what he had been striving to
avoid—precipitated an immediate reaction from Marsh, who promptly tele-
graphed to Samuel Williston in Kansas. Williston rushed to Como, arriving on
the 18th of April, and promptly reported to Marsh:

> One of Cope's men was here—on which my brother telegraphed. He first
> purported to be selling groceries!! Gave his name as *"Haines"*, thick heavy
> set sullen portly man of about 40, shaven except moustache and whiskers.
> Made some botanical collections and was anxious to learn as much as pos-
> sible about the fossils and *whether I* was coming out here. They said he
> walked a little lame. You may perhaps recognize him.

In a second letter written that same day, Williston commented:

> I have been talking further with Carlin about this man "Haines". There is
> no doubt but that he is direct from Cope. . . . Carlin at the time thought it
> was Cope and tried very hard to catch him. The chief reason that I *know*
> it was not he is that the man wrote a very neat fine and legible hand and I
> have seen Cope's writing! He was anxious to know if the *head* had been
> found and if many small saurians had been found. He gained *no definite*
> information from Carlin or my brother. He went up into the hill and re-
> turning said that he had found no fossils,—*of course* he lied. He was gone
> about 3 hours. . . . may have seen deserted Quarry No. 2, not some others
> . . . had been in Peabody Museum. Didn't mention Cope's name, but yours
> frequently—*rather* disparagingly. When Carlin called Cope a "damned
> thief", sneered . . . If you recognize him let me know as soon as possible
> and I will have a little fun at his expense. If you care to telegraph it, please
> choose simple words—*the initials of which will indicate his name.*

"Haines" was mentioned again in several subsequent letters, but no record of his identity has been preserved; he was the first, but far from the last, of Cope's collectors to come to Como.

Work continued at Quarry 4, but at a declining pace, because of the hazards of crossing Rock Creek and the difficulties of transporting the fossil materials to the railroad. Increasing amounts of time and effort were devoted to prospecting and exploration of new areas by the Williston brothers and Reed. Apparently it was during this phase of prospecting that Reed found a number of small bones which were immediately expressed to Marsh. In early May an urgent wire from Marsh instructed his collectors to find and send more of these remains. Among the small bones was the major part of a mammal jaw, which Marsh described in June as *Dryolestes priscus* (YPM 11820), the first Jurassic mammal from North America. The precise site of the *Dryolestes* discovery is unfortunately not recorded in any of the preserved field records or correspondence, but there are indications that it was very near Quarry 5. In response to Marsh's inquiry about this find, Williston wrote on May 19th:

Dear Professor:

Description of jaw just received—understand perfectly where it came from and will send original fragment of rock with more bones in it in a few days. I did not see it. Reed obtained it and was intending to examine the place thoroughly as soon as weather permitted—Near the top of the ridge in a distinct layer of rock—not far above the layer that is most productive of small saurians. Has been snowing for two days.

In haste,
S.W.W.

Quarry 5 had been opened only a week or so before (it is mentioned for the first time in Williston's letter of May 16th) and the "layer that is most productive of small saurians" is quite likely a reference to that site, for Quarry 5 was the only excavation then active which was producing small bones. A letter from Reed dated 25 May seems to support this interpretation:

I suppose you are aware that the jaw of small mammal was found by me and I have colected all fragments that could be found in the same rock I have also found the deposit of small bones and toe bones sent in last box you are getting prompt work and got returns now it would pleas me to receive the same from you in the shape of two checks due at this date.

Reed's habit of running his sentences together obscures matters somewhat, but *if* the phrase "in the same rock" is read as the beginning of a new sentence rather than the end of the preceding remark, the *Dryolestes* jaw seems to have been associated with other small bones which probably were those of *Dryosaurus* from Quarry 5. Confusing the issue still further, however, is Lakes' sketch of the geologic section exposed in the main bluff, in which he marked the level of *Dryolestes* slightly higher than that of Quarry 5.

The discovery of *Dryolestes* greatly accelerated prospecting activities and brought work in Quarry 4 to a complete stop. Most of the prospecting was concentrated along the north slope of the bluff south and southeast of Como Station, apparently from about the vicinity of Quarry 1 westward to Quarry 5 (northeast quarter of Section 17). Samuel Williston first refers to Quarry 5 as such in his May 16th letter, where he makes a parenthetic reference to "small bones." Evidently the search was concentrated particularly in this area. On June 1st, Williston commented:

> I think the horizon of Quarry 5 (small) [bones] is the same with the mammal and most if not all the small bones so far found. ... The Laosaurus is from the same level.

The *Laosaurus* referred to by Williston was the only major find specifically recorded from Quarry 5; it was the type skeleton of *Dryosaurus altus* (YPM 1876). The only other remains recovered from this quarry were a fragmentary sauropod jaw and some isolated sauropod teeth. The quarry was abandoned in early June 1878.

At this point, activity at Como began to decline. S. W. Williston left Como about the end of June to return to New Haven. In August, Frank Williston, at his brother's instructions, returned to the Williston home in Kansas. Frank Williston's departure may have been related to Marsh's continued interest in Niobrara fossils from the Kansas area, but his reports to New Haven indicated that the Como vicinity had been thoroughly searched and "bones were very hard to find."

With the departure of the Willistons, Reed again was left as Marsh's sole collector at Como, although Carlin was still residing at the station. Carlin had done almost no work for Marsh since early spring, and there are indications that before the summer of '78 was over he had made contacts with other fossil collectors in the area. Reed continued to prospect and ship collections to New Haven, but his principal responsibility that summer seems to have been to keep other parties away. Late in August, Marsh terminated all contracted collecting at Como, but Reed was forced to remain there for nearly a month awaiting his wages. During this time, he prospected on his own and discovered the first of several *"Sauranodon"* (=*Ophthalmosaurus*) or ichthyosaur skeletons in the Jurassic marine strata (Sundance formation) underlying the Morrison formation. On his own, he collected *Sauranodon* No. 1, which was ultimately purchased many months later by Marsh. Unfortunately, the precise location and stratigraphic position of this specimen were never recorded, presumably because Reed considered it as his own private specimen. Finally, on September 10th, after disagreements with Carlin finally had come to a head, Reed left for Central City, Nebraska—still without his wages—where he spent the winter. Thus ended the first year at Como Bluff.

Work was not begun again at Como until February 1879, at which time Reed, on orders from Marsh, returned to the "bone business." His first letter to Williston complained that he had been very poorly received at the station upon his arrival (except by his old friend Kennedy) and he had immediately moved out of the station and set up camp on Rock Creek close to Quarry 4—in February! Although working and living completely alone in the dead of winter, and in a tent at that, Reed worked diligently and "turned out bones by the ton." But he was not above complaining to his friend Samuel Williston that it "is just meerly H_____ H_____ H_____." Most of the bones recovered by Reed pertained to the skeletons found earlier (*Camarasaurus, Apatosaurus, Barosaurus,* and *Diplodocus,* plus fragments of *Stegosaurus* and *Antrodemus*). The difficult, if not hostile, relations between Reed and Carlin at this time made it almost impossible for Reed to ship anything from Como Station. Carlin was still acting as the station agent and had nearly absolute control of matters there.

Numerous letters from Reed at "Camp Misery" near Quarry 4, both to Williston and to Marsh, reported that Carlin was prospecting for Cope and reporting to him almost daily. Early in March, Reed reported that Carlin had opened a quarry (see Fig. 3, map of Como Bluff) several hundred yards west of the small saurian site (Quarry 5) and was now making shipments to Cope. This was the beginning of a long and busy freight season at Como Station, with rival parties boxing collections within a few yards of each other for shipment to New Haven and Philadelphia. But, whereas Carlin boxed his collections for Cope in the comfort of the freight room, Reed complained that he was forced to crate his specimens for Marsh outside on the freight platform.

Work in Quarry 4 was abandoned in early March, apparently on orders from Marsh, who instructed that all fragments were to be recovered from Quarries 1 and 3. Reed reported that when he abandoned Quarry 4, he had "taken the liberty to demolish to the best of my ability [all remaining bones] as there are other parties in the field colecting." From that time until mid-April, Reed focused his excavating in Quarries 1 and 3. Occasionally, one of the railroad men working at the station (Kennedy, in particular) would give Reed a hand hauling fossil bones down from the bluff, otherwise Reed worked by himself. However, when one of the quarries was invaded by two strangers and Reed was confronted by the prospects of physical battle, he began to look about for a companion to accompany him to the quarries. Reed reported the quarry confrontation incident to his "Friend Williston":

> peace and harmoney does not prevail here to any extent there are two more men here hunting bones they came up from rock creek last weak they came in the evening and said they wer going to work in quarey no. 1 and Kennedy came out [from the station to Reed's camp on Rock Creek] that night and told me so I went down the next morning and got there as soon as they did ... I asked them what they wer goind to do they said dig for bones I told them they could not get any bones there they said they would see I went to the top of the back wall with a pick and commenced to let down dirt and rocks they told me to leave but I was not quite ready to go and I staid with them 4 four days I have got a big pile of dirt in that hole in the ground more I think than they wil want to dig out at any rate I can get there before they get in to where there are any bones they are doing lots of talking down at the Station but talk does not hurt me nor scare me much either.

In the ensuing months, activity by other collecting parties in the Como area increased. Reed frequently commented in his letters to Marsh on the activities of Carlin and his men and, while there was open hostility between Reed and Carlin and occasional flare-ups occurred between them when they chanced to meet at the station, there seems to have been no further direct confrontation like that of the Quarry 1 incident during the season of '79. Reed hired three men from Kennedy and undertook extensive digging operations at Quarry 3. He reported excellent results every several weeks until early May when he apparently shifted his attention to Quarry 5, hoping no doubt to get more of the small saurian *Dryosaurus*.

Although Reed seems not to have written Marsh about the Quarry 1 incident, Williston, who was in New Haven at the time, undoubtedly relayed the matter. Very soon thereafter, Marsh instructed Arthur Lakes to leave Morrison and assist Reed in his operations at Como. At that point Lakes had been in Colorado only a few weeks, having spent the winter in New Haven. It would seem that Marsh considered the situation at Como sufficiently critical to interrupt the work at Morrison and reinforce his interests at Como Bluff. Lakes arrived at Como on the 14th of May 1879, and together the two men continued to work in Quarry 3.

THE BUSY YEARS (1879–1883)

The summer of 1879 was perhaps the most active interval, and certainly one of the most productive periods in the entire history of Como Bluff. All the remaining major quarry sites were found during the three months from June to September and excavation, crating, and shipping reached its peak. Quarry 6 and the second ichthyosaur or *"Sauranodon"* quarry were found by Reed in the latter half of May. The Three Trees Quarry (No. 7) and Quarry 8 were discovered in early June. Then, in rapid succession, came the discoveries of Quarries 9, 10, and 11, all during July. Quarry 12 was found in early August and Quarry 13 followed in early September.

Quarry 6 is mentioned only infrequently in Reed's letters, apparently because it was not considered a site of any particular promise. Priority was given to the Three Trees Quarry and to Quarry 8, both of which were cleared out and abandoned before work on No. 6 was finally completed. This quarry, which was only a few hundred yards west of the highly productive Quarry 3 in Section 11, ultimately proved to be one of the least important of the numerous Como quarries, producing only isolated crocodilian remains (probably *Goniopholis*) and miscellaneous fragments.

Quarry 7, on the other hand, produced the very fine remains of a new hollow-boned saurian that later was designated the type of *Laosaurus consors* (YPM 1882). This quarry was nearly four miles from Quarries 3 and 6, at the far west end of the Bluff. The Laosaurian remains were removed quickly, in a matter of three or four days, probably at the insistence of Professor Marsh. As a matter of fact, Marsh himself is credited as the discoverer of Quarry 7. No mention is made in either Lakes' or Reed's letters about the discovery of this site, whereas discovery of each of the other quarries is promptly reported in their correspondence. The reason for this is simply that no letters were written then because Marsh was at that moment visiting his collectors at Como. Fortunately, however, Arthur Lakes kept a rather detailed day-by-day journal of the activities and discoveries. His entry for June 6 reads:

> Three Trees Quarry
> This quarry (Quarry 7) discovered by Professor Marsh June 6 from a few vertebrae lying at the extreme base varigated clays forming Atlantosaurus beds and full 100 feet lower than any quarry so far opened.

Upon completion of the Three Trees Quarry, Reed turned to prospecting again and about the middle of June discovered a new site about a quarter mile east of No. 3. This site, designated Quarry 8, occupied Reed for the remainder of

June, during which time he and his helper Ashley (and occasionally Lakes) unearthed a moderate number of large and small bones, chiefly of *Camarasaurus* and *Antrodemus,* plus fragmentary *Diplodocus,* turtle, and crocodilian remains.

While Reed was busy at quarry work, Lakes spent much of his time at the sketching board, drawing bones as they were unearthed and making large sketches of the region (see Frontispiece and Figs. 4–11), together with detailed stratigraphic sections. These drawings of course were of great value to Marsh and to posterity. Most of the quarries could be relocated in recent years and recorded in this volume chiefly because of Lakes' scenic sketches of the Como area and his geologic sections. Without them, much (if not all) of this information would now be lost. Reed, however, could not see the value of the drawings, and they became a source of increasing irritation to him. Before the summer was out, the matter had developed into an open feud between the two men.

Both Reed and Lakes kept Marsh informed about the activities of Cope's parties, noting Carlin's departure in late June to work again for the railroad, the take-over by the Hubbel brothers,[6] and the pending visit in July of Professor Cope himself. Another minor confrontation between Reed and Cope men was rather casually reported by Reed:

> I yesterday morning learned that the Hubbels wer going over *across* the lake to that carnivorous quarey [No. 1½] to work ... I got a pick and shovel and went across the lake and went to work and very soon H. and Co. arived but did not stay to argue the matter.

In the same letter, Reed noted the discovery of *Sauranodon* No. 3 (found on his way back from Quarry 1½) and made his first specific reference to the new quarry—No. 9.

Probably no other single fossil locality has generated as much interest as this famous "mammal quarry" (Fig. 8) of Como Bluff (No. 9). This site yielded an amazing diversity of reptilian and amphibian as well as mammalian remains, but the mammal finds were the spectacular items and by far the most important (see Faunal Lists, pp. 55–57). Of the 250 Jurassic mammal specimens currently known from North America, all but three were collected at Como Bluff, and all of these, except the type jaw of *Dryolestes* and two isolated teeth from Quarry 1 and

6. The Cope collection of fossil vertebrates was obtained by the American Museum after Cope's death. The most important specimens in this collection were collected by F. F. Hubbel in 1879: (1) an almost complete skeleton of *Antrodemus valens* (AMNH 5753) from "Cope Quarry No. 3" (now mounted in the *Brontosaurus* Hall of that Museum over a prostrate *Apatosaurus*) and (2) some *Stegosaurus* vertebrae (AMNH 5754) from "Cope Quarry No. 1." (The latter probably constitutes the type of Cope's *Hypsirhophus seeleyanus,* but this is not established as yet.)

Fig. 6. Benjamin Mudge contemplating the "colossal" bones of *Atlantosaurus* found by Arthur Lakes near Morrison, Colorado, in early April 1877.

Fig. 7. Professor Marsh (*right*) lunching near Robber's Roost with his collectors W. H. Reed and E. G. Ashley. It was during this visit that Marsh discovered the Three Trees Quarry (No. 7) which produced the type of *Laosaurus consors*. The scene was painted by Arthur Lakes in early June 1879.

Quarry 11, were recovered from Quarry 9. The first indication of this site appeared in Arthur Lakes' letter of July 5th, 1879:

> Left No. 8 for today to prospect East along bluff. At 400 yds E of No. 8—600 from No. 3 and 200 from Indian Fort—found a low bluff . . . opened long trench 50 feet . . . turtle scutes . . . striated teeth . . . crocodile scutes, several small vertebrae . . . herbiv and carniv good sized teeth . . . claw bones . . . small hollow vertebrae, etc. etc. We got out quite a lot all mingled together. Strata about 1 foot thick, lower portion full of small rounded concretions upper a loose grey shale stained with lignitic marks . . . I believe the resources of Como are very abundant!

This was followed on the 10th of July by a letter from Reed:

> Professor Lakes found a beautiful little jaw with teeth which I wil send you by mail in the morning . . . P.S. the jaw was found in our new quarey or no. 9 which is turning out very good.

Lakes' journal notes this first mammal find: "At No. 9 I found a small jaw about ½ inch long with teeth in it. Also a portion of another in a lump of grey shale." This was the beginning of what must be considered one of the most important paleontologic finds in all of North America. It was not long before letters from Reed came, as follows:

> July 18, 1879
>
> Dear Sir:
>
> I have the plasure of sending you by mail with this letter three small jaws.

> July 22, 1879
>
> Dear Sir:
>
> I send you by mail tonight another cann of bones 4 jaws.

> August 7, 1879
>
> I send also by this mail what I believe is a mammal jaw from quarey no 9 I think it is the best yet found here.

Quarry 9 proved to be every bit as rich as Lakes had predicted, and it consumed a great deal of human effort and time. The quarry was worked almost continuously over a period of nearly ten years by Reed and his successors, finally being abandoned by Fred Brown in June 1889.

From the early part of July on, Reed and Lakes had both been warning Marsh of another "first" pending at Como—a visit by Professor Cope. The event finally came to pass on the 2nd of August, Cope apparently staying at Como

Fig. 8. The famous Mammal Quarry (No. 9) at the eastern end of Como Bluff. William Reed and E. Kennedy are shown at work looking for small bones while E. G. Ashley and a hired hand quarry out more "pay dirt." The "Indian Fort" is at the top of the distant ridge, just east of the Mammal Quarry. From a watercolor painted by Arthur Lakes in 1879.

Fig. 9. W. H. Reed and E. Kennedy in the process of removing bones of *"Brontosaurus" excelsus* from Quarry 10. This specimen is the one that is now on exhibit in the Peabody Museum of Natural History at Yale University. The view here is looking almost due west along Como Bluff. From a water-color painted by Arthur Lakes in 1879.

just a single day, presumably to reinforce his position there. Reed observed that he did not think Cope saw much, but he had made inquiries about the mammal jaw (probably a reference to the *Dryolestes* jaw, which had been published a few weeks before, rather than to the new finds at Quarry 9). Reed was careful to add that Cope got no satisfaction. Many hours had been spent by Reed, Lakes, Ashley, and Kennedy preparing for this visit by Cope, most of it directed toward securing all of Marsh's quarries from Cope's forces. This necessitated frequent treks back and forth between existing quarries, as well as full-time occupancy of the most highly valued quarries. The result was that July turned out to be a very profitable month for Marsh—both in terms of collections made from exposed portions of various quarries and in the discovery of several new sites. At the end of July, immediately before Cope's visit, Reed reported to Marsh about the discovery of new Quarries 10 and 11:

> I have a few more jaws which I wil send by mail with this quarey no. 9 does not turn out so wel as it did at first for the bank is geting higher and the rock harder but stil we find something every day we found two new quaries 10 and 11 of large bones and as soon as we have time wil tak up a box from each one and send you and then you can tell whether you want them worked or not.

Lakes' diary—August 9, 1879:

> Glancing over the record of the past two weeks the time has mainly been occupied with work at No. 9, resulting in the discovery of many small bones some jaws and finally as we hope at last a small mammal jaw. Three new quarries of large bones two of them of gigantic proportions [Quarries 10 and 11] and the third [Quarry 12] at Robber's roost of carnivorous? hollow bones[7] of a large size and probably of interest. Prof. Cope dropped in for a couple of days . . . on his way to Salt Lake or Green River. The work has been carried on steadily under Mr. Reed's excellent management and Mr. Ashley's keen eyes in prospecting we are indebted for 3 new quarries and a sauranodon [*Sauranodon* No. 3 and 4] Sauranodon No. 5 party returned [from near Rock Creek Gap three miles north of the main bluff] with the news of the discovery of very large vertebrae and bones between No 8 and No. 9.

7. Lakes and Reed almost always referred to large hollow limb bones as "carnivorous"—in contrast to the solid limb bones of the "herbivorous" dinosaurs (sauropods). *Stegosaurus* and *Camptosaurus* limb bones, which often displayed a hollow structure, were thus referred to as of the carnivorous type in their correspondence. The specimen referred to in this letter is the type specimen of *Stegosaurus ungulatus* (YPM 1853), which is now exhibited in the Yale Peabody Museum.

These were the first notices of the discovery of Quarry 10—the now famous *Brontosaurus* Quarry (Fig. 9). According to Lakes, Quarry 10 was approximately a hundred yards west of Quarry 9 and at the same level as Quarries 3 and 1. Ashley discovered No. 11 some fifty yards west of Quarry 10 on July 31st, just before the dreaded visit of Professor Cope.

Reed, Lakes, and Ashley (and unofficially, Kennedy) had spread themselves very thin over the Como Bluff area in an attempt to occupy and secure the largest possible area from Cope and his collectors. Reed worked at Quarry 1½ and at *Sauranodon* Quarries 3 and 4. Ashley worked *Sauranodon* Quarry 5, and, together with Lakes, patrolled Quarries 1, 3, 5, 6, and 9—and in so doing stumbled on the sites of future Quarries 10 and 11. Lakes worked in Quarry 9 for much of this hazardous month, but he also tried to keep tabs on the now abandoned Cope Quarry (probably Cope Quarry No. 3, opened several months before by Carlin) south of the station and on the Three Trees Quarry at the west end of the ridge. Although there is no record prior to this time of any serious attempt by Cope's men to move in on any of the Yale quarries, these precautionary moves on the part of Reed and his men may have helped discourage such action. In later years, however, such invasions did occur.

After Cope's visit, Marsh's men returned to the business of collecting again. Reed, assisted by Ashley, divided his duties among Quarries 9, 8, and 6, but he also managed to find and collect *Sauranodon* No. 6 and No. 7 from about a hundred yards west of the Three Trees Quarry. This probably was about the time that Ashley found the Robber's Roost Quarry (No. 12) early in August. Lakes worked alone in Quarries 9 and 10, when he was not engaged in prospecting or in sketching the Como scene. Lakes also maintained his diary, or journal as he called it, recording the items collected and other pertinent data. Portions of his journal contain rather interesting and amusing items:

August 11, 1879

The Monstrum horrendum Cope has been and gone and I must say that what I saw of him I liked very much his manner is so affable and his conversation very agreeable. I only wish I could feel sure he had a sound reputation for honesty.

Such frank observations certainly must have done little to improve Marsh's humor, but, on the other hand, the following item from a later part of the same journal must have amused Marsh considerably:

the remainder of the day was spent in remodeling and refining our camp which much needed it as well as pitching and fixing up my new tent which had just arrived. A heavy thunderstorm and rain occurred in afternoon in evening our tents were inundated with *Siredons* [=*Amblystoma*] who swarmed in such numbers insinuating themselves under every box and bed that although we threw out and killed dozens it became useless to stop the horde of slimy lizards that waddled leisurely into the tents as if they had a perfect right to them and resenting any attempt at interference by a vigorous curling up of their tails. What with the noise of these creatures working their way under our boxes papers and bed, the baying of wild geese on the lake, the gnawing of mice at our furniture and the roar of the thunder, the voices of the night were not conducive to slumber.

August passed in this manner (apparently much to the discomfort of Arthur Lakes), great progress was made in the quarries, and prospects looked excellent. However, relations between Reed and Lakes, which had never been particularly good, were rapidly deteriorating. Finally, in late August, Reed wrote to both Williston and Marsh that he could take it no longer and that he was quitting at the end of the month. Marsh was well aware of the value of a man like Reed and recognized that he could not be replaced easily. For more than two years Reed had been steadfast in his loyalty to Marsh and had worked hard and long in the quarries at Como, both summer and winter. It was Reed who had stood up to the threats of Cope's collectors and had defended Marsh's sites; yet Lakes also was a most useful assistant. His geologic training and his ability with pen and paint were of great value. Marsh could ill afford at that particular moment to lose either one. So Marsh instructed the two men to work independently and to keep out of each other's way. From that time until he left Como the following spring, Lakes worked alone at the west end of the bluff at Robber's Roost (Quarry 12) or at a new site that he had discovered, the Big Canyon Quarry (Quarry 1A) southwest of Como Station. Reed worked at the opposite end of the bluff some five miles distant, chiefly in Quarries 9 and 10 and the new site that was designated Quarry 13. The discovery of the latter, which was to turn out to be one of the most important sites in the Como Bluff region, was reported by Reed in his letter of September 4th:

> we have today found an entirely new bone yard it is something new I hope and think it is it is in a formation below Iaosaurus and above Sauranodon it is the same as the place where Mr. L. has made his discovery which he says he found and which I object to that statement for I found bones in that horison and on the same ground where he is at work [Quarry 12] . . . but about my new one the bones are all holow and are very pleanty and in good preservation, and are located about 1½ miles east of Quarey no. 4 on Rock Creek there is about two acres of ground that is full of bones.

Reed's letter of September 5th noted:

> I and Mr. Ashley have bin exploring the new discovery that I wrote you
> about yesterday and have found it very rich in all kinds of bones we got out
> six jaw bones with the teath in them the teath look like laosaurus but are
> much larger [*Camptosaurus*].

The first excavations at Quarry 13 were referred to as 13 east (other later
excavations at the same site were designated 13 west, 13 middle and 13½ by
various members of Marsh's collecting staff, but the locality was a solitary bone
deposit in a single stratum). Quarry 13 (east) occupied Reed and Ashley throughout most of September and October, after which they returned to Quarries 9 and
10. Work was still carried on intermittently at 13 by Reed and his successors
until the fall of 1887 when it was finally abandoned by Fred Brown. Quarry 13
proved to be one of the richest of the Como sites and second only to Quarry 9 in
abundance and diversity of fossil vertebrate remains. This quarry yielded the
type specimens of *Camarasaurus lentus* (YPM 1910); *Coelurus fragilis* (YPM
1991); *Coelurus agilis* (YPM 2010); four species of *Camptosaurus: C. dispar*
(YPM 1877), *C. medius* (YPM 1880), *C. nanus* (USNM 2210), *C. browni*
(USNM 4282); *Diracodon laticeps* (YPM 1885); *Stegosaurus affinis* (YPM uncatalogued); and *Stegosaurus sulcatus* (USNM 4937). In addition, Quarry 13
produced a variety of other sauropod, ornithopod, and stegosaur remains (including the large sauropod skull, YPM 1911 [see Plates 5 and 6] arbitrarily referred
by Marsh to *Brontosaurus*) during the nearly eight years the quarry was actively
worked by Yale collectors.

Arthur Lakes, as instructed by Professor Marsh, kept well out of Reed's path
in the months following Reed's "blow-up." During most of August and September he concentrated his efforts on Quarry 12, the site that both he and Reed
claimed as their own discovery, but which appears to have been first spotted by
Ashley. Besides No. 12, Lakes also opened several other small quarries which
he had discovered "back of the station" between Cope's abandoned Quarry 3 and
Reed's Quarry 5. The only one of these to amount to any significance was that
designated 1A or the "Big Canyon Quarry." Lakes was quite certain that this was
a highly promising site and he repeatedly returned to it even when Marsh was
pressing him for more *Stegosaurus* bones from Quarry 12. The remains of a
large "carnivorous saurian" (*Antrodemus*) attracted Lakes' attention at first, but
then he unearthed a number of large vertebrae, as well as foot and limb bones,
of *Camarasaurus*. Finally, Big Canyon Quarry yielded the type specimen of
Camptosaurus amplus (YPM 1879), which, unfortunately consists only of a
right foot. However, these limited remains still represent the largest camptosaur

specimen known. Lakes continued to work the Big Canyon Quarry throughout most of the fall, but at Marsh's insistence he returned to Robber's Roost and re-opened Quarry 12 (the site of *Stegosaurus ungulatus*) during late September, and thereafter alternated his efforts between these two sites.

Reed and Ashley, meanwhile, divided their time between Quarries 9 and 13 during September and October. In November they shifted to Quarry 10, which was to become the site of Reed's greatest conquest. For the remainder of the autumn and much of the winter, Reed and Ashley exhumed many tons of great bones from this site, the final result being the recovery of the nearly complete skeleton of *Apatosaurus excelsus* (YPM 1980), now exhibited in the Peabody Museum at Yale. This specimen is still one of the finest "brontosaur" skeletons ever found and in many ways stands as Reed's greatest achievement as a collector.

The great quantities of fossil bones collected during the winter of 1879–80 are remarkable testimony to the hardiness and diligence of Marsh's assistants. Two men alone, Reed and Ashley, collected nearly all of the great "brontosaur" from Quarry 10 during that winter, and Lakes, working alone almost all of the time, expanded Quarry 12 at Robber's Roost from a shallow pit to an enormous vertical trench more than eighty feet long and nearly forty feet deep. In spite of his "haughty Oxford ways" that so irritated Reed, Lakes proved himself to be a man of almost incredible fortitude and industry. The conditions under which he pursued the stegosaur skeleton are almost beyond belief, at least in terms of modern collecting. Few of us in this century could *or would want to* register field reports comparable to those submitted by Lakes during that winter:

Feb. 5th, 1880

Collecting at this season is under many difficulties. At the bottom of a narrow pit 30 feet deep into which drift snow keeps blowing and fingers benumbed with cold from thermo between 20 and 30 below zero and snow often blowing blindingly down and covering up a bone as fast as it is unearthed.

Robber's Roost is located almost precisely on the nose of the Como Anticline (Fig. 11) and at this point the strata have a near-vertical attitude. Consequently, in order to follow the bone-bearing stratum, Lakes was required to dig almost straight down, rather than horizontally into the hillside. The result was that Quarry 12 developed as a very narrow trench only four or five feet wide at the bottom and more than forty feet deep before it was ultimately abandoned. In January, a great fracture developed parallel to the north wall, which threatened to cave in the whole north side of the quarry. At this point, Lakes became fearful for his life, but he braced the threatening wall with heavy timbers and continued

Fig. 10. William Reed (*center*) and two helpers at their winter camp on the bank of Lake Como near Como Station. Painted during the winter of 1879–80 by Arthur Lakes.

Fig. 11. The "Pleasures of Science"—the title originally given to this view of winter excavations at Quarry 12 (Robber's Roost) by Arthur Lakes (*standing*), with his hired helper Hallett. From a watercolor by Arthur Lakes, February 1880.

to deepen the trench in quest of more *Stegosaurus* bones. The first cave-in occurred in late February, fortunately when no one was in the quarry, but it required several days to dig out the debris. Further cave-ins were a certainty, but before these occurred another problem interrupted the work in Quarry 12—and it is probably fortunate that it arose, because the next cave-in would almost certainly have killed anyone who was in the quarry. The life-saving interruption was the flooding of all the lowest parts of the quarry floor. At a depth of about forty feet, Lakes struck a "spring," or water-bearing fracture zone, which inundated the quarry faster than he could bail it out. This development came as bad news to Marsh, who was extremely anxious to obtain every last bone of the "fine" *Stegosaurus* skeleton from this quarry, but as we now know, Lakes would have been forced to abandon Quarry 12 very shortly in any case, because of a cave-in, had he remained at Como. Lakes did try to unearth more bones from beneath the flooded sections, as he notes in a later letter:

> All these bones have been got out with considerable difficulty owing to the spring bursting out and covering them with a lot of water. I had to bale with one hand and dig out bone as I got a glimpse of it with the other, sitting at the time in a frog pond more like fishing for eels than digging for bones meanwhile snowing and freezing hard so what with water mud and slush it is no wonder if some small pieces are missing.

Soon after this, about the middle of March, Lakes left the "bone business" to accept a teaching position at the newly organized State School of Mines in Golden, Colorado (now the Colorado School of Mines). Except for a few brief instances, Lakes did no further collecting for Marsh after he moved to Golden. Shortly after his departure, Reed reported to Lakes (and also Marsh) that the wall had fallen in at No. 12, and he estimated it would require four men an entire month to dig it out.

Winter was no less severe at the eastern end of Como Bluff, although Reed was perhaps more matter-of-fact in reporting conditions to Marsh than was Lakes. Reed did note periods of bitter cold and numerous days when wind or snow made it impossible to walk the four miles from the station to the quarry. In January, Reed and Ashley placed a tent over the active part of Quarry 10 in order to provide some shelter from the high winds, but it offered little protection against the cold. A second helper, Fred Brown, was hired in January and Reed put him and Ashley to work in nearby Quarry 11 to recover more of the *Stegosaurus* skeleton there. Reed himself finally gave up hope of recovering any more of the large skeleton in Quarry 10, and in early February he joined Ashley and Brown in No. 11.

Quarry 11 was not quite as rich or as spectacular as the two adjacent quarries, but it did yield the types of *Stegosaurus duplex* (YPM 1858) and *Apatosaurus amplus* (YPM 1981). The latter resulted in some rather interesting incidental remarks in several of Reed's letters.

> March 20, 1880
>
> have taken up the Femur. it is a beauty, but so heavy that I canot pack it on a horse. one end is all three of us can cary. shall get it down to the RR and Bring it in on the hand car.

> March 24, 1880
>
> that Femur is a poser we tried today to get the head down to the R.R. got it part way and had to leave it will get it down to morrow.

> March 31, 1880
>
> we are geting the Bones down to the station today all except the head of the Femur that is a bad one we have got it half way to the R.R. we give it a lift every day but can't cary it far.

How long it finally took to drag the femur down to the tracks, a distance of about half a mile, Reed never reveals, but recent efforts to move this impressive object have generated estimates of a 400-pound weight and considerable admiration for the durability and energy of Reed and his men.

With the weather improving each day, Reed expressed an eagerness to get back to Quarry 13. Marsh, however, was still anxious for more of the *Stegosaurus* skeleton at Robber's Roost and had other plans for Reed. A very emphatic telegram arrived from New Haven early in April:

> Superintend or stop work. quarry twelve or send Ashley there.
>
> Marsh

Reed was left with no alternative but to take the entire force—Ashley, Brown, Kennedy (who had been hired by Marsh a few weeks before), and Lakes' hired man Hallett—to Quarry 12. On April 12th, he wrote:

> I had Ashley and Brown and the man of Lakes diging they got down about two feet and the south side of the quarey gave way and let in over six feet of rock they just got out of the way or would have bin buried the north side is all loos and ready to fall I have stoped the work there for at the way it is it would be 3 weeks befor we could get down to the Bones and I am very shure that you can do Better in 13 east or 13 west rather for there is a lot of stegosaur Bones in the west wash and a good many sticking out of the Bank.

Thus Quarry 12 was once again temporarily abandoned, and Marsh was once again frustrated in his efforts to obtain more of the *Stegosaurus*. At this point, Reed decided to reopen No. 9, putting Kennedy to work there while he and Ashley went to work in Quarry 13. For most of April and May, Reed directed the work in these two quarries, alternating daily between them. A steady flow of mammal jaws from No. 9 and of larger bones from No. 13 was dispatched to New Haven during this time. At one point Reed requested Marsh to send Frank Williston back to Como to take charge of one of these quarries and thus step up the rate of collecting. In general, however, the excavations seem to have progressed quite smoothly and productively under Reed's direction. Cope's parties, under the command of the Hubbel brothers, seem to have been relatively inactive,[8] a state which Reed attributed to money problems. At the end of May, Reed wrote that Cope's field boss (Hubbel) had come to him offering to sell packing materials and equipment. He purportedly had told the station agent Chase that there were no more bones in the Como hills and that Cope was sending him farther west. This event did not come to pass, however.

Early in June, hostilities among Marsh's collectors again came to the forefront and again, as with the quarrel between Reed and Lakes, the source of the difficulties seems to have been the independent hiring of Kennedy by Marsh. Reed was resentful that Marsh did not allow him to do all the hiring. Kennedy, feeling that he was not responsible to Reed since Reed had not employed him, refused to take orders from Reed. The result was a bitter blow-up between the two men, and both Brown and Ashley quit because of the continued friction (although Ashley returned a few weeks later). After the dust had settled, only Reed and Kennedy remained of the original force. Two new men, Kenny and Dixon, were hired to replace Brown and Ashley, and Frank Williston arrived from New Haven to calm things down and look after Marsh's interests. But new developments resulted from Williston's return that could hardly have been sought by Marsh, although he should have anticipated them.

By mid-June, collecting operations were once again at full steam with Frank Williston and Kennedy working Quarry 9 and Ashley and Dixon at Quarry 13. Reed, still considering himself very much the boss, divided his time between the two quarries. Reed's enthusiasm from Quarry 13 was entirely justified, as the growing collections soon proved. In mid-July Reed noted that bone was exposed continuously over more than seventy feet of quarry face, and he revised his earlier estimate of the total area involved to twenty acres: "there is maney tons of

8. The only known specimens recovered by F. F. Hubbel in 1880 from Como Bluff were some scattered *Stegosaurus* bones (AMNH 5752) from Cope Quarry No. 4 and a few "*Brontosaurus*" bones (AMNH 5755) from Cope Quarry No. 5.

bones [in No. 13] more than has ever bin shiped from Como." Consequently, the summer and fall of 1880 were devoted almost entirely to Quarries 9 and 13. When Marsh himself visited Como in September, he directed that work be pushed at these two sites. Museum records indicate that the only specimens collected from Como localities other than 9 and 13 for the remainder of that year were restricted to five newly discovered specimens of *Sauranodon.* These were found at undisclosed localities some eight miles north of Como.

After Marsh's visit in September, a feud developed between Frank Williston and the other men. Precisely what precipitated the difficulties is not clear, but apparently Williston had been given considerable freedom of action by Marsh. Naturally, Reed and the other men resented this independence, and Williston was ostracized by the rest of the party. Williston subsequently moved out of the Marsh camp and boarded at Carlin's new ranch on Rock Creek. On November 18th Marsh learned from Reed that: "F.H.W. and another man are at work between no. 10 and 11." Scrawled at the bottom of this letter in Marsh's own hand is the comment: "Recd. Nov. 18th, 1880. FHW working for Cope."

That Carlin, a total stranger, had deserted him for his "adversary" probably came as no surprise to Marsh, but the shock of Williston's betrayal must have been great. On November 25th, Reed wrote:

> Your telegram recd wil do all I can to keep all parties out of the places you mention they have shiped a Box to Cope to day so *it is a shure* thing that that is what they mean if you wish I can tell you something by which you can make them some trouble.
>
> Yours
> [signed] W.H. Reed

Reed's suggestion for solving the problem was sent on November 30th, 1880.

> the C. party came over there [Quarries 9, 10, and 11] twice to the ridge in front of the quaries and took a look at us and went Back they must be at work some where else[9] for they have another Box to ship . . . there is one way in which to keep them away from our quaries and that is to preempt or take the land under the desert act by this act we can pay 25 cents per acre and hold the land three years and then by paying one dolar per acre more get a deed but three years is ample time the least amount we can take is 160

9. F. H. Williston did most of his collecting for Cope farther north at the Bone Cabin Quarry, which was later worked so successfully by American Museum parties nearly 20 years later. Quite probably, Frank Williston was responsible for the discovery of this famous site, although this is not verified at present.

> acres if we do this myself and Ashley can take 160 each one at 13 and the
> other at 9, 10, 11 and that will take the best of the ground.

The loss of Frank Williston, who was very thoroughly acquainted with all the
Yale localities and quarries at Como, was followed by a sudden and alarming
increase in activity by the Cope parties. These two events together apparently
convinced Marsh that the measures proposed by Reed were indeed necessary.
Steps were taken almost immediately for filing on the lands mentioned. December and January brought repeated warnings from Reed that Cope men were looking for small bones near Quarry 3 and others were digging near No. 1½. Then
on December 5th Marsh received the following:

> the Cope party was up to 13 yesterday. they did not come to the quarey but
> was all around it the went to those big Bones west of the quarey and I
> started out to see them and they left . . . I find their tracks all around no. 9
> but they have not done any work there.

This was followed by further notice that Cope men were digging near Quarry
1, and then a cryptic wire to Marsh on December 13th: "Man sent crystal to C.
today by mail. R."

Anxiety must have been high in New Haven as well as at Como, for each
letter brought further notice of trouble and increasing encounters with Cope's
men. To add to the problem, the large crew that Marsh had maintained throughout most of the fall had been reduced to only two men. Williston had deserted,
Dixon had quit, and Ashley had returned to the railroad. This left Reed and
Kennedy who were valiantly trying to occupy the critical areas around No. 9
and No. 13—nearly three miles apart—while the Cope party of four to six men
moved about freely. The processing of Marsh's application for the lands around
Quarries 9 and 13 proceeded very slowly, but finally on February 15th, 1881,
the claims were completed and filed in Reed's and Kennedy's names. However,
further delays resulted from difficulties in determining the precise location of
Quarry 13 (it lies almost precisely on the line between Sections 4 and 5 of
Township 22 north and Range 76 west). Thus, the claims were not approved
until late spring apparently, for as late as April 4th, Reed registered his extreme
anxiety and requested that these papers be rushed out to him.

During all this furor, which dominated Reed's correspondence from November 1880 until the following April, Reed was, surprisingly enough, recovering
large quantities of small bones and jaws from the "pay dirt" of Quarry 9. Between
January 1st and April 1st, Reed worked alone most of the time (Kennedy, although he did assist Reed at times, actually was working for the railroad at Como
during that winter), but in April Reed hired Kennedy and a new man, Phelps,

and his own brother in preparation for the coming summer season. The threat from Cope's parties, so great during the fall and winter, seems to have subsided, in spite of the fact that Cope maintained several collectors at Como throughout the spring and summer of 1881. As the "dangers" declined, Reed and his men increased their efforts to expand Quarry 9 and shipped back to New Haven considerable quantities of small bones recovered from the pay dirt. Letters from Reed repeatedly refer to "quite a lot of jaws," or "I sent you cann jaws by todays mail," etc. and contained fewer and fewer references to Cope's men.

These conditions were soon to change and shortly Reed would again feel the pressure of outside collectors, but the scene was disrupted, if only briefly, by tragedy. On July 19th, 1881, Reed somberly reported:

> My Brother that was working for you got hurt and died last Friday. it took all the money I could raise to pay his funeral expeses and doctor.

July 31, 1881:

> You will likely wish to know how my Brother met his death. we had him clearing of in no 9 and the wind was very high and the dirt was very bad, so he started sunday morning to go to rock creek to wash up with Phelps. he thinking the water was deep took off his clothes and dove in striking on the Bottom and causing Paralysis from the head down. he only lived a short time.

That Reed felt this loss deeply is reflected in the tone of his letters, and in the sharp decline in the frequency of his reports to Marsh. He appears to have accelerated his efforts in the quarries, perhaps to occupy himself completely, and isolate himself from the fact of his brother's death, yet the pathetic picture still comes through. This tragedy may well have been the initial factor in the disillusionment of Reed with the work at Como. From that moment on, he seems to have become more cynical and less enthusiastic about the activities around the Bluff.

However, all things change and, with the coming of fall, came an invasion of other collecting parties. On September 1st, Reed wrote:

> this country is run over with bone hunters and have bin trying to hire my men. they offerd Phelps more than you are paying me but I told him they would not give him steady work and you would not hire him again. I think McDermott the section foreman is going to work for them there has bin six men here looking for fossils the past week. I flowed one party two days up in the vicinity of 13. they was looking for that place but did not find it. I have *stuck up* a notice that the land is taken.

This was followed by the announcement that one of these parties was from Harvard College. At this point Reed began to keep what he called his "historical notes." From these notes:

> about the 15th of August a man in the imploy of Prof. Agassizs came here and wanted to imploy colectors and offered Phelps $85.00 per month but failed to hire him he inquired for Fred Brown who was out prospecting at the time . . . a few days after this Prof. A's man came to no. 9 where we was at work wanted to know if that was the place we found the little jaws I told him to look around and see. we was taking of Bank and had the Pay dirt covered 3 or 4 feet deep. he said he thought ower prospects very poor, said he did not want to interfeer with Prof. Marsh in eney way. I told him there was no dainger for all the important quaries was owned by Prof. Marsh. he said he did not see how that could be and I explained the desert land act to him with slight verations.

If one accepts Reed's historical notes at face value, it is clear that Marsh was extremely fortunate to have a man of Reed's loyalty and industry in charge of the collecting for Yale College. Cope's interests at Como appear to have suffered seriously because he was not able to keep trustworthy men on the job, and Professor Agassiz seems to have fared no better, at least as far as Como Bluff is concerned. Reed's historical notes continue:

> Prof. A's man failed that time [to hire Fred Brown] but hired the section foreman here Petter McDermott by name. McD. did not know a bone from a stone. So he went and talked to F.H.W. [Cope's man] and as near as I can find out divided with him . . . Carlin says he is going to report F.W. to Prof. Cope. I took a little trip last Sunday out on the litle Medicene and folowed the wagon tracks made the day before by W. and one of McD. men and saw where the Bones was loaded[10] and on Monday there was Boxes on the platform marked for Prof. A and others marked for Prof. C—and they all came from one quarey.

This must have been the organization of what Reed referred to as the "Bone Company" which seems to have operated in the Como area until about mid-fall as an independent collecting agency ready to do business with anyone who was interested in fossil bones. About this particular event, Reed is quite clear in his accusations, but how long this company operated, or how many individuals were party to its business, Reed does not say.

10. The famous Bone Cabin Quarry.

As the fall of 1881 progressed, Reed terminated the work at Quarry 13 and closed it for the winter. Then he shifted all efforts to Quarry 9, where large amounts of overburden had been blasted and the bank cut back to expose large areas of "pay dirt." The fossil-bearing seam was carefully quarried out and immediately placed on large white cloths laid out on the floor of the quarry. By this procedure, every possible fragment of pay dirt was recovered. Apparently this innovation was Marsh's idea but, wherever it originated, it seems to have reduced the number of jaw fragments lost. With Reed's team of horses and "ambulance," large wagonloads of pay dirt were hauled from the quarry to Reed's shanty at the station. The plan was to haul as much pay dirt as possible before winter set in and store it at the station where it could be worked over carefully in relative comfort. Reed had purchased a large window which he installed in the roof of the shanty to provide the maximum amount of light for scrutinizing the pay dirt.

During December, Marsh's crew began to separate for the winter—Brown to Colorado, Kenney to Philadelphia and Brooklyn. This left Reed and Phelps at work on the Quarry 9 matrix. Throughout the winter and on into April, they processed ton after ton of clay matrix, sending one can after another of jaws and teeth and various other small bones to Marsh in New Haven. Whenever they ran out of pay dirt, they returned to the quarry and brought back fresh supplies of matrix for processing in the shanty.

In April, most of the old hands returned, Kenney, Kennedy, Ashley, and Brown, all of whom were rehired by Reed for the season of 1882. But almost immediately trouble arose because Kennedy preferred to arrange his own contract directly with Marsh. Reed, who had already survived two prior insurrections, both of which had resulted from independent contracts between Marsh and individual collectors who subsequently felt no responsibility to Reed and therefore challenged his authority, voiced his strong opposition to such dealings by Marsh. It was to no avail, however, and Kennedy was subsequently hired by Marsh quite independent of Reed. Consequently, Kennedy felt himself to be quite outside of Reed's authority and free to act on his own. The result was that, like Frank Williston and Arthur Lakes before him, Kennedy soon considered himself boss of Marsh's enterprises at Como—with authority over the men hired by Reed. Whether Marsh was aware of the practical problems presented by two bosses is not clear. Marsh may have taken this action in order to have some independent and reliable check on his field marshal, or it may have been an attempt to induce greater productivity by generating greater competition among his collectors. It seems unlikely that Marsh was unable to foresee the demoralizing effect on employees of having to satisfy two bosses, especially in view of the prior incidents with Lakes and Williston. In any event, the result of the situation was quite predictable, and it followed earlier patterns. Phelps could not satisfy both Kennedy and Reed and consequently was discharged.

At this point Reed was anticipating a return visit by Professor Cope, and he was preparing once again to occupy the critical sites (Nos. 9 and 13). In order to dispose his forces effectively, Reed had to amend his relations with Kennedy and Ashley and rehire Phelps. The reconciliation appears to have been at least partially successful during the early weeks of the summer. In the midst of these activities, a new locality, Quarry 14, was discovered between Quarries 9 and 10. This was the last major discovery[11] made while Reed was still in command of Marsh's forces at Como. The remains found in No. 14 consisted of a partial skeleton of a large carnivore, *Antrodemus ferox* (*Allosaurus*) (YPM 1893).

For more than a year Como Station had been operated on a sort of on-again-off-again basis by the Union Pacific Railroad. Frequently the station would be locked and no agent available. The post office had been closed for many months, necessitating frequent trips to Rock Creek or Medicine Bow in order to mail parcels to New Haven and to pick up mail from Marsh. Indications were that the railroad management considered Como an expendable station. In June 1882, the telegraph station at Como was renamed Aurora, apparently in a move to separate the telegraph and railroad services there. For the first few months, W.W. Brownson served as agent of both stations but, from the time of the separation, Como was doomed as an active station of the Union Pacific Railroad.

The summer of 1882[12] appears to have been a calm—even humdrum—time for everyone at Como Bluff, in spite of the fact that rival parties roamed about seeking "mammal quarries" for Marsh, Cope, and Agassiz. Reed, Phelps, and Kenney (Kennedy and Ashley had left early in the summer presumably to go into mining) divided their time between Quarries 9 and 13, working somewhat halfheartedly. It is evident from the majority of Reed's letters of that summer and fall that he had become quite disenchanted with the bone business. Whether this was due to the increasing monotony of quarry work, the frequent unpleasant encounters with rival parties, the not infrequent flare-ups between men under his charge, or the rather unpredictable schedule of payment of his "poor" wages, is not clear. Any or all of these may have contributed to Reed's growing restlessness and dissatisfaction. He complained about all of them at one time or

11. An important quarry site that is not recorded here is that of *Nodosaurus textilis* (YPM 1815). Reed placed this site as at least 100 feet above the *Atlantosaurus* beds in the Cretaceous (Dakota) sandstone, but never located it closer than 1½ miles east of Quarry 13.

12. This was about the time that Marsh was appointed Vertebrate Paleontologist of the United States Geological Survey.

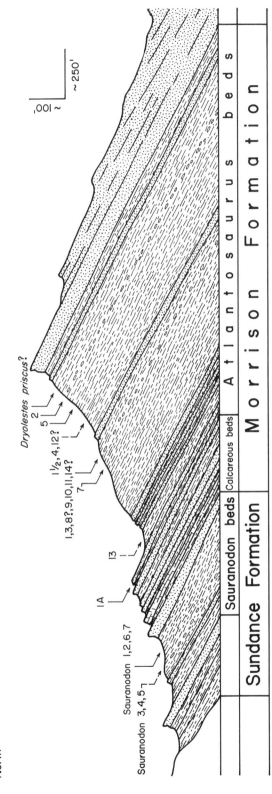

North   South

~ 100'

~ 250'

Dryolestes priscus?

2

5

1½, 4, 12?

1,3,8?,9,10,11,14?

7

13

1A

Sauranodon 1,2,6,7

Sauranodon 3,4,5

Sundance Formation	Morrison Formation	
Sauranodon beds	Calcareous beds	Atlantosaurus beds

STRATIGRAPHIC SECTION - COMO BLUFF

Taken from a sketch by Arthur Lakes

Fig. 12. Generalized stratigraphic section of the main ridge at Como Bluff as sketched by Arthur Lakes in 1879 from near Robber's Roost. The approximate stratigraphic positions of the fossil quarries located on the main bluff are indicated by solid-line arrows. The levels of fossil quarries located elsewhere on the Como Anticline are shown by dashed-line arrows.

other. Whatever the reasons, by mid-fall Reed had served informal notice of his intention to leave Marsh's employment in the spring.

December, January, and February were spent much as the previous winter had been, with Reed and his helpers Phelps and Kenney hauling pay dirt from Quarry 9 down to the shanty where it was processed for small bones, jaws, and teeth. The productivity, however, was far from what it had been in preceding years. Phelps and Kenney quite understandably grew anxious about their future in the "bone business" as Reed's protestations about leaving Como became more emphatic. In January Reed tried to sell his house and land to Marsh for a future headquarters at Como, but Marsh declined.

On April 2nd, 1883, almost six years to the day after his entrance into the bone business for Marsh, Reed resigned, announcing that he had turned over all of Marsh's property and interests to Kennedy, so that he could take advantage of an opportunity to go into the sheep business. Reed had served a remarkable tenure as a collector for Marsh; he had supervised most of the collecting at Como, vigorously defended Marsh's sites from poachers, and carefully collected and shipped to New Haven literally hundreds of specimens, most of them new, and many of them among the most important paleontologic finds in all of North America.

Reed, unfortunately, never received due reward or recognition for his services at Como, but his departure failed to bring him better times. His venture into the sheep business in the nearby Shirley Basin proved to be a near disaster, for he lost almost half of his herd of 2,400 sheep during the severe winter of 1883–84. The following year Reed was back at the bone business as an independent collector.

THE FINAL YEARS (1883–1889)

Kennedy assumed command of the Yale paleontologic enterprises at Aurora (Como) on April 1st and immediately set out to clear the winter and spring debris from Quarry 9. To help him with this heavy work, he hired a new man, William Beck. Kenney and Phelps in the meantime had been put to work re-opening Quarry 13. The Kenney–Phelps combination failed to work, however, and Phelps quit early in July. Fred Brown, who had worked at Como before and had been working for Marsh at Garden Park, Colorado, during the preceding year, returned unannounced to Como as an independent collector only a few days before Phelps left. Marsh, quite naturally, rehired Brown to fill the vacancy left by Phelps, but in so doing he set up another potentially explosive situation.

Brown, who was well known for his independent attitude, refused to work either for or with Kennedy and demanded that he be allowed to work alone. Marsh once again was faced with a divided field force. Before long, Brown, who neither liked to boss nor be bossed, had convinced Marsh that he could be more useful to Marsh if he were free of all others, but nevertheless, Brown left about six months later in order to be free once again to operate as an independent collector.

Both Quarries 9 and 13 prospered during the summer and fall of '83 under the efforts of Kennedy in No. 9 and Brown in No. 13. During the fall, Beck and Kennedy (who had adopted many of Reed's procedures) back-packed numerous loads of pay dirt from Quarry 9 to Kennedy's quarters at Reed's place for processing during the coming winter months. (Kennedy had been married the previous summer, and he and his wife had moved into Reed's house situated about three quarters of a mile east of the station.) Kennedy, although not in a class with Reed as a collector, performed very creditably in fulfilling his responsibilities to Marsh for the better part of two years. He was able to nearly double the size of the excavation at Quarry 9 through his skills with powder and his ability to blast off considerable quantities of overburden that covered the precious pay dirt. But, while the fossil shipments continued to arrive at New Haven from Quarry 9, fossils from Quarry 13 stopped almost completely when Brown left in midwinter, in spite of the fact that Brown still considered his chief allegiance was to Marsh. Kennedy, already annoyed that Marsh had hired Brown the summer before, became very angry with Marsh during that winter for interfering with his supervision of the collecting procedures at Como. When Marsh attempted to solve the problem by putting Brown in complete charge of Yale operations during January 1884, Kennedy warned Marsh that he was likely to lose both of his prime sites (9 and 13), indicating that one of his most trusted parties was apt to betray him.

In spite of Kennedy's warnings, Brown was rehired in March, and for the next twelve months Marsh had two field generals—Kennedy who refused to give up his control of Quarry 9 and Brown who assumed charge of No. 13. Kennedy continued to expand Quarry 9 and ship occasional finds to Marsh. He still lived in Reed's house near the station. Brown and Beck, on the other hand, lived in a tent camp on Rock Creek near Quarry 13. And so the situation remained for nearly a year, with the teams producing moderate collections from their respective quarries, trying to outdo the other, but having as little contact as possible with each other. Kennedy appears to have been most bitter that he had not been given full command of all Marsh's activities at Como.

Both Kennedy and Brown were hot-headed but the incidents between them were relatively minor—save one, that is. In December, Kennedy wrote of the most serious encounter:

> i shiped you 3 cans fossils 16th and came near being my last shipment to you for a man working for you by the name of Brown assaulted me at station with two revolvers and wanted me to fight him. i Refused on account of my family and he said to agents wife before i get thear he would shoot me. he has Been my Enemy since you left hear for what Reasons i dont Know and more don't care from this out. he must not molest me or i will put him under Bonds to keep the Peace. i have Been in this territory 10 years and it is the first time i had my life threatened and the only Enemies i have is the McDermotts and him.

This perilous episode seems to have marked a strong change of the tide in Brown's favor. Although Kennedy continued to work Quarry 9 and occasionally send a new jar or can of bones to Marsh, he became less aggressive, complained less about his curtailed authority, and wrote more frequently of leaving Como. Brown, on the other hand, perhaps more confident as a result of Marsh's wire nearly a year before instructing him to take over the Como operations, moved about more and more freely. By March, Brown had shifted his efforts from No. 13 to the old Quarry 10 site—barely a hundred yards from Kennedy in Quarry 9—in an effort to recover the skull of the "Brontosaurus" skeleton.

On April 2nd, Kennedy finally pulled out, turning all the equipment and materials over to Beck. At this point, Fred Brown assumed full command of Yale's collecting program at Como. This was the last major event at Como Bluff, except for a few incidental excursions into the region by other parties at infrequent intervals in subsequent years. Brown remained at Como and continued to explore and excavate, and to ship occasional specimens for another four years. During this time, he made further important collections from Quarries 9 and 13, reopened No. 10, and opened seven new quarries of his own in the vicinity of No. 13 (Quarries A–G).[13] None of these new sites, however, matched any of the previous quarries, and some were never even located in his correspondence with Marsh.

It appears from Brown's letters, and from several of Marsh's, for the years 1888 and 1889, that Marsh kept Brown on at Como partly to guard his quarry sites from other collectors (the University of Wyoming had collectors in the area during the spring of 1889), but also to have him work at Quarry 9. Marsh

---

13. Fred Brown also provided the most detailed quarry maps of any of Marsh's collectors, and many of his quarry diagrams have been published in Gilmore's papers. It is largely due to this scrupulous care on Brown's part that the many skeletons of Quarry 13 could be sorted out.

seemed to have had some irrepressible hope that the mammal quarry was not really played out after all. But after many months with practically no production from Quarry 9, Marsh terminated his interests at Como Bluff. There is no record available of the precise reasons for the final cessation of activities, nor even any indication of its approach. Brown's last letter to Marsh, dated June 17, 1889, marks the last word from this amazing locale to the Peabody Museum. It noted the rarity of small bones in No. 9, but did describe bones cropping out all along the side running into the hill. Brown's departure is unrecorded, but a letter from Henry Kessler, one of Brown's assistants during those last years, informed Marsh of Brown's death in mid-March of 1890, less than nine months after his departure from Como.

EPILOGUE

As a postscript, it might be added that more than a decade after Fred Brown abandoned Quarry 13, Como Bluff was revisited by American Museum parties under the leadership of Jacob Wortman and University of Wyoming parties led by W. C. Knight. Pickings were very slim, however, the most significant finds being those of partial skeletons of *Apatosaurus* (AMNH 222) and *Diplodocus* (AMNH 223). The discouraging yield caused these and subsequent collecting parties to concentrate their activities farther north in the Bone Cabin and Freeze Out Hills localities.[14]

The Como Bluff era spanned an interval of slightly more than twelve years, from early April 1877 to mid-June 1889. During that time a great many men contributed to the legend of this place, exactly how many can never be known. An unbelievable wealth of paleontologic specimens was unearthed, the total amount of which is still not definitely known. Thus, Como Bluff left an impressive mark on the history of the American West, the Peabody Museum, and our present understanding of ancient life and evolution.

14. In recent years Yale parties under the direction of the senior author have made several surveys of the Como Bluff region in attempts to rediscover Marsh's quarry sites. To date only four (Nos. 1½, 2, 4, and 5) of the main quarries in the Morrison formation have not yet been found or at least placed within a few yards of the actual site. Precise locations of those Como Bluff quarries that have been relocated (Quarries 1, 1A, 3, 6, 7, 8, 9, 10, 11, 12, 13, and 14) have been recorded on enlarged (scale 1″=1,650′) aerial photographs and are preserved in the records of the Peabody Museum.

FAUNAL LISTS

COMO BLUFF QUARRIES

The asterisk denotes throughout that the holotype came from the quarry under which it is listed. Marsh's original names are given in parentheses.

REED'S YPM QUARRY 1, T. 22 N., R. 77 W., SEC. 10.

Class: Reptilia
  Order: Saurischia
  Suborder: Sauropoda
      Camarasaurus grandis (*Morosaurus*) (YPM 1901)
      Camarasaurus impar (*Morosaurus*) (YPM 1900) [=*Camarasaurus grandis*]
      Camarasaurus robustus (*Morosaurus*) (YPM 1902) [=*Camarasaurus grandis*]
      Pleurocoelus montanus (YPM 1908)
      Diplodocus sp.
  Suborder: Theropoda
      Antrodemus atrox (*Creosaurus*) (YPM 1890)
Class: Mammalia
  Unspecified tooth

LAKES' YPM QUARRY 1A (BIG CANYON QUARRY), T. 22 N., R. 77 W., SEC. 17.

Class: Reptilia
  Order: Saurischia
  Suborder: Sauropoda
      Camarasaurus sp.
  Suborder: Theropoda
      Antrodemus sp.

51

Order: Ornithischia
  Suborder: Ornithopoda
    Camptosaurus amplus (*Camptonotus*) (YPM 1879)

REED'S YPM QUARRY 1½, T. 22 N., R. 77 W., SEC. 8.

Class: Reptilia
  Order: Saurischia
    Suborder: Sauropoda
      Unidentifiable sp.
    Suborder: Theropoda
      Antrodemus valens

REED'S YPM QUARRY 2, T. 22 N., R. 77 W., SEC. 16.

Class: Reptilia
  Order: Saurischia
    Suborder: Sauropoda
      Apatosaurus sp.

REED'S YPM QUARRY 3, T. 22 N., R. 77 W., SEC. 11.

Class: Reptilia
  Order: Saurischia
    Suborder: Sauropoda
      Camarasaurus grandis (*Morosaurus*)
    Suborder: Theropoda
      Antrodemus lucaris (*Labrosaurus*) (YPM 1931)
  Order: Ornithischia
    Suborder: Ornithopoda
      Laosaurus sp.

REED'S YPM QUARRY 4, T. 22 N., R. 76 W., SEC. 6.

Class: Reptilia
  Order: Saurischia
    Suborder: Sauropoda
      Apatosaurus sp.

       Camarasaurus sp.

       Barosaurus sp.

    Suborder: Theropoda

       Antrodemus valens

  Order: Ornithischia

    Suborder: Stegosauria

       Stegosaurus sp.

REED'S YPM QUARRY 5, T. 22 N., R. 77 W., SEC. 17.

Class: Reptilia

  Order: Saurischia

    Suborder: Sauropoda

       Diplodocus sp.

  Order: Ornithischia

    Suborder: Ornithopoda

       Dryosaurus altus (YPM 1876) [=*Laosaurus altus?*]

  Order: Pterosauria

       Dermodactylus montanus (YPM 2020)

REED'S YPM QUARRY 6, T. 22 N., R. 77 W., SEC. 11.

Class: Reptilia

  Order: Crocodilia

    Suborder: Mesosuchia

       Goniopholis sp.

REED'S YPM QUARRY 7 (THREE TREES QUARRY), T. 22 N., R. 77 W., SEC. 18.

Class: Reptilia

  Order: Ornithischia

    Suborder: Ornithopoda

       Laosaurus consors (YPM 1882)

REED'S YPM QUARRY 8, T. 22 N., R. 77 W., SEC. 11.

Class: Reptilia
  Order: Saurischia
    Suborder: Sauropoda
       Diplodocus sp.
       Camarasaurus sp.
    Suborder: Theropoda
       Antrodemus sp.
       "Coelurus fragilis"
  Order: Ornithischia
    Suborder: Stegosauria
       Stegosaurus sp.
  Order: Crocodilia
    Suborder: Mesosuchia
       Goniopholis sp.
  Order: Chelonia
       Species indeterminate

REED'S YPM QUARRY 9 (MAMMAL QUARRY), T. 22 N., R. 77 W., SEC. 12.

Class: Osteichthyes
 Subclass: Choanichthyes
  Order: Dipnoi
       Ceratodus guntheri
Class: Amphibia
  Order: Anura
    Suborder: Aglossa?
       Eobatrachus agilis (YPM 1862)
    Suborder: Neobatrachia
       Comobatrachus aenigmatis (YPM 1863)
  Order: Urodela
       Comonecturoides marshi (YPM 3919)
Class: Reptilia
  Order: Chelonia
    Suborder: Amphichelydia
       Glyptops ornatus

Order: Crocodilia
  Suborder: Mesosuchia
     Goniopholis sp.
Order: Rhynchocephalia
     Opisthias rarus (USNM 2860)
     Theretairus antiquus (YPM 13764)
Order: Saurischia
  Suborder: Sauropoda
     Camarasaurus sp.
  Suborder: Theropoda
     Coelurus fragilis
     Antrodemus valens
Order: Ornithischia
  Suborder: Ornithopoda
     Laosaurus gracilis[1] (YPM 1875)
     Laosaurus ?consors
     Laosaurus celer[1] (YPM 1874)
     Dryosaurus sp. [=*Laosaurus* sp.]
     Camptosaurus sp.
  Suborder: Stegosauria
     Stegosaurus sp.
Order: Squamata
  Suborder: Lacertilia
     Cteniogenys antiquus (USNM 6134)
Order: Crocodilia or Eosuchia?
  Suborder: Mesosuchia or Choristodera?
     Macellognathus vagans (YPM 1415)
Class: Aves?
     Laopteryx priscus (YPM 1800)
Class: Mammalia
  Order: Multituberculata
     Ctenacodon serratus (YPM 11833)
     Ctenacodon nanus (YPM 11832) [=*Ctenacodon serratus*]
     Ctenacodon scindens (YPM 10366)
     Ctenacodon laticeps (*Allodon*) (YPM 11761)
     Psalodon potens (*Ctenacodon*) (YPM 11834)

---

1. This specimen may have come from Quarry 9, but records in the Peabody Museum do not establish this.

Psalodon fortis (*Allodon*) (YPM 11760)

Psalodon marshi (USNM 2684)

Order: Triconodonta

Phascolodon gidleyi (USNM 2703)

Aploconodon comoënsis (USNM 2791)

Trioracodon bisulcus (*Triconodon*) (YPM 11851)

Priacodon ferox (*Tinodon*) (YPM 606)

Priacodon robustus (*Tinodon*) (YPM 11846)

Priacodon lulli (YPM 13625)

Priacodon grandaevus (YPM 10349)

Order: Symmetrodonta

Tinodon bellus (YPM 11843)

Tinodon lepidus (YPM 11845)

Menacodon rarus (USNM 2131) [=*Tinodon lepidus*]

Amphidon superstes (YPM 13638)

Eurylambda aequicrurius (YPM 13639)

Order: Pantotheria

Paurodon valens (USNM 2143)

Archaeotrigon brevimaxillus (USNM 2793)

Archaeotrigon distagmus (YPM 13641)

Tathiodon agilis (YPM 13649)

Dryolestes priscus

Laolestes eminens (YPM 13719)

Laolestes vorax (*Dryolestes*) (USNM 2727)

Laolestes grandis (YPM 13727)

Laolestes segnis (*Asthenodon*) (USNM 2862)

Amblotherium gracilis (*Stylacodon*) (YPM 11883)

Laodon venustus (USNM 2142) [=*Amblotherium gracilis*]

Amblotherium debilis (YPM 11821)

Herpetairus arcuatus (*Dryolestes*) (YPM 11822)

Herpetairus humilis (YPM 13745)

Herpetairus obtusus (*Dryolestes*) (YPM 11819A)

Melanodon oweni (YPM 10663)

Melanodon goodrichi (YPM 13738)

Euthlastus cordiformis (YPM 13755)

Miccyclotyrans minimus (USNM 2754)

Malthacolestes osborni (YPM 13751)

Pelicopsis dubius (YPM 13754)

Stylacodon validus (USNM 2722) [=*Dryolestes priscus*]

Order: Docodonta
    Docodon victor (Diplocynodon) (YPM 11826)
    Docodon striatus (YPM 11823)
    Docodon crassus (Enneodon) (USNM 2130)
    Docodon affinis (Enneodon) (USNM 2129)
    Docodon superus (YPM 10647)

REED'S YPM QUARRY 10, T. 22 N., R. 77 W., SEC. 12.

Class: Reptilia
  Order: Saurischia
    Suborder: Sauropoda
      Apatosaurus excelsus (Brontosaurus) (YPM 1980)

REED'S YPM QUARRY 11, T. 22 N., R. 77 W., SEC. 12.

Class: Reptilia
  Order: Saurischia
    Suborder: Sauropoda
      Apatosaurus amplus (Brontosaurus) (YPM 1981)
  Order: Ornithischia
    Suborder: Stegosauria
      Stegosaurus duplex (YPM 1858) [=*Stegosaurus ungulatus*]
Class: Mammalia
  Unspecified tooth

REED'S YPM QUARRY 12, T. 22 N., R. 77 W., SEC. 18.

Class: Reptilia
  Order: Saurischia
    Suborder: Sauropoda
      Camarasaurus sp.
      Diplodocus sp.
    Suborder: Theropoda
      Antrodemus sp.
      Coelurus sp.

Order: Ornithischia
    Suborder: Stegosauria
        Stegosaurus ungulatus (YPM 1853)
    Suborder: Ornithopoda
        Laosaurus sp.
Order: Crocodilia
    Suborder: Mesosuchia
        Goniopholis sp.
Order: Chelonia
        Species indeterminate

REED'S YPM QUARRY 13, T. 22 N., R. 76 W., SEC. 4 OR 5.

Class: Reptilia
    Order: Saurischia
    Suborder: Sauropoda
        Camarasaurus lentus (*Morosaurus*) (YPM 1910)
        Diplodocus sp.
    Suborder: Theropoda
        Coelurus agilis (YPM 2010)
        Coelurus fragilis (YPM 1991)
    Order: Ornithischia
    Suborder: Ornithopoda
        Camptosaurus dispar (*Camptonotus*) (YPM 1877)
        Camptosaurus medius (*Camptonotus*) (YPM 1880)
        Camptosaurus nanus (*Camptonotus*) (USNM 2210)
        Camptosaurus browni (*Camptonotus*) (USNM 4282)
        Camptosaurus depressus
        Laosaurus sp.
    Suborder: Stegosauria
        Stegosaurus affinis (YPM uncatalogued)
        Stegosaurus sulcatus (USNM 4937)
        Stegosaurus stenops
        Stegosaurus ungulatus
        Stegosaurus laticeps (*Diracodon*) (YPM 1885)

Order: Chelonia
  Suborder: Amphichelydia
    Glyptops plicatulus
Order: Crocodilia
  Suborder: Mesosuchia
    Goniopholis sp.

REED'S YPM QUARRY 14, T. 22 N., R. 77 W., SEC. 12.

Class: Reptilia
  Order: Saurischia
    Suborder: Theropoda
      Antrodemus ferox (Allosaurus) (YPM 1893)

REED'S YPM LOWER CRETACEOUS QUARRY
(Location Unknown)

Class: Reptilia
  Order: Ornithischia
    Suborder: Ankylosauria
      Nodosaurus textilis (YPM 1815)

BROWN'S YPM QUARRY A (Location Unknown)

Class: Reptilia
  Order: Ornithischia
    Suborder: Stegosauria
      Stegosaurus sp.

BROWN'S YPM QUARRY B, T. 22 N., R. 76 W., SEC. 5.

Class: Reptilia
  Order: Ornithischia
    Suborder: Stegosauria
      Stegosaurus sp.

BROWN'S YPM QUARRY C, T. 22 N., R. 76 W., SEC. 5.

Class: Reptilia
  Order: Saurischia
    Suborder: Theropoda
      Antrodemus valens

BROWN'S YPM QUARRY D, T. 22 N., R. 76 W., SEC. 5.

Class: Reptilia
  Order: Saurischia
    Suborder: Theropoda
      Antrodemus valens

BROWN'S YPM QUARRY G (Location Unknown)

Class: Reptilia
  Order: Saurischia
    Suborder: Sauropoda
      Camarasaurus sp.

LAKES' YPM QUARRY 1, T. 4 S., R. 70 W., SEC. 26.

Class: Reptilia
  Order: Saurischia
    Suborder: Sauropoda
      Atlantosaurus montanus (YPM 1835)
    Suborder: Theropoda
      Antrodemus sp.
  Order: Crocodilia
    Suborder: Mesosuchia
      Goniopholis felise (*Diplosaurus*) (YPM 517)

LAKES' YPM QUARRY 5, T. 4 S., R. 70 W., SEC. 26.

Class: Reptilia
  Order: Saurischia
    Suborder: Sauropoda
      Diplodocus lacustris (YPM 1922)
  Order: Ornithischia
    Suborder: Stegosauria
      Stegosaurus armatus (YPM 1850)

LAKES' YPM QUARRY 8, T. 4 S., R. 70 W., SEC. 26.

Class: Reptilia
  Order: Saurischia
    Suborder: Sauropoda
      Apatosaurus ajax

61

LAKES' YPM QUARRY 10, T. 4 S., R. 70 W., SEC. 35.

Class: Reptilia
  Order: Saurischia
    Suborder: Sauropoda
        Apatosaurus ajax (YPM 1860)
        Apatosaurus laticollis (YPM 1861)
        Atlantosaurus immanis (YPM 1840)
    Suborder: Theropoda
        Antrodemus sp.
  Order: Chelonia
        Species indeterminate

FELCH'S YPM QUARRY 1, T. 17 S., R. 70 W., SEC. 28.

Class: Osteichthyes
  Subclass: Choanichthyes
    Order: Dipnoi
      Ceratodus guntheri
Class: Reptilia
  Order: Saurischia
    Suborder: Sauropoda
      Haplocanthosaurus priscus (CM 572)
      Haplocanthosaurus utterbackii (CM 879)
      Brachiosaurus sp.
      "Morosaurus" agilis (USNM 5384)
      Apatosaurus sp.
      Diplodocus longus (YPM 1920)
    Suborder: Theropoda
      Antrodemus fragilis (*Allosaurus*) (YPM 1930)
      Labrosaurus ferox (USNM 2315)
      Ceratosaurus nasicornis (USNM 4735)
      Coelurus agilis
  Order: Ornithischia
    Suborder: Ornithopoda
      Laosaurus gracilis
      Camptosaurus medius
    Suborder: Stegosauria
      Stegosaurus stenops (USNM 4934)
      Stegosaurus armatus (?)
  Order: Crocodilia
    Suborder: Mesosuchia
      Goniopholis sp.
  Order: Chelonia
    Suborder: Amphichelydia
      Probaena sculpta
      Glyptops plicatulus

Class: Mammalia
    Order: Pantotheria
        Kepolestes coloradensis (USNM 2723)
    Order: Docodonta
        Docodon sp.

FELCH'S YPM QUARRY 2, T. 17 S., R. 70 W., SEC. 28.

Class: Reptilia
    Order: Saurischia
      Suborder: Sauropoda
        Camarasaurus (?) sp.
      Suborder: Theropoda
        Antrodemus sp.

MARSH'S SAUROPOD PLATES

PLATE 1

Diplodocus longus Marsh (1878) USNM 2672
Lateral view (1) and anterior view (2) of restored skull[1]

HORIZON: Morrison formation

LOCALITY: Felch YPM Quarry 1, Garden Park, T. 17 S., R. 70 W., Sec. 28, Fremont County, Colo.

ABBREVIATIONS:

a	antorbital fossa
an	angular
b	antorbital fenestra
c	external nares
d	orbit
dn	dentary
e	infratemporal fenestra
fr	frontal
j	jugal
m	maxilla
n	nasal
oc	occipital condyle
pf	prefrontal
pm	premaxilla
po	postorbital + postfrontal
q	quadrate
qj	quadratojugal
sq	squamosal

1. Marsh considered this part of the holotype, but Felch's quarry map shows that it was far removed from the type caudals.

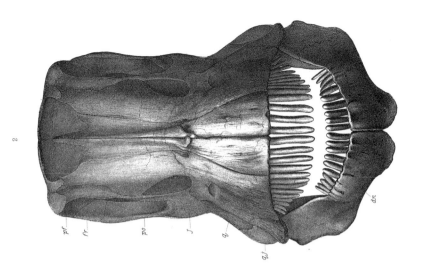

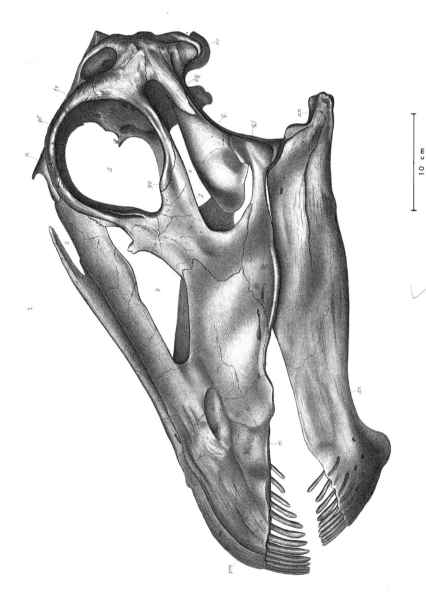

PLATE 2

Diplodocus longus Marsh (1878) USNM 2672

Dorsal view (1) and posterior view (2) of restored skull;[1] medial view (3) of right mandible

HORIZON: Morrison formation

LOCALITY: Felch YPM Quarry 1, Garden Park, T. 17 S., R. 70 W., Sec. 28, Fremont County, Colo.

ABBREVIATIONS:

a	antorbital fossa
an	angular
ar	articular
b	antorbital fenestra
c	external nares
d	orbit
dn	dentary
e	infratemporal fenestra
f	fontanel
fp	postorbital + postfrontal
fr	frontal
g	supratemporal fenestra
m	maxilla
n	nasal
oc	occipital condyle
p	parietal
p'	paroccipital process
pf	prefrontal
pm	premaxilla
pt	pterygoid
q	quadrate
qj	quadratojugal
s	symphysis
sp	splenial
sr	surangular

---

1. Marsh considered this part of the holotype, but Felch's quarry map shows that it was far removed from the type caudals.

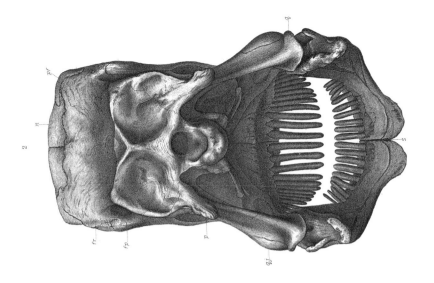

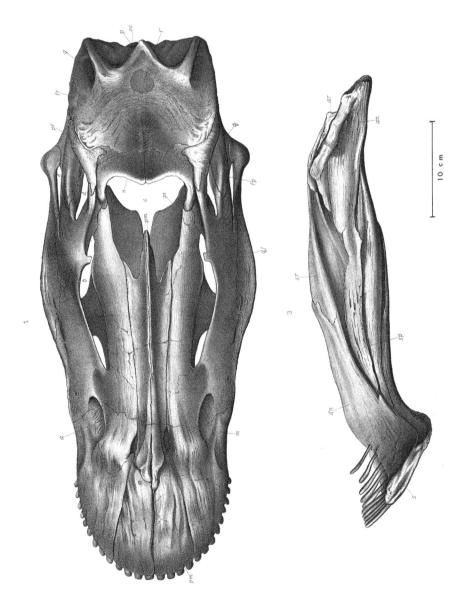

PLATE 3

Morosaurus grandis[1] Marsh (1877) YPM 1905

1. Basicranium in lateral (1), dorsal (1a), anterior (1b), ventral (1c), and posterior (1d) views

2. Left exoccipital–opisthotic complex in lateral (2), anterior (2a), medial (2b), posterior (2c), and dorsal (2d) views

3. Supraoccipital (3) in ventral view

   HORIZON: Morrison formation

   LOCALITY: YPM Quarry 1, Como Bluff, T. 22 N., R. 77 W., Sec. 10, Albany County, Wyo.

4. (a–d) Postfrontal (?), YPM 1912

   HORIZON: Morrison formation

   LOCALITY: YPM Quarry 3, Como Bluff, T. 22 N., R. 77 W., Sec. 11, Albany County, Wyo.

   ABBREVIATIONS:
b	endocranial cavity
bo	basioccipital tubercle
bp	basipterygoid process
bs	basisphenoid suture
es	exoccipital suture
l	lateral wall of braincase
oc	occipital condyle
p	paroccipital process
pf	pituitary fossa
s	parasphenoid
ss	supraoccipital suture

1. Now referred to *Camarasaurus grandis*.

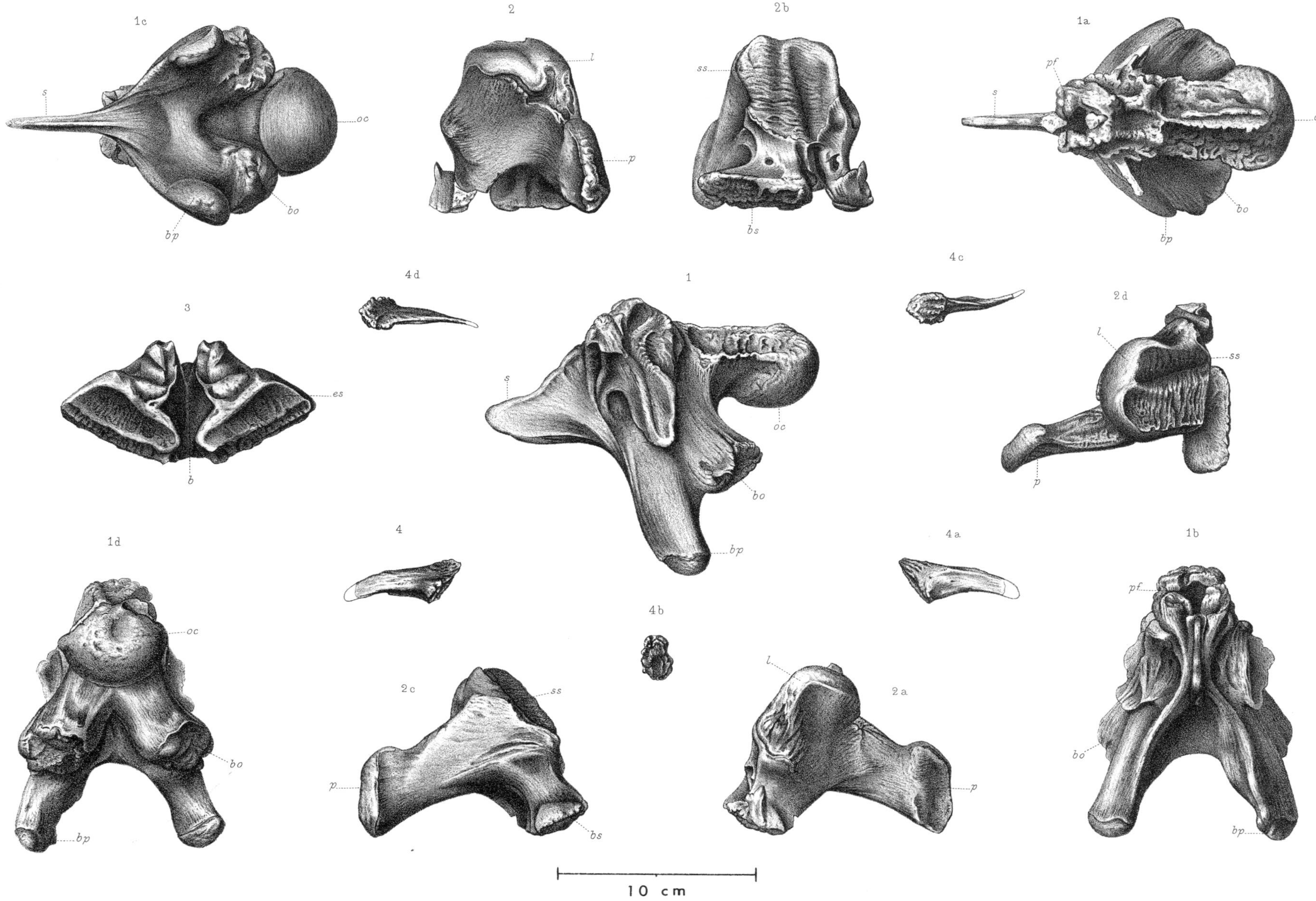

1a
oc
bo
bp
pf
s

2d
ss
l
p

1b
bp
pf
bo

4c

4a

2a
p
l
bp

10 cm

2b
ss
bs

1
oc
bo
bp
s

4b

2c
ss
bs
p

4

4d

2
l
p

1c
oc
bo
bp
s

3
es
b

1d
oc
bo
bp

PLATE 4

Morosaurus grandis[1] Marsh (1877) YPM 1905

1. Left quadrate in lateral (1), anterior (1a), medial (1b), posterior (1c), and ventral (1d) views

2. Left pterygoid in lateral (2), medial (2a), posterior (2b), and dorsal (2c) views

3. Left quadratojugal in lateral (3), anterior (3a), medial (3b), and posterior (3c) views

4. Left squamosal in lateral (4), anterior (4a), medial (4b), posterior (4c), and dorsal (4d) views

HORIZON: Morrison formation

LOCALITY: YPM Quarry 1, Como Bluff, T. 22 N., R. 77 W., Sec. 10, Albany County, Wyo.

ABBREVIATIONS:

ar	articular surface for articular
f	fossa for basipterygoid process
h	head of quadrate
pf	articulation for postorbital + postfrontal
pl	palatine process of pterygoid
pp	pterygoid process of quadrate
ps	articular surface for pterygoid
q	articular surface for quadrate
qj	quadratojugal suture
tp	pterygoid flange

1. Now referred to *Camarasaurus grandis.*

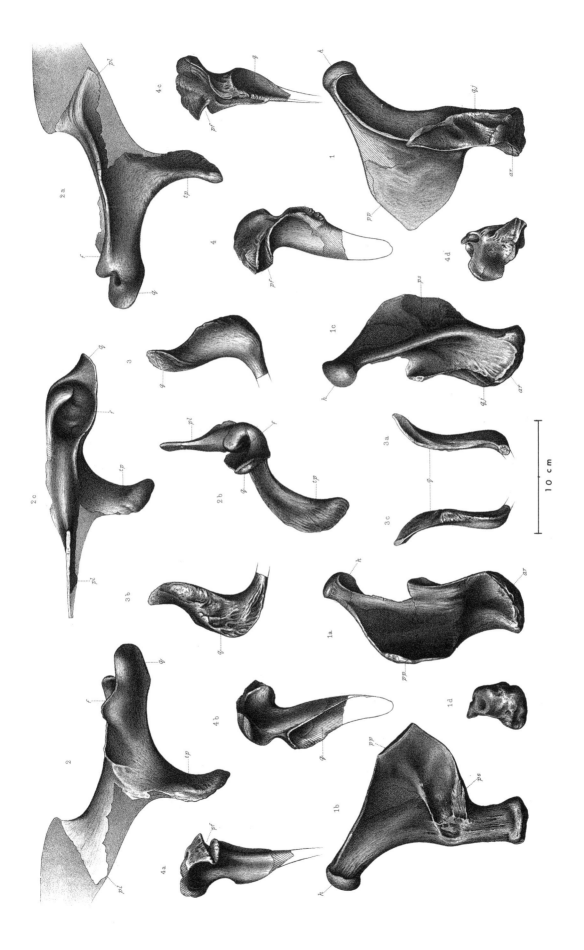

10 cm

PLATE 5

Brontosaurus excelsus[1] Marsh (1879) YPM 1911[2]

Left premaxilla in lateral (1), medial (2), and posterior (3) views

Left maxilla in lateral (4), and medial (5) views; anterior views (6) of premaxillae and maxillae

HORIZON: Morrison formation

LOCALITY: YPM Quarry 13 East, Como Bluff, T. 22 N., R. 76 W., Sec. 4 or 5, Albany County, Wyo.

ABBREVIATIONS:
a	ascending maxillary process
m	maxilla
ms	maxilla suture
n	nasal
pm	premaxilla
pms	premaxilla suture
s	symphysis

1. Now referred to *Apatosaurus excelsus*.

2. Probably assignable to *Camarasaurus* sp. Marsh used these skull elements in his first restoration of *Brontosaurus; Amer. Jour. Sci.,* 1883. They were found isolated in the south end of Quarry 13 East. No other bones of *Apatosaurus* (*Brontosaurus*) have been identified from Quarry 13.

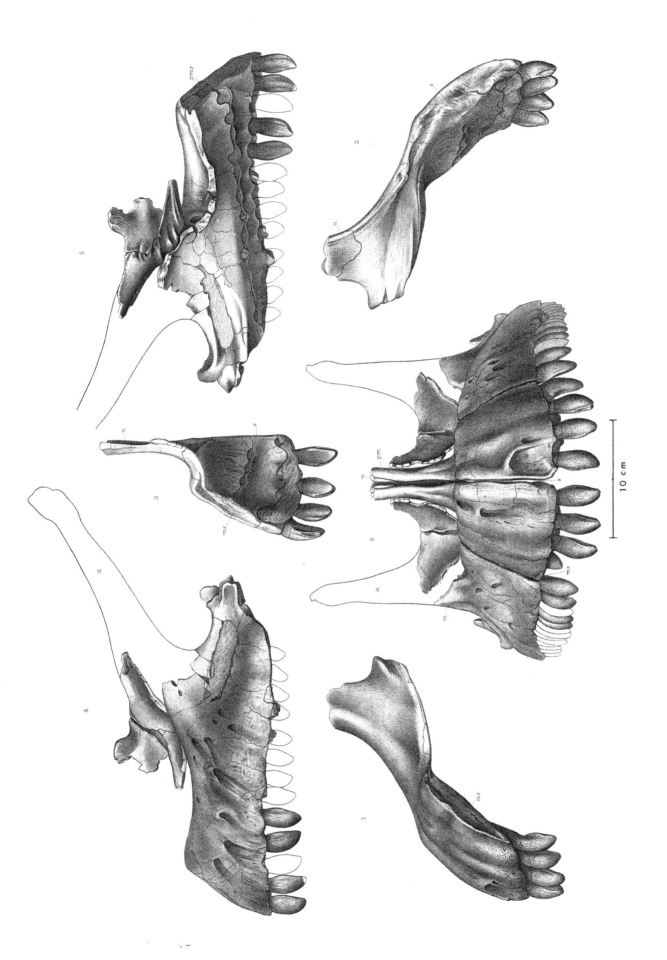

10 cm

PLATE 6

Brontosaurus excelsus[1] Marsh (1879) YPM 1911[2]

Left dentary in lateral (1), dorsal (2), ventral (3), and medial (4) (reversed) views

HORIZON: Morrison formation

LOCALITY: YPM Quarry 13 East, Como Bluff, T. 22 N., R. 76 W., Sec. 4 or 5, Albany County, Wyo.

ABBREVIATIONS: *a*   alveolus
               f   dental foramen
               mg Meckelian groove
               s   symphysis

1. Now referred to *Apatosaurus excelsus*.
2. Probably assignable to *Camarasaurus* sp. See note 2 to Plate 5.

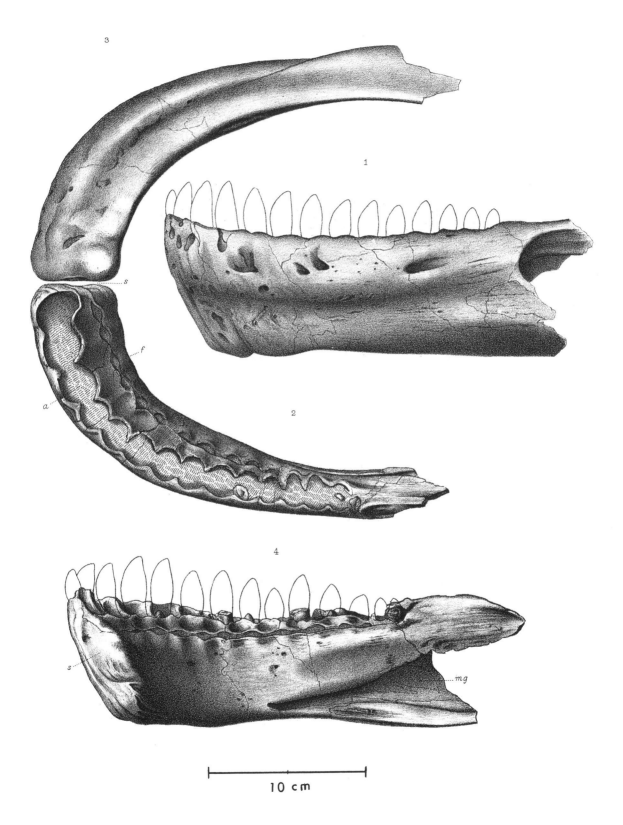

10 cm

PLATE 7

Morosaurus grandis[1] Marsh (1877) YPM 1905?

Unworn tooth in lateral (1), anterior (2), medial (3), posterior (4), and ventral (5) views

Worn tooth in lateral (6), anterior (7), medial (8), and dorsal (9) views

Unworn replacement? tooth in medial (10), anterior (11), lateral (12), and posterior (13) views

HORIZON: Morrison formation

LOCALITY: YPM Quarry 1, Como Bluff, T. 22 N., R. 77 W., Sec. 10, Albany County, Wyo.

1. Now referred to *Camarasaurus grandis.*

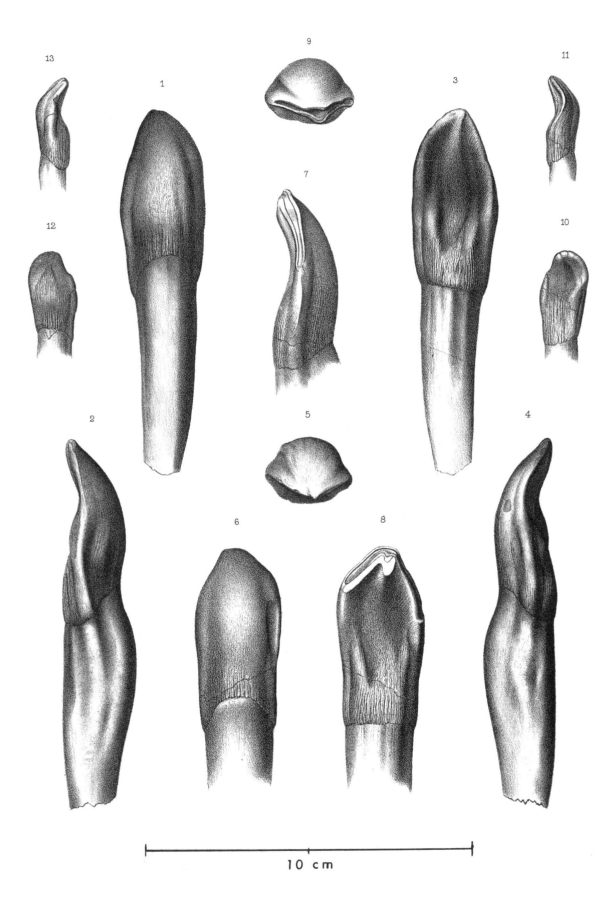

10 cm

PLATE 8

Morosaurus grandis[1] Marsh (1877) YPM 1905
Endocranial cast in lateral (1), ventral (2), and dorsal (3) views

HORIZON: Morrison formation

LOCALITY: YPM Quarry 1, Como Bluff, T. 22 N., R. 77 W., Sec. 10, Albany County, Wyo.

ABBREVIATIONS:
a	artery
c	cerebrum
cb	cerebellum
m	medulla
ol	olfactory stalk
p	pituitary body
I	olfactory nerve
II	optic nerve
V	trigeminal nerve
X	vagus nerve
XI	accessory nerve
XII	hypoglossal nerve

1. Now referred to *Camarasaurus grandis*.

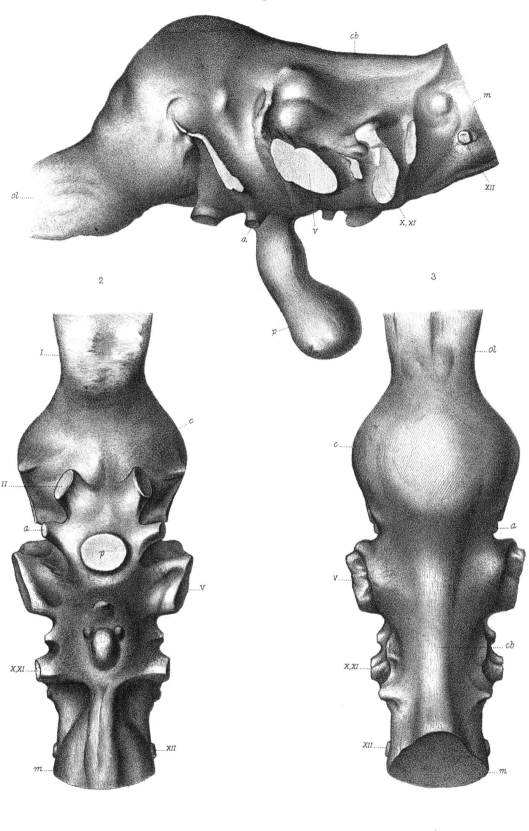

1

2

3

10 cm

PLATE 9

Morosaurus grandis[1] Marsh (1877) YPM 1905

Atlas–axis complex; left atlas neural arch in lateral (1) and medial (2) views

Axis in lateral (3), dorsal (4), anterior (5), ventral (6), and posterior (7) views

Transverse section of axis (8)

HORIZON: Morrison formation

LOCALITY: YPM Quarry 1, Como Bluff, T. 22 N., R. 77 W., Sec. 10, Albany County, Wyo.

ABBREVIATIONS:
- *a* intercentrum of the axis
- *c* centrum
- *d* diapophysis
- *f* lateral pleurocoel
- *n* neural canal
- *o* odontoid process
- *s* neural spine
- *z* prezygapophysis
- *z'* postzygapophysis

1. Now referred to *Camarasaurus grandis*.

10 cm

PLATE 10

Morosaurus grandis[1] Marsh (1877) YPM 1905

Third cervical vertebra in lateral (1), dorsal (2), anterior (3), ventral (4), and posterior (5) views; transverse section (6)

HORIZON: Morrison formation

LOCALITY: YPM Quarry 1, Como Bluff, T. 22 N., R. 77 W., Sec. 10, Albany County, Wyo.

ABBREVIATIONS: *b*   anterior articular facet of centrum

            c   centrum

            d   diapophysis

            f   lateral pleurocoel

            n   neural canal

            p   parapophysis

            s   neural spine

            z   prezygapophysis

            z'   postzygapophysis

1. Now referred to *Camarasaurus grandis*.

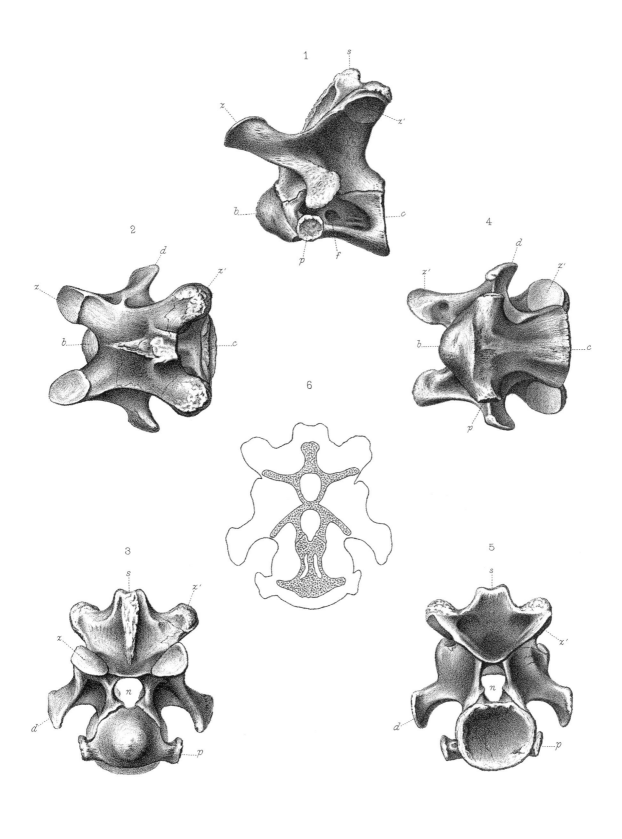

10 cm

PLATE 11

Morosaurus grandis[1] Marsh (1877) YPM 1905

Fifth cervical vertebra in lateral (1), dorsal (2), anterior (3), ventral (4), and posterior (5) views

HORIZON: Morrison formation

LOCALITY: YPM Quarry 1, Como Bluff, T. 22 N., R. 77 W., Sec. 10, Albany County, Wyo.

ABBREVIATIONS:
- *b* anterior articular facet of centrum
- *c* centrum
- *d* diapophysis
- *f* lateral pleurocoel
- *n* neural canal
- *ns* neural arch–centrum suture
- *p* parapophysis
- *s* neural spine
- *z* prezygapophysis
- *z′* postzygapophysis

1. Now referred to *Camarasaurus grandis*.

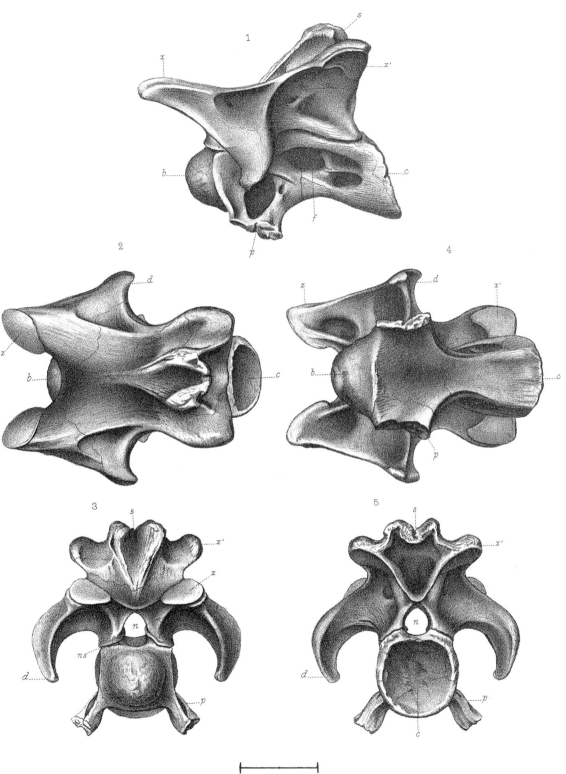

1
2
4
3
5

10 cm

PLATE 12

Brontosaurus excelsus[1] Marsh (1879) YPM 1980 (holotype)

Eighth cervical vertebra in lateral (1) and anterior (2) views (neural spine is missing)

HORIZON: Morrison formation

LOCALITY: YPM Quarry 10, Como Bluff, T. 22 N., R. 77 W., Sec. 12, Albany County, Wyo.

ABBREVIATIONS:

b	anterior articular facet of centrum
c	centrum
d	diapophysis
f	lateral pleurocoel
lf	lateral fenestra
n	neural canal
p	parapophysis
r	cervical rib
z	prezygapophysis
z'	postzygapophysis

1. Now referred to *Apatosaurus excelsus*.

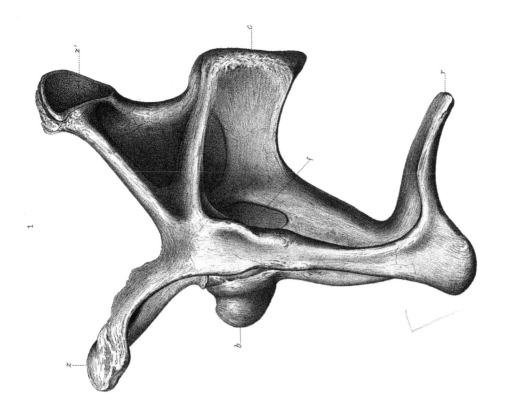

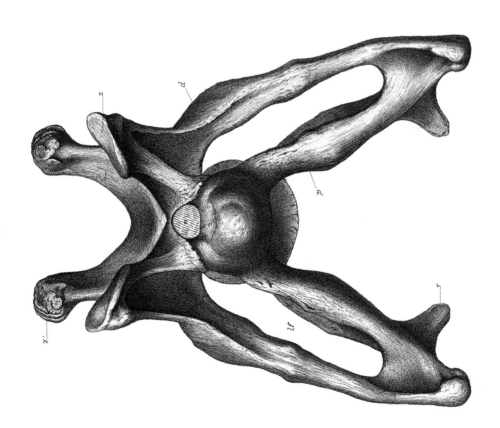

10 cm

PLATE 13

Brontosaurus excelsus[1] Marsh (1879) YPM 1980 (holotype)
Eighth cervical vertebra in ventral (1) and posterior (2) views

HORIZON: Morrison formation

LOCALITY: YPM Quarry 10, Como Bluff, T. 22 N., R. 77 W., Sec. 12, Albany County, Wyo.

ABBREVIATIONS:
- b — anterior articular facet of centrum
- c — centrum
- d — diapophysis
- lf — lateral fenestra
- n — neural canal
- p — parapophysis
- r — cervical rib
- rs — rib suture
- z — prezygapophysis
- z' — postzygapophysis

1. Now referred to *Apatosaurus excelsus*.

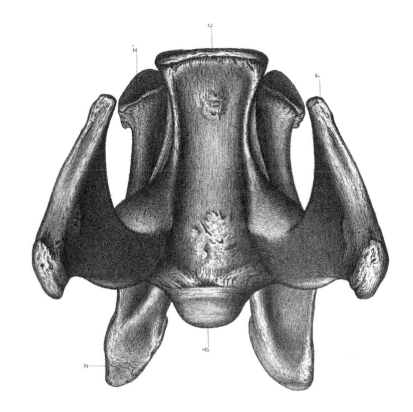

1

10 cm

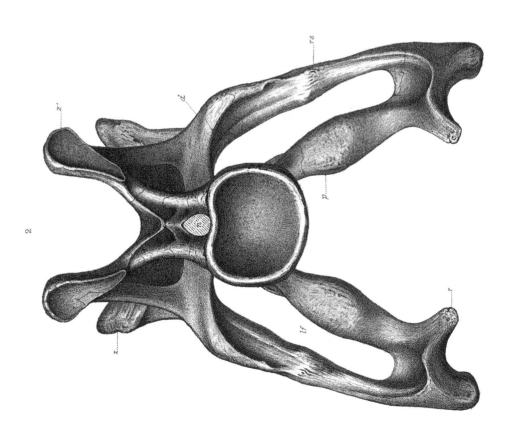

2

PLATE 14

Atlantosaurus immanis Marsh (1878) YPM 1840 (holotype)
Ninth (?) cervical vertebra in lateral (1) and anterior (2) views

HORIZON: Morrison formation

LOCALITY: YPM Quarry 10, Morrison, T. 4 S., R. 70 W., Sec. 35, Jefferson County, Colo.

ABBREVIATIONS:
b	anterior articular facet of centrum
c	centrum
d	diapophysis
lf	lateral fenestra
n	neural canal
p	parapophysis
r	cervical rib
z	prezygapophysis
z'	postzygapophysis

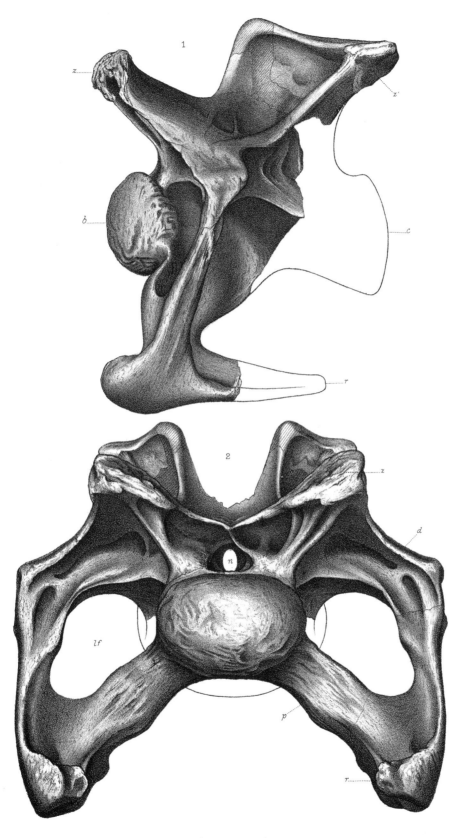

10 cm

PLATE 15

Apatosaurus laticollis Marsh (1879) YPM 1861 (holotype)
  Thirteenth (?) cervical vertebra in lateral (1) and posterior (2) views

HORIZON: Morrison formation

LOCALITY: YPM Quarry 10, Morrison, T. 4 S., R. 70 W., Sec. 35, Jefferson
  County, Colo.

ABBREVIATIONS: *c* centrum
  d diapophysis
  lf lateral fenestra
  p parapophysis
  r rib
  z' postzygapophysis

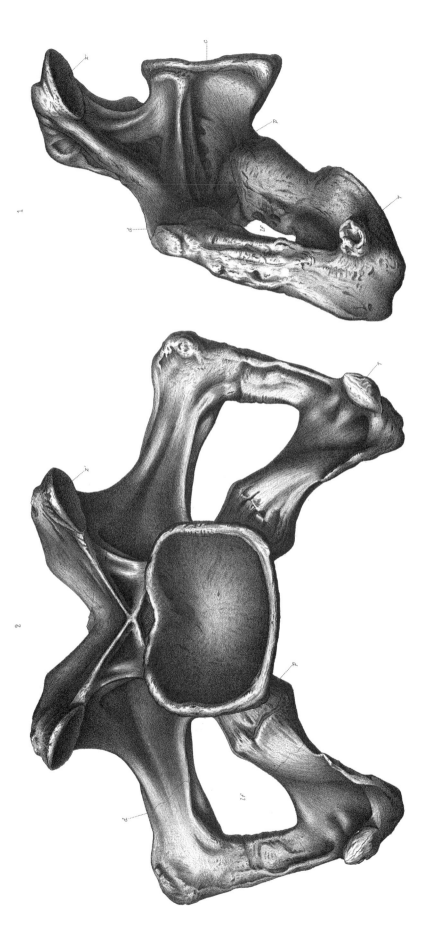

10 cm

PLATE 16

Atlantosaurus immanis Marsh (1878) YPM 1840 (holotype)
Third dorsal vertebra in lateral (1) and posterior (2) views.[1]

> HORIZON: Morrison formation
>
> LOCALITY: YPM Quarry 10, Morrison, T. 4 S., R. 70 W., Sec. 35, Jefferson County, Colo.
>
> ABBREVIATIONS: *b*   anterior articular facet of centrum
>   *c*   centrum
>   *d*   diapophysis
>   *f*   lateral pleurocoel
>   *m*   lateral neural spine
>   *n*   neural canal
>   *p*   parapophysis
>   *z'*   postzygapophysis

1. This same vertebra was figured by Marsh as *Apatosaurus ajax* in *Dinosaurs of North America* (U.S. Geol. Surv., 16th Ann. Rept., 1896), but its size indicates that it belongs with YPM 1840 which is the holotype of *Atlantosaurus immanus*.

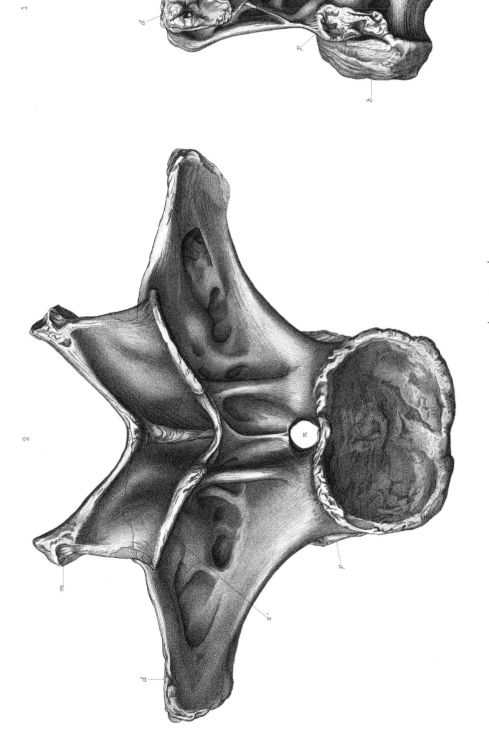

1

2

10 cm

PLATE 17

Brontosaurus excelsus[1] Marsh (1879) YPM 1980 (holotype)
Third dorsal vertebra in lateral (1) and anterior (2) views

HORIZON: Morrison formation

LOCALITY: YPM Quarry 10, Como Bluff, T. 22 N., R. 77 W., Sec. 12, Albany County, Wyo.

ABBREVIATIONS:
- *b*   anterior articular facet of centrum
- *c*   centrum
- *d*   diapophysis
- *f*   lateral pleurocoel
- *m*   lateral neural spine
- *n*   neural canal
- *p*   parapophysis
- *z*   prezygapophysis
- *z'* postzygapophysis

1. Now referred to *Apatosaurus excelsus*.

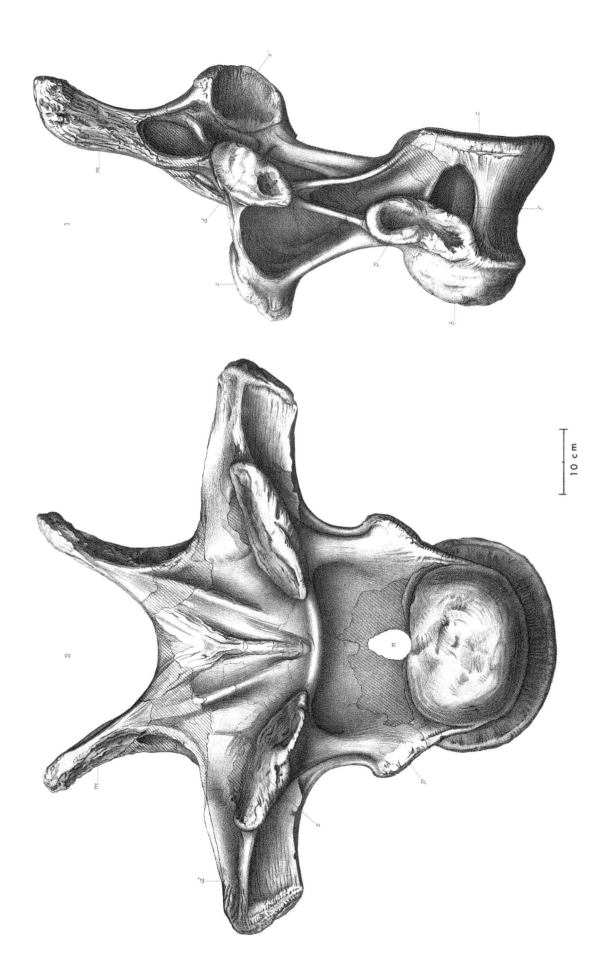

10 cm

PLATE 18

Brontosaurus excelsus[1] Marsh (1879) YPM 1980 (holotype)
Third dorsal vertebra in posterior view

HORIZON: Morrison formation

LOCALITY: YPM Quarry 10, Como Bluff, T. 22 N., R. 77 W., Sec. 12, Albany County, Wyo.

ABBREVIATIONS:
- *d* diapophysis
- *m* lateral neural spine
- *n* neural canal
- *p* parapophysis
- *z'* postzygapophysis

1. Now referred to *Apatosaurus excelsus.*

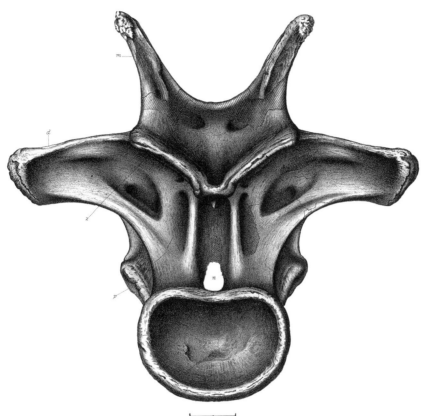

10 cm

PLATE 19

Brontosaurus excelsus[1] Marsh (1879) YPM 1980 (holotype)
Fourth dorsal vertebra in lateral (1) and anterior (2) views

HORIZON: Morrison formation

LOCALITY: YPM Quarry 10, Como Bluff, T. 22 N., R. 77 W., Sec. 12, Albany County, Wyo.

ABBREVIATIONS:
d   diapophysis
f   lateral pleurocoel
n   neural canal
p   parapophysis
x   hyposphene
z   prezygapophysis
z' postzygapophysis

1. Now referred to *Apatosaurus excelsus*.

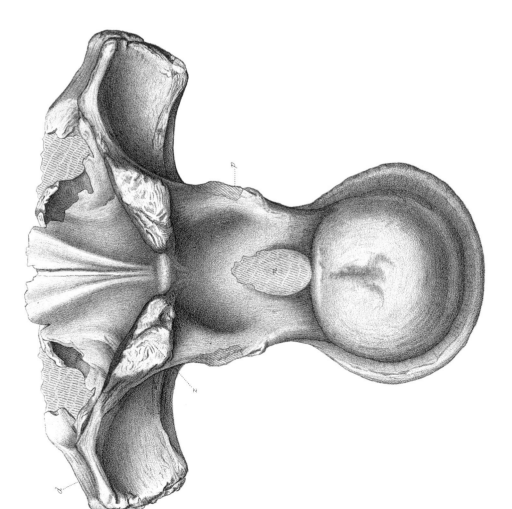

1

2

10 cm

PLATE 20

Brontosaurus excelsus[1] Marsh (1879) YPM 1980 (holotype)
Fourth dorsal vertebra in posterior view

HORIZON: Morrison formation

LOCALITY: YPM Quarry 10, Como Bluff, T. 22 N., R. 77 W., Sec. 12, Albany County, Wyo.

ABBREVIATIONS:
d	diapophysis
n	neural canal
p	parapophysis
x	hyposphene
z'	postzygapophysis

1. Now referred to *Apatosaurus excelsus.*

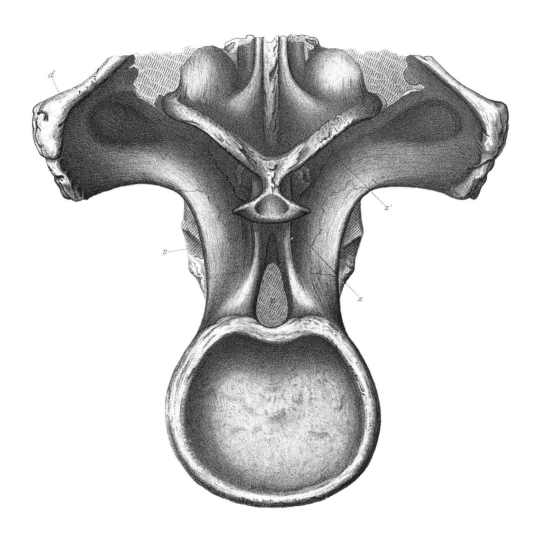

10 cm

PLATE 21

Brontosaurus excelsus[1] Marsh (1879) YPM 1980 (holotype)
Fifth dorsal vertebra in lateral (1) and anterior (2) views

HORIZON: Morrison formation

LOCALITY: YPM Quarry 10, Como Bluff, T. 22 N., R. 77 W., Sec. 12, Albany County, Wyo.

ABBREVIATIONS:
- *d*   diapophysis
- *f*   lateral pleurocoel
- *n*   neural canal
- *p*   parapophysis
- *s*   neural spine
- *z*   prezygopophysis
- *z'*   postzygapophysis

1. Now referred to *Apatosaurus excelsus*.

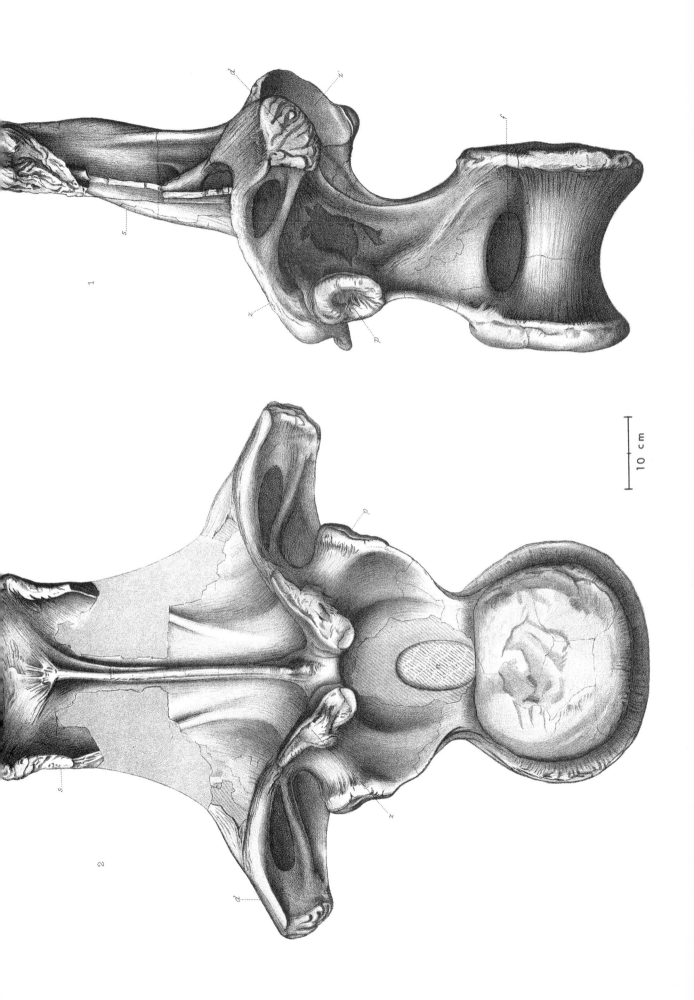

1

2

10 cm

PLATE 22

Brontosaurus excelsus[1] Marsh (1879) YPM 1980 (holotype)
Fifth dorsal vertebra in posterior view

HORIZON: Morrison formation

LOCALITY: YPM Quarry 10, Como Bluff, T. 22 N., R. 77 W., Sec. 12, Albany County, Wyo.

ABBREVIATIONS:
- *d*   diapophysis
- *n*   neural canal
- *p*   parapophysis
- *s*   neural spine
- *x*   hyposphene
- *z'*   postzygapophysis

1. Now referred to *Apatosaurus excelsus.*

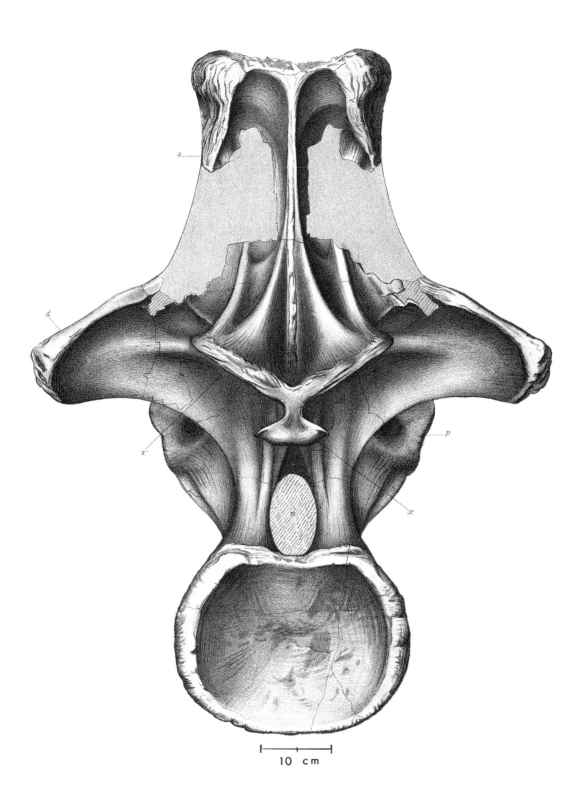

10 cm

PLATE 23

Morosaurus grandis[1] Marsh (1877) YPM 1901 or 1902 (holotype)

Anterior dorsal vertebra in lateral (1), anterior (2), and posterior (3) views; horizontal longitudinal (4) and vertical transverse (5) sections through the centrum

HORIZON: Morrison formation

LOCALITY: YPM Quarry 1, Como Bluff, T. 22 N., R. 77 W., Sec. 10, Albany County, Wyo.

ABBREVIATIONS:
b anterior articular facet of centrum
c centrum
d diapophysis
f lateral pleurocoel
m lateral neural spine
n neural canal
ns neural arch–centrum suture
x hyposphene
z prezygapophysis
z' postzygapophysis

1. Now referred to *Camarasaurus grandis.*

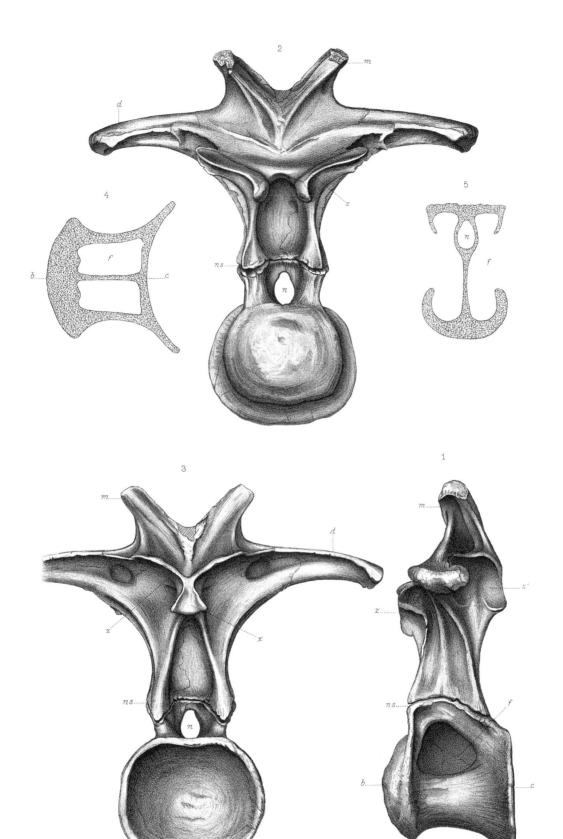

10 cm

PLATE 24

Morosaurus grandis[1] Marsh (1877) YPM 1901 or 1902 (holotype)

Anterior dorsal vertebra in lateral (1), anterior (2), and posterior (3) views; horizontal longitudinal (4) and vertical transverse (5) sections through the centrum

HORIZON: Morrison formation

LOCALITY: YPM Quarry 1, Como Bluff, T. 22 N., R. 77 W., Sec. 10, Albany County, Wyo.

ABBREVIATIONS:
- *b*   anterior articular facet of centrum
- *c*   centrum
- *d*   diapophysis
- *f*   lateral pleurocoel
- *m*   lateral neural spine
- *n*   neural canal
- *ns*   neural arch–centrum suture
- *x*   hyposphene
- *z*   prezygopophysis
- *z'*   postzygapophysis

1. Now referred to *Camarasaurus grandis*.

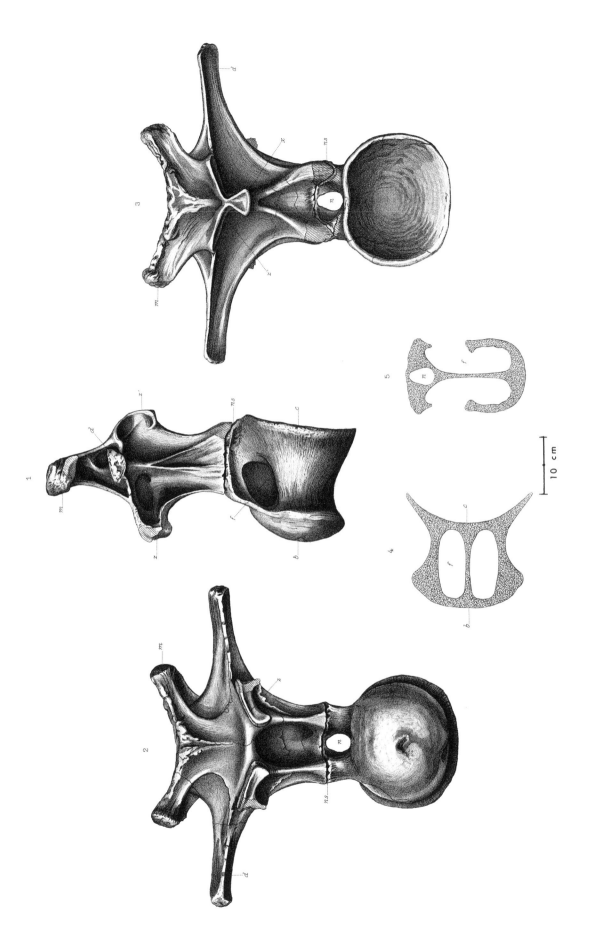

10 cm

PLATE 25

Morosaurus grandis[1] Marsh (1877) YPM 1901 (holotype)

Posterior dorsal vertebra in lateral (1), anterior (2), and posterior (3) views; horizontal longitudinal (4) and vertical transverse (5) sections through centrum

HORIZON: Morrison formation

LOCALITY: YPM Quarry 1, Como Bluff, T. 22 N., R. 77 W., Sec. 10, Albany County, Wyo.

ABBREVIATIONS:
b	anterior articular facet of centrum
c	centrum
d	diapophysis
f	lateral pleurocoel
n	neural canal
ns	neural arch–centrum suture
p	parapophysis
s	neural spine
z	prezygapophysis
z′	postzygapophysis

1. Now referred to *Camarasaurus grandis*.

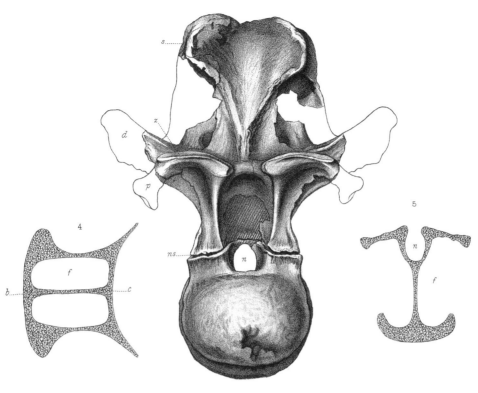
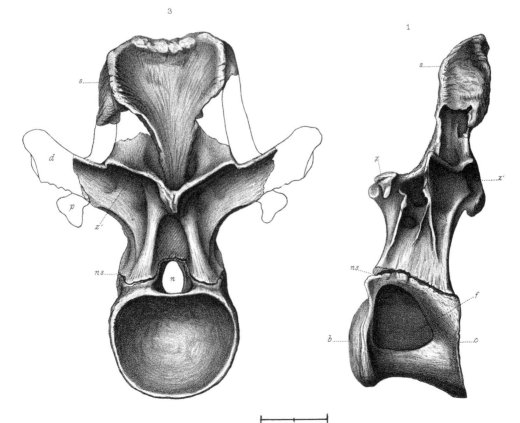

10 cm

PLATE 26

Brontosaurus excelsus[1] Marsh (1879) YPM 1980 (holotype)
    Eighth dorsal vertebra in posterior view

    HORIZON: Morrison formation
    LOCALITY: YPM Quarry 10, Como Bluff, T. 22 N., R. 77 W., Sec. 12,
                Albany County, Wyo.
    ABBREVIATIONS: *d*   diapophysis
                    n   neural canal
                    s   neural spine
                    z'   postzygapophysis

1. Now referred to *Apatosaurus excelsus*.

116

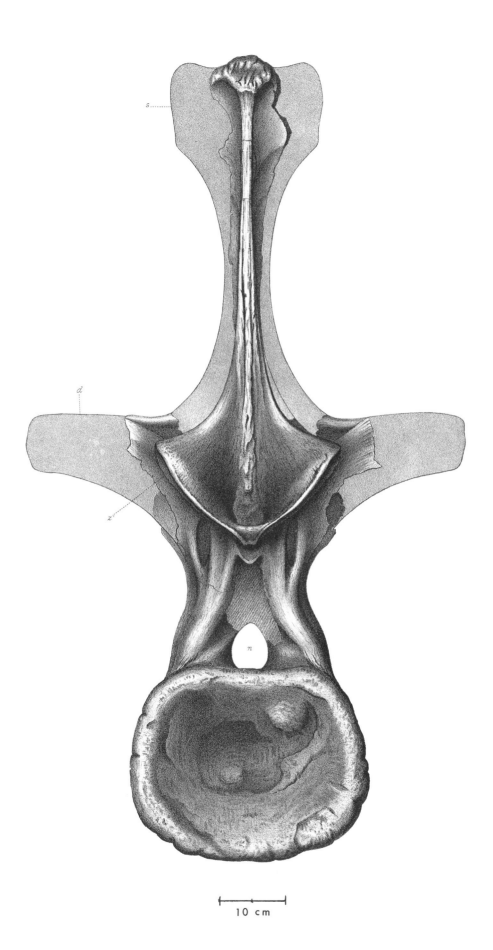

10 cm

PLATE 27

Brontosaurus excelsus[1] Marsh (1879) YPM 1980 (holotype)
Sacrum in ventral view

HORIZON: Morrison formation

LOCALITY: YPM Quarry 10, Como Bluff, T. 22 N., R. 77 W., Sec. 12, Albany County, Wyo.

ABBREVIATIONS:

a	first sacral centrum
b	first sacral rib
c	second sacral rib
d	third sacral rib
e	fourth sacral rib
f, f', f'', f'''	intervertebral fenestrae
g	iliac bar
l	dorsal 10 centrum
p	last sacral centrum

1. Now referred to *Apatosaurus excelsus*.

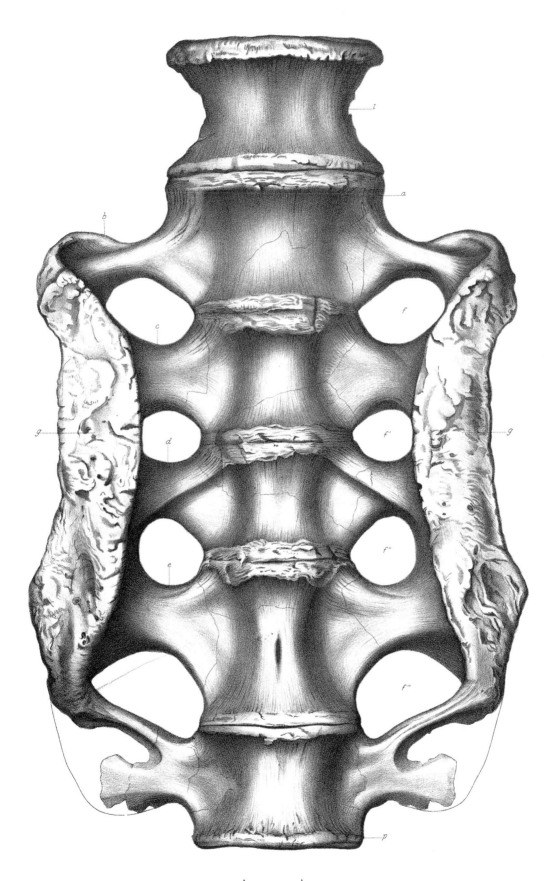

10 cm

PLATE 28

Brontosaurus amplus[1] Marsh (1881) YPM 1981 (holotype)
Sacrum in ventral view

HORIZON: Morrison formation

LOCALITY: YPM Quarry 11, Como Bluff, T. 22 N., R. 77 W., Sec. 12, Albany County, Wyo.

ABBREVIATIONS:
a	first sacral centrum
b	first sacral rib
c	second sacral rib
d	third sacral rib
e	fourth sacral rib
f, f′, f″	intervertebral fenestrae
g	iliac bar
l	dorsal 10 centrum
p	fourth sacral centrum

1. Now referred to *Apatosaurus amplus.*

120

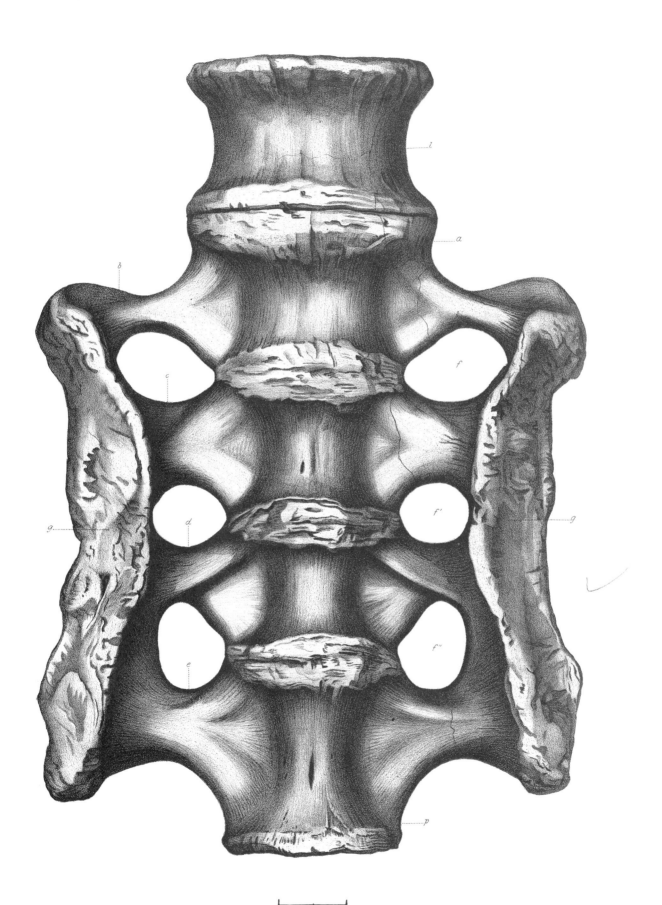

10 cm

PLATE 29

Apatosaurus ajax Marsh (1877) YPM 1860 (holotype)
Sacrum in ventral view

HORIZON: Morrison formation

LOCALITY: YPM Quarry 10, Morrison, T. 4 S., R. 70 W., Sec. 35, Jefferson
County, Colo.

ABBREVIATIONS: *a*   anterior sacral centrum
  b   second sacral rib
  c   third sacral rib
  d   fourth sacral rib
  f, f′   intervertebral fenestrae
  g   iliac bar
  p   posterior sacral centrum

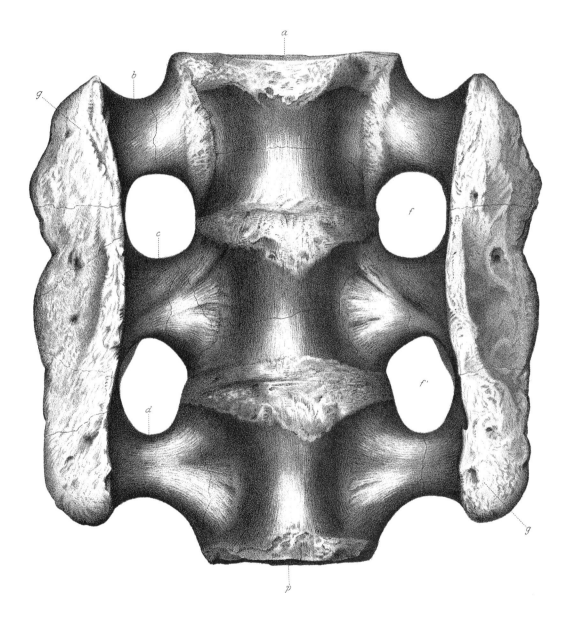

10 cm

PLATE 30

Apatosaurus ajax Marsh (1877) YPM 1860 (holotype)
Last (fifth) sacral vertebra in anterior (1), and dorsal (2) views

HORIZON: Morrison formation

LOCALITY: YPM Quarry 10, Morrison, T. 4 S., R. 70 W., Sec. 35, Jefferson County, Colo.

ABBREVIATIONS: *a* anterior articular facet of centrum
        e fifth sacral rib
        g iliac bar
        n neural canal
        p posterior articular facet of centrum

1

2

g

a

10 cm

p

n

a

e

g

PLATE 31

Morosaurus grandis[1] Marsh (1877) YPM 1900[2]
Sacrum in ventral view (1) and in transverse section (2)

HORIZON: Morrison formation

LOCALITY: YPM Quarry 1, Como Bluff, T. 22 N., R. 77 W., Sec. 10, Albany County, Wyo.

ABBREVIATIONS:
a	anterior or first sacral centrum
b	first sacral rib
c	second sacral rib
d	third sacral rib
e	fourth sacral rib
f, f′, f″	intervertebral fenestrae
g	iliac bar
n	neural canal
p	posterior sacral centrum

1. Now referred to *Camarasaurus grandis*.
2. This specimen is the holotype of *Morosaurus impar*.

126

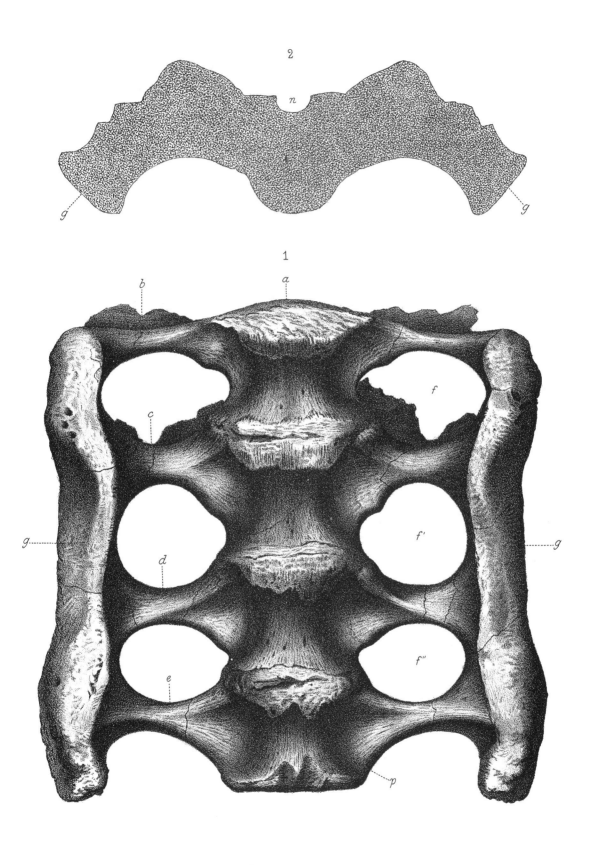

2

n

g   *g*

1

b   *a*

f

c

g   *g*

d   *f'*

e   *f''*

p

10 cm

PLATE 32

Brontosaurus excelsus[1] Marsh (1879) YPM 1980 (holotype)
Second caudal vertebra in anterior view

HORIZON: Morrison formation

LOCALITY: YPM Quarry 10, Como Bluff, T. 22 N., R. 77 W., Sec. 12, Albany County, Wyo.

1. Now referred to *Apatosaurus excelsus*.

PLATE 33

Brontosaurus excelsus[1] Marsh (1879) YPM 1980 (holotype)
Third caudal vertebra in lateral (1), ventral (2), and posterior (3) views

HORIZON: Morrison formation

LOCALITY: YPM Quarry 10, Como Bluff, T. 22 N., R. 77 W., Sec. 12, Albany County, Wyo.

ABBREVIATIONS:
- *f*   lateral canal
- *n*   neural canal
- *s*   neural spine
- *t*   transverse process
- *z*   prezygapophysis
- *z'* postzygapophysis

1. Now referred to *Apatosaurus excelsus.*

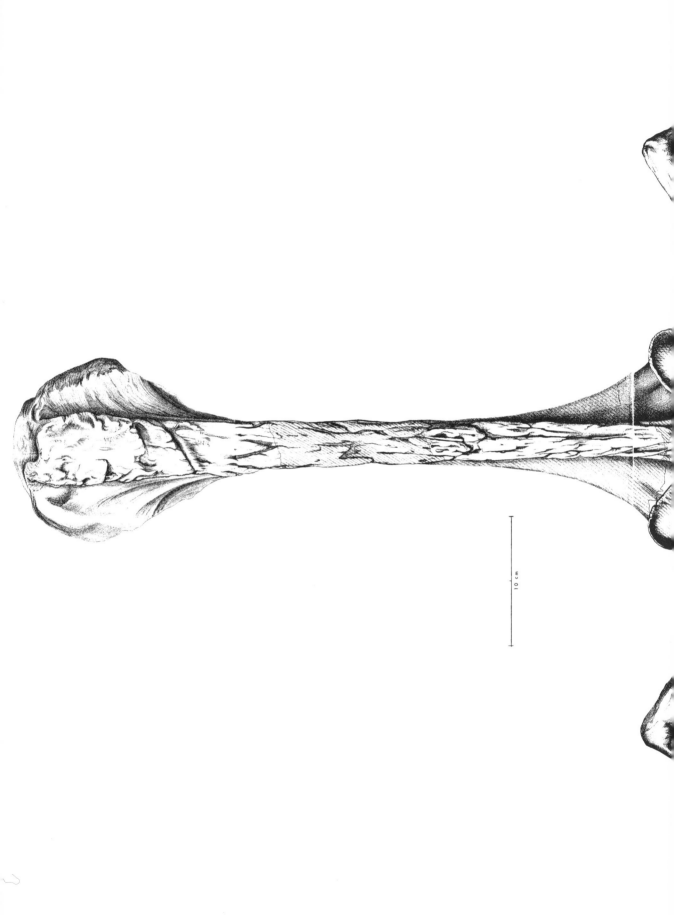

10 cm

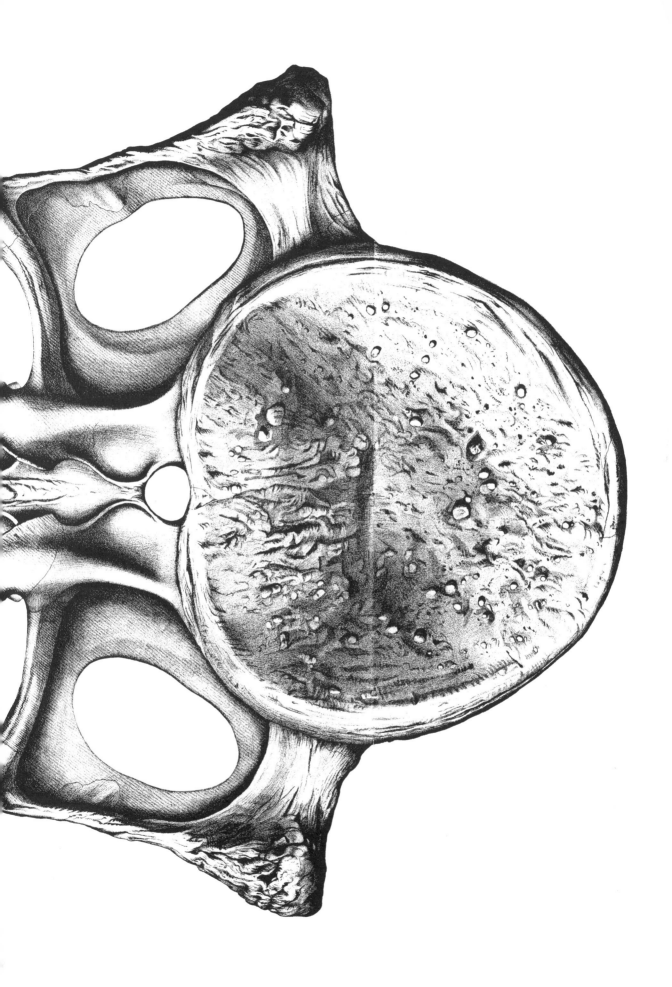

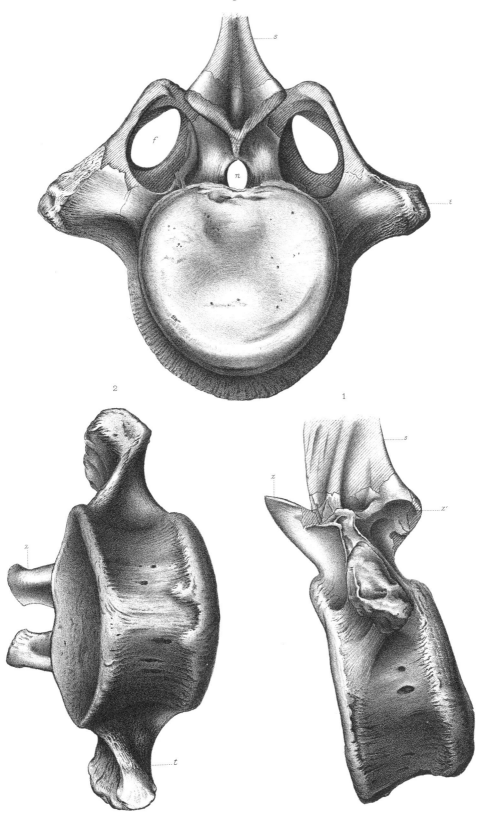

10 cm

PLATE 34

Brontosaurus excelsus[1] Marsh (1879) YPM 1980 (holotype)
Fourth caudal vertebra in lateral (1) and posterior (2) views

HORIZON: Morrison formation

LOCALITY: YPM Quarry 10, Como Bluff, T. 22 N., R. 77 W., Sec. 12,
Albany County, Wyo.

ABBREVIATIONS:
- *c*   centrum
- *f*   lateral canal
- *n*   neural canal
- *s*   neural spine
- *t*   transverse process
- *z*   prezygapophysis
- *z'*   postzygapophysis

1. Now referred to *Apatosaurus excelsus*.

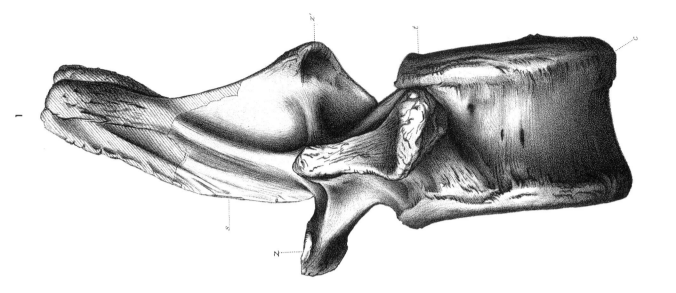

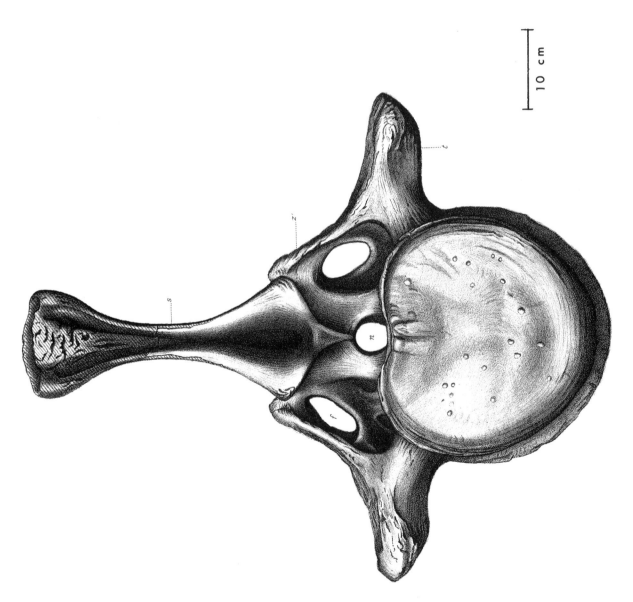

10 cm

PLATE 35

Brontosaurus excelsus[1] Marsh (1879) YPM 1980 (holotype)
Fifth caudal vertebra in lateral (1) and anterior (2) views, dorsal view of neural spine extremity (3), and lateral (4) and posterior (5) views of the chevron

HORIZON: Morrison formation

LOCALITY: YPM Quarry 10, Como Bluff, T. 22 N., R. 77 W., Sec. 12, Albany County, Wyo.

ABBREVIATIONS:
    c   centrum
    h   haemal canal
    n   neural canal
    s   neural spine
    t   transverse process
    z   prezygapophysis
    z′ postzygapophysis

1. Now referred to *Apatosaurus excelsus*.

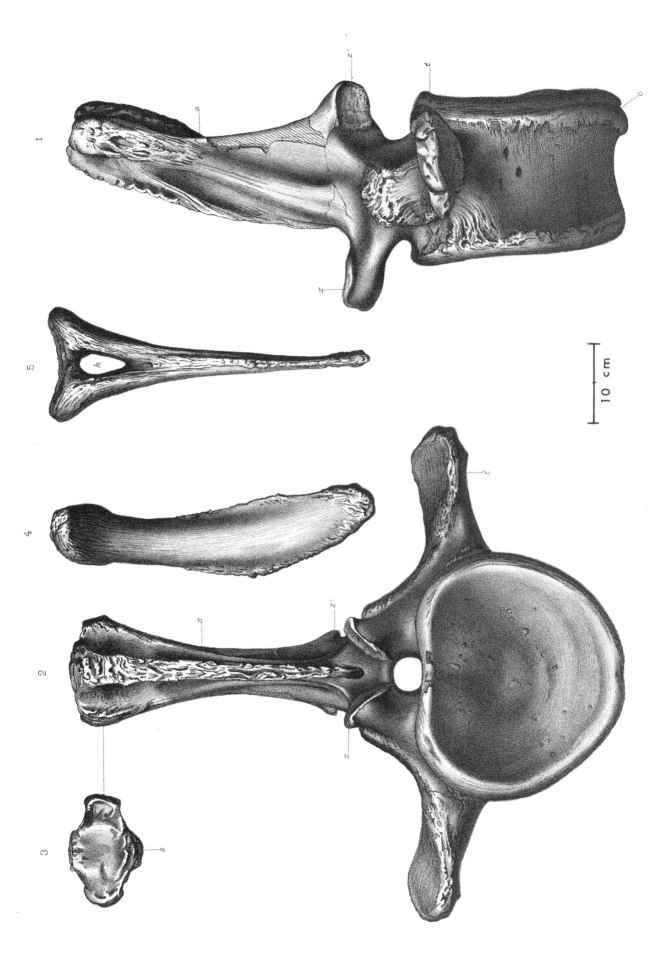

10 cm

PLATE 36

Diplodocus longus Marsh (1878) YPM 1920 (holotype)
Distal caudal vertebra in lateral (1), anterior (2), ventral (3), and posterior (4) views; distal chevrons in lateral (5) and dorsal (6) views

HORIZON: Morrison formation
LOCALITY: Felch YPM Quarry 1, Garden Park, T. 17 S., R. 70 W., Sec. 28, Fremont County, Colo.

Diplodocus longus YPM 4675
Distal chevron in lateral (7) and dorsal (8) views

HORIZON: Morrison formation
LOCALITY: YPM Quarry 1, Como Bluff, T. 22 N., R. 77 W., Sec. 10, Albany County, Wyo.

ABBREVIATIONS:
a	anterior process of haemal arch
c	anterior articulation for chevron
c'	posterior articulation for chevron
n	neural canal
p	posterior process of haemal arch
s	neural spine
v	articular facet for succeeding centrum
v'	articular facet for preceding centrum
z	prezygapophysis
z'	postzygapophysis

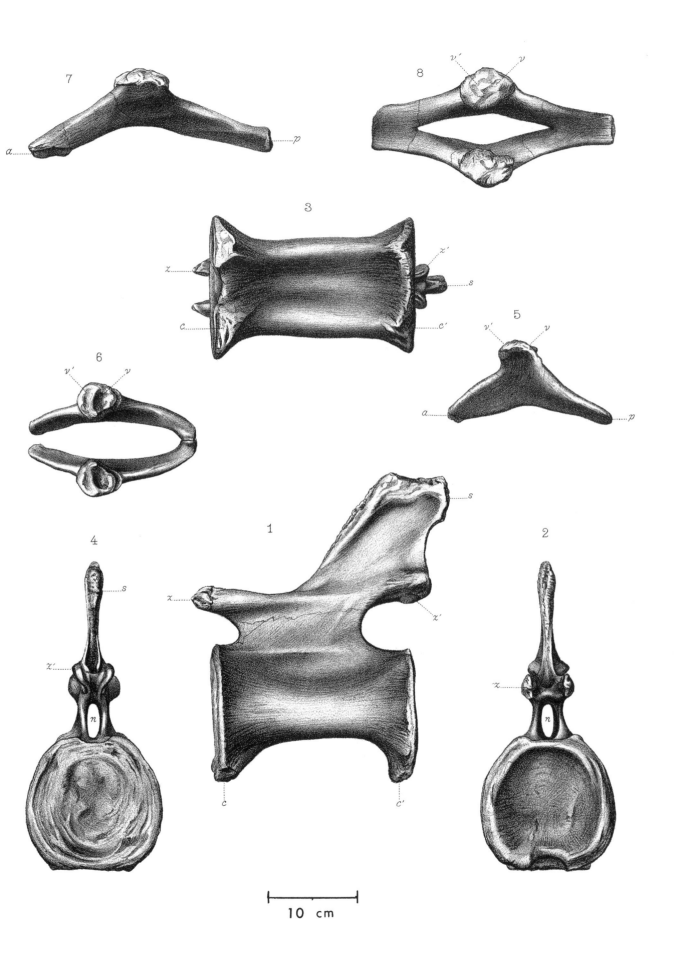

PLATE 37

Morosaurus grandis[1] Marsh (1877) YPM 1901 (holotype)

Anterior (second?) caudal vertebra in lateral (1) and anterior (2) views; mid-caudal (eleventh?) vertebra in lateral (3) and anterior (4) views; middle chevron in lateral (5) and posterior (6) views

HORIZON: Morrison formation

LOCALITY: YPM Quarry 1, Como Bluff, T. 22 N., R. 77 W., Sec. 10, Albany County, Wyo.

ABBREVIATIONS:
h	haemal canal
n	neural canal
s	neural spine
t	transverse process
z	prezygapophysis
z'	postzygapophysis

1. Now referred to *Camarasaurus grandis.*

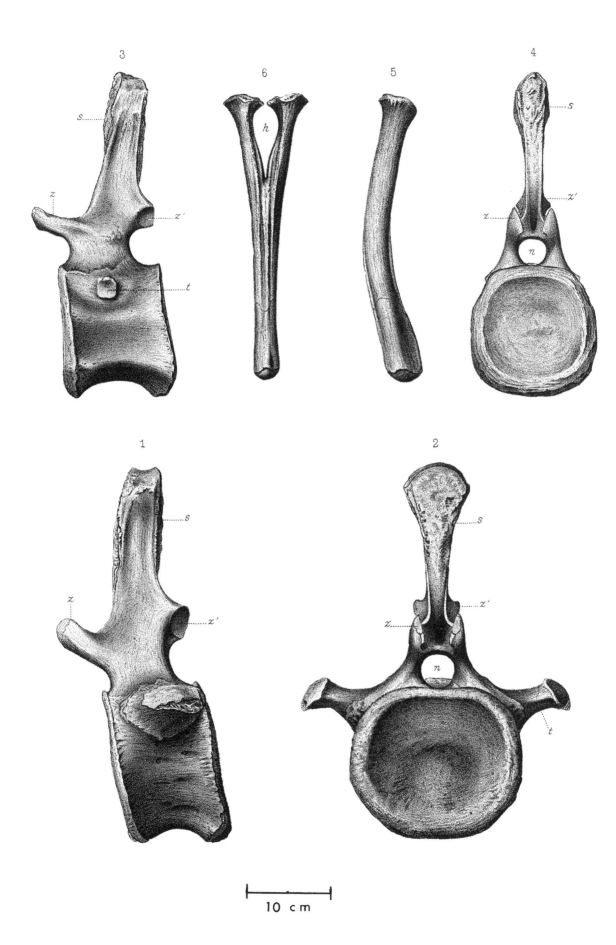

10 cm

PLATE 38

Morosaurus grandis[1] Marsh (1877) YPM 1901 (holotype)

Mid-caudal (twelfth?) vertebra in lateral (1), anterior (2), and posterior (3) views; a mid-caudal (thirteenth?) vertebra in lateral (4) and posterior (5) views; a mid-caudal (sixteenth?) vertebra in lateral (6), anterior (7), and posterior (8) views

HORIZON: Morrison formation

LOCALITY: YPM Quarry 1, Como Bluff, T. 22 N., R. 77 W., Sec. 10, Albany County, Wyo.

ABBREVIATIONS:
c anterior articulation for chevron
c' posterior articulation for chevron
n neural canal
s neural spine
t transverse process
z prezygapophysis
z' postzygapophysis

1. Now referred to *Camarasaurus grandis*.

140

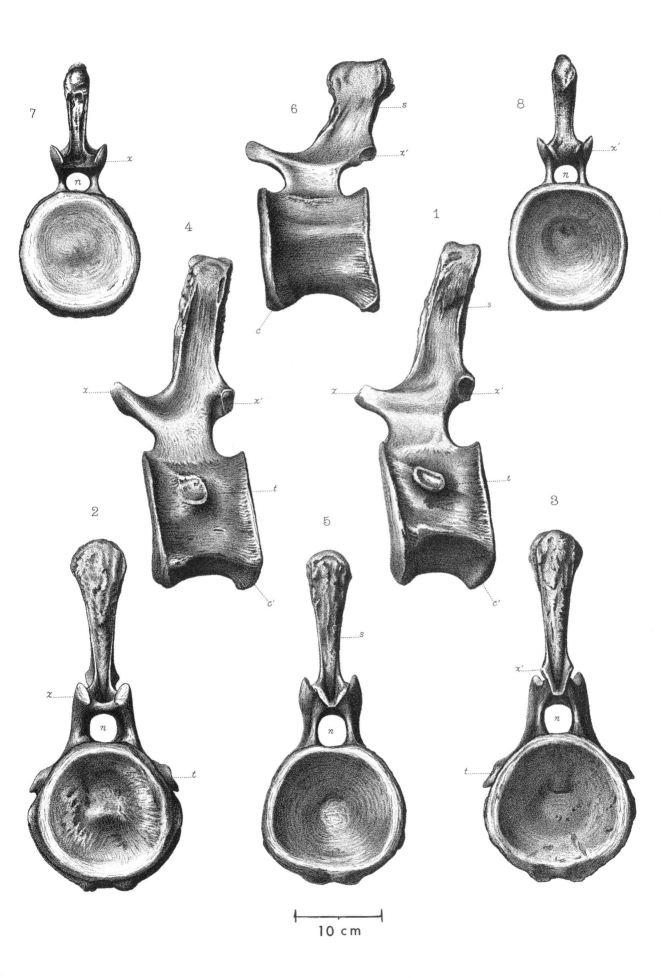

10 cm

PLATE 39

Brontosaurus excelsus[1] Marsh (1879) YPM 1980 (holotype)
Anterior dorsal rib in anterior (1), posterior (2), medial (3), and dorsal views

HORIZON: Morrison formation

LOCALITY: YPM Quarry 10, Como Bluff, T. 22 N., R. 77 W., Sec. 12, Albany County, Wyo.

ABBREVIATIONS: *h*   capitulum
t   tuberculum

1. Now referred to *Apatosaurus excelsus.*

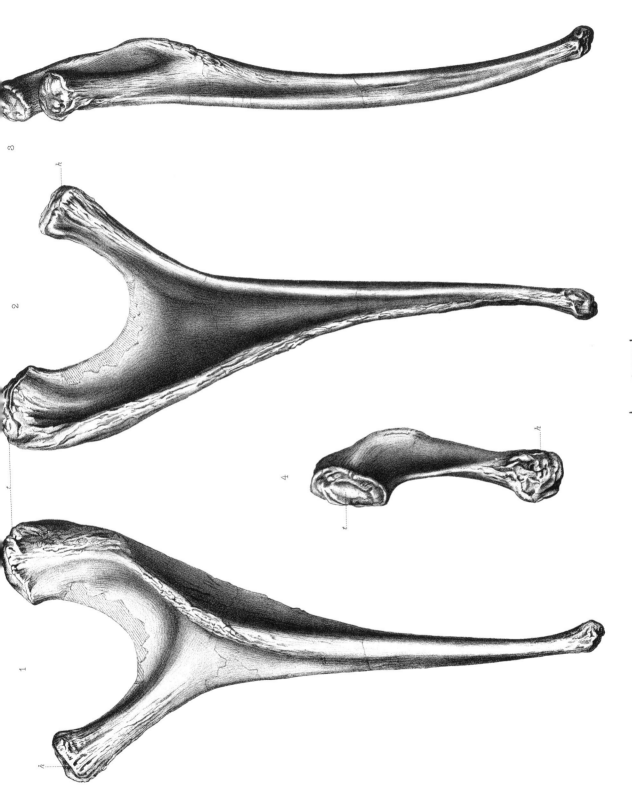

h

t.

10 cm

4

h

t

h

PLATE 40

Brontosaurus excelsus[1] Marsh (1879) YPM 1980 (holotype)
Mid-dorsal rib in anterior (1), medial (2), and dorsal (3) views

HORIZON: Morrison formation

LOCALITY: YPM Quarry 10, Como Bluff, T. 22 N., R. 77 W., Sec. 12, Albany County, Wyo.

ABBREVIATIONS: *h*   capitulum
                     t   tuberculum

1. Now referred to *Apatosaurus excelsus.*

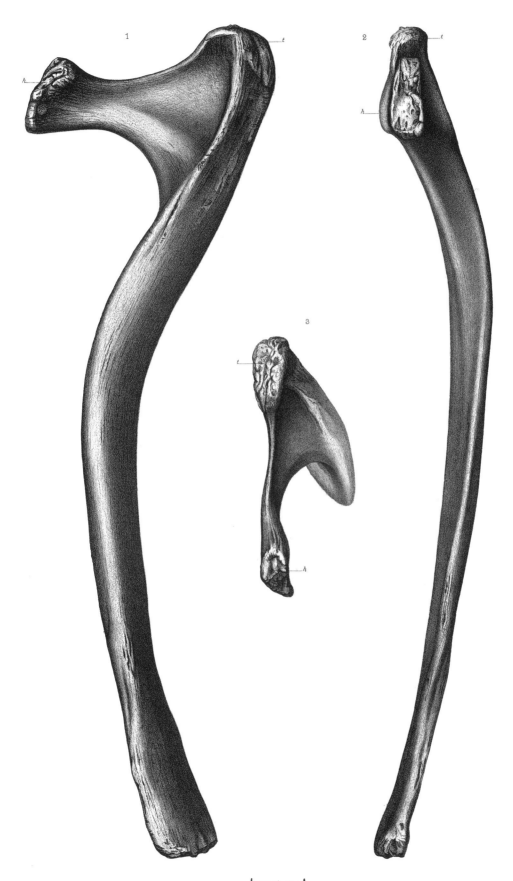

10 cm

PLATE 41

Brontosaurus excelsus[1] Marsh (1879) YPM 1980 (holotype)
Posterior dorsal rib in anterior (1), medial (2), and dorsal (3) views

HORIZON: Morrison formation

LOCALITY: YPM Quarry 10, Como Bluff, T. 22 N., R. 77 W., Sec. 12, Albany County, Wyo.

ABBREVIATIONS: *h* capitulum
t tuberculum

1. Now referred to *Apatosaurus excelsus.*

146

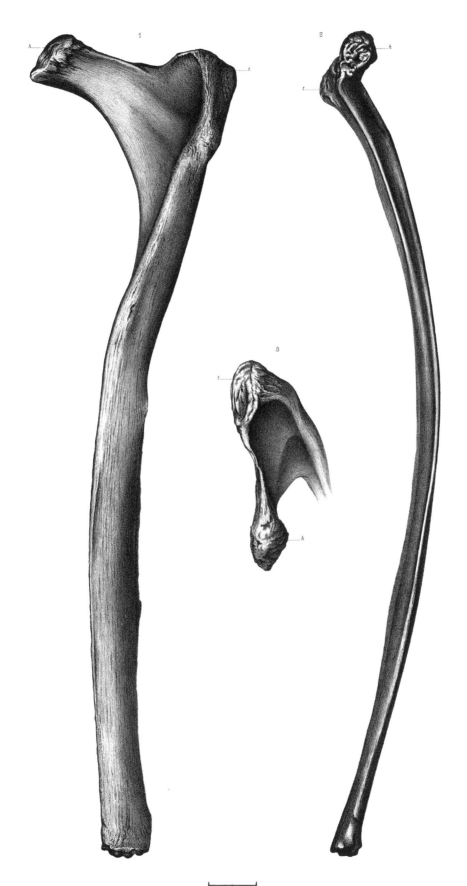

10 cm

PLATE 42

Brontosaurus excelsus[1] Marsh (1879) YPM 1980 (holotype)
Left scapula in lateral (1), ventroanterior (2), and posterior (3) views; transverse section of shaft (4)

HORIZON: Morrison formation

LOCALITY: YPM Quarry 10, Como Bluff, T. 22 N., R. 77 W., Sec. 12, Albany County, Wyo.

ABBREVIATIONS:
- *a* scapular portion of glenoid
- *b* articular margin for coracoid
- *c* dorsal process
- *d* dorsoposterior end

1. Now referred to *Apatosaurus excelsus.*

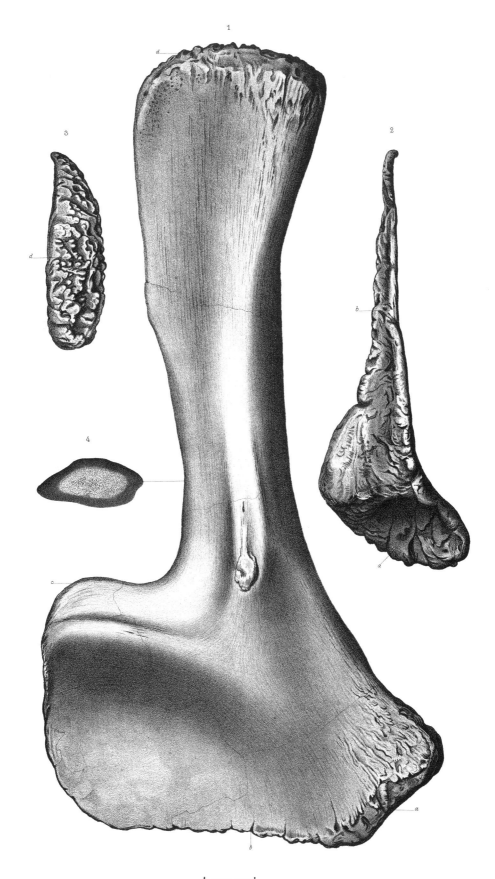

10 cm

PLATE 43

Morosaurus grandis[1] Marsh (1877) YPM 1901 (holotype)
Left scapula in lateral (1) and dorsoanterior (2) views

HORIZON: Morrison formation

LOCALITY: YPM Quarry 1, Como Bluff, T. 22 N., R. 77 W., Sec. 10, Albany County, Wyo.

ABBREVIATIONS: *a* scapular portion of glenoid
b articulation for coracoid
c dorsal process
d dorsoposterior end

1. Now referred to *Camarasaurus grandis*.

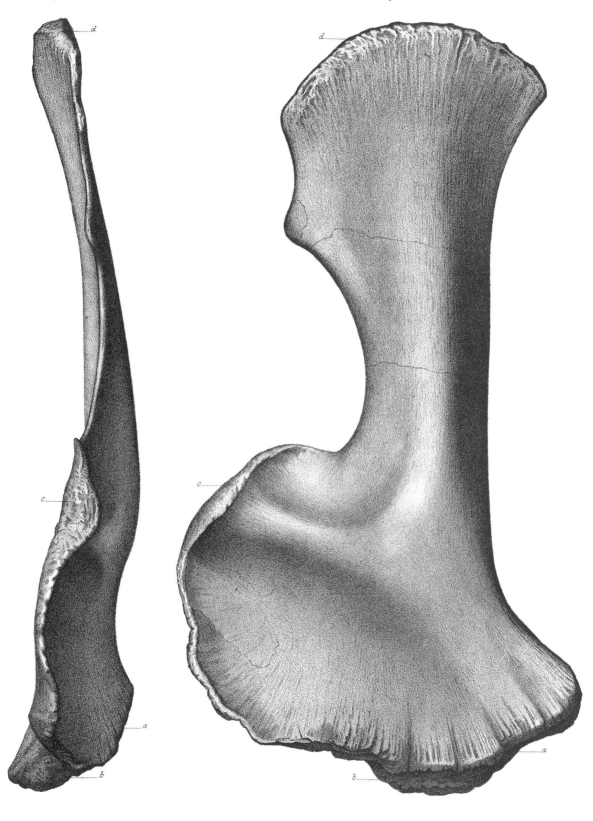

10 cm

PLATE 44

Brontosaurus excelsus[1] Marsh (1879) YPM 1980 (holotype)
Left coracoid in lateral (1) and dorsal (2) views

HORIZON: Morrison formation

LOCALITY: YPM Quarry 10, Como Bluff, T. 22 N., R. 77 W., Sec. 12,
Albany County, Wyo.

ABBREVIATIONS: *a*   coracoid margin of glenoid
               b   articular surface for scapula
               c   anterior margin
               f   coracoid foramen

1. Now referred to *Apatosaurus excelsus*.

152

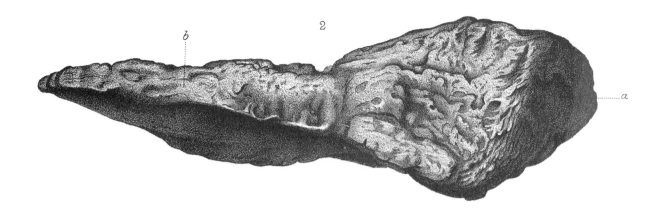

2

b

a

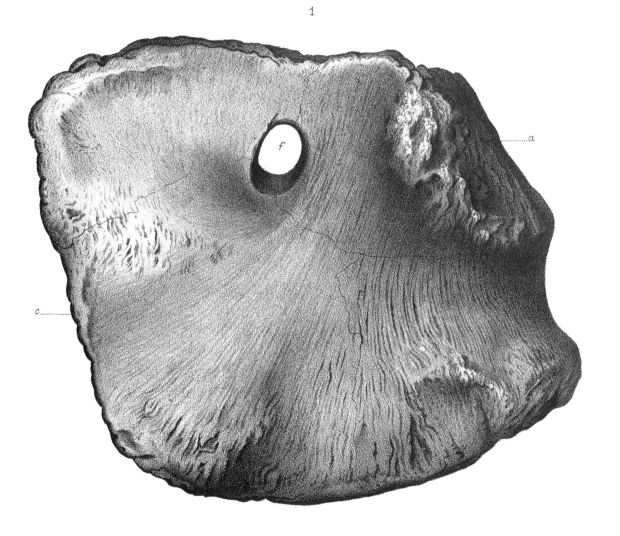

1

a

f

c

10 cm

PLATE 45

Apatosaurus ajax Marsh (1877) YPM 1860 (holotype)
Left coracoid in lateral (1) and dorsal (2) views

HORIZON: Morrison formation

LOCALITY: YPM Quarry 10, Morrison, T. 4 S., R. 70 W., Sec. 35, Jefferson County, Colo.

ABBREVIATIONS: *a* coracoid margin of glenoid
b articular surface for scapula
c anterior margin
f coracoid foramen

2

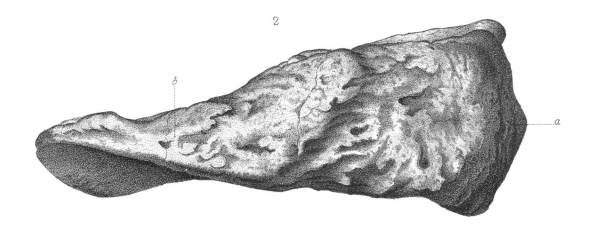

1

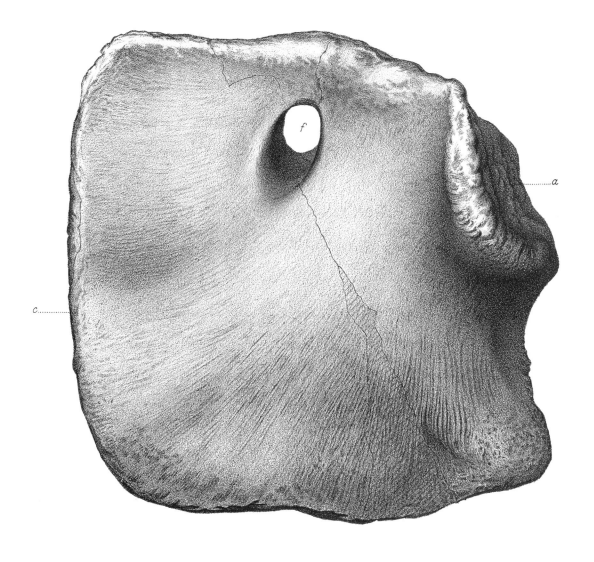

10 cm

PLATE 46

Morosaurus grandis[1] Marsh (1877) YPM 1901 (holotype)
Right coracoid in lateral (1), dorsoposterior (2), and medial (3) views

HORIZON: Morrison formation

LOCALITY: YPM Quarry 1, Como Bluff, T. 22 N., R. 77 W., Sec. 10
Albany County, Wyo.

ABBREVIATIONS: *a* coracoid margin of glenoid
b articular surface for scapula
c anterior margin
f coracoid foramen

1. Now referred to *Camarasaurus grandis.*

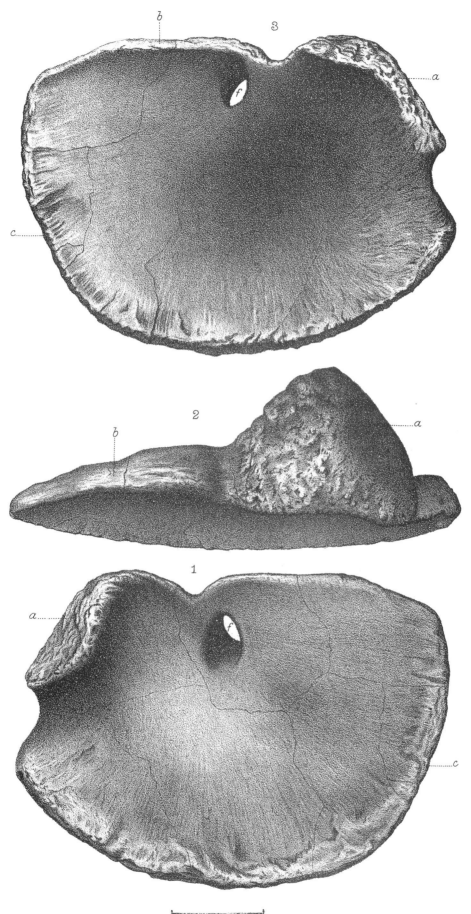

10 cm

PLATE 47

Brontosaurus excelsus[1] Marsh (1879) YPM 1980 (holotype)
Left sternal bone in dorsal (1), ventral (2), medial (3), and anterior (4) views

HORIZON: Morrison formation

LOCALITY: YPM Quarry 10, Como Bluff, T. 22 N., R. 77 W., Sec. 12, Albany County, Wyo.

ABBREVIATIONS:
- *c*   anterior end
- *d*   medial margin
- *e*   anteromedial margin
- *p*   posterior margin

1. Now referred to *Apatosaurus excelsus.*

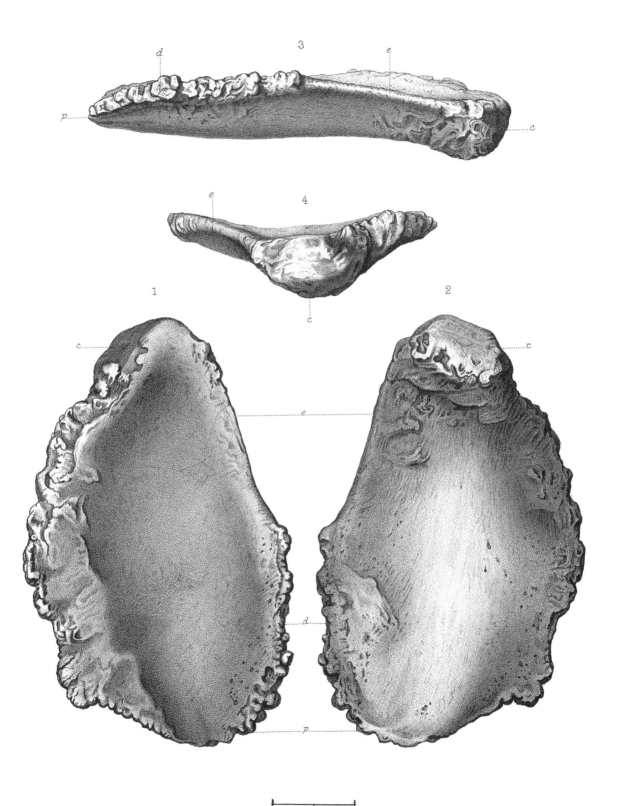

10 cm

PLATE 48

Brontosaurus excelsus[1] Marsh (1879) YPM 1980 (holotype)
  Left humerus in posterior (1), lateral (2), proximal (3), and distal (4) views

  HORIZON: Morrison formation
  LOCALITY: YPM Quarry 10, Como Bluff, T. 22 N., R. 77 W., Sec. 12,
       Albany County, Wyo.
  ABBREVIATION: *r* deltopectoral crest

  1. Now referred to *Apatosaurus excelsus.*

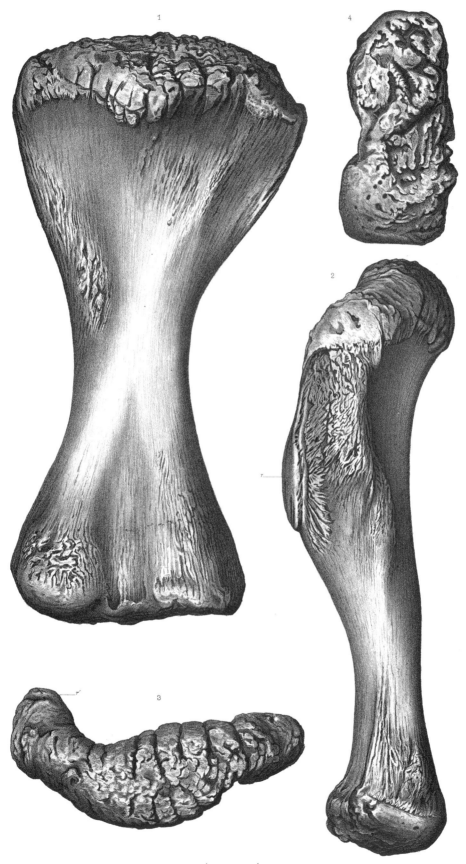

10 cm

PLATE 49

Morosaurus grandis[1] Marsh (1877) YPM 1901 (holotype)
Left humerus in anterior (1), posterior (2), lateral (3), proximal (4), and distal (5) views

HORIZON: Morrison formation
LOCALITY: YPM Quarry 1, Como Bluff, T. 22 N., R. 77 W., Sec. 10, Albany County, Wyo.

ABBREVIATION: *r* deltopectoral crest

1. Now referred to *Camarasaurus grandis*.

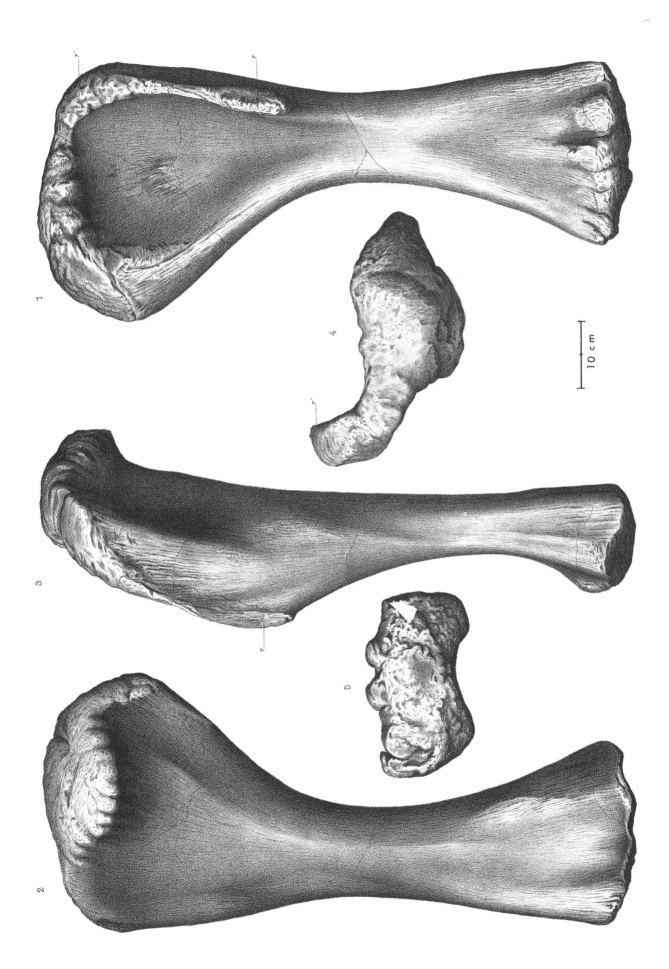

PLATE 50

Brontosaurus excelsus[1] Marsh (1879) YPM 1980 (holotype)
Right radius in medial (1), anterior (2), proximal (3), and distal (4) views; transverse section of shaft (5)

HORIZON: Morrison formation
LOCALITY: YPM Quarry 10, Como Bluff, T. 22 N., R. 77 W., Sec. 12, Albany County, Wyo.

1. Now referred to *Apatosaurus excelsus.*

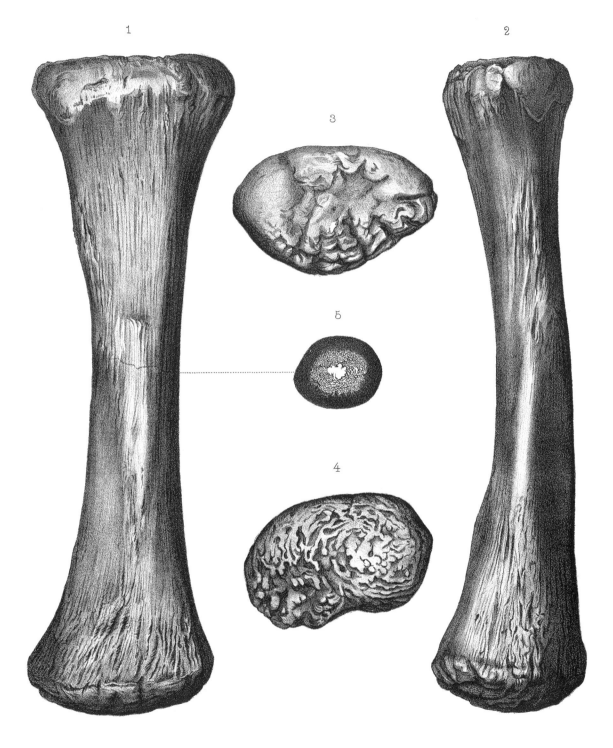

1   2   3   5   4

10 c m

PLATE 51

Morosaurus grandis[1] Marsh (1877) YPM 1901 (holotype)

Left radius in lateral (1), distal (1a), posterior (2), medial (3), proximal (3a), and anterior (4) views; transverse section through shaft (5)

HORIZON: Morrison formation

LOCALITY: YPM Quarry 1, Como Bluff, T. 22 N., R. 77 W., Sec. 10, Albany County, Wyo.

1. Now referred to *Camarasaurus grandis*.

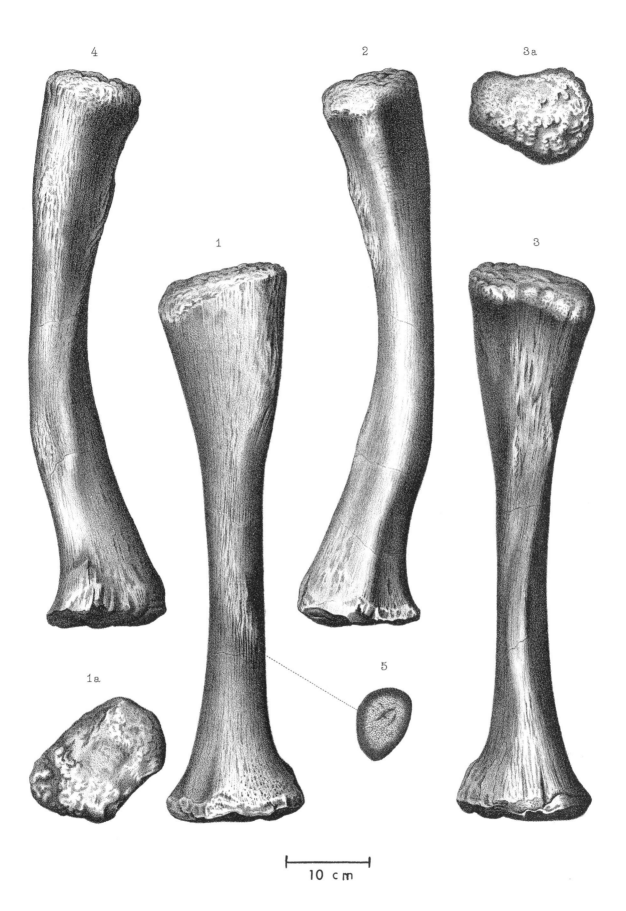

4 2 3a

1

1a 5 3

10 cm

PLATE 52

Brontosaurus excelsus[1] Marsh (1879) YPM 4633[2]

Left (?) ulna in posterior (1), lateral (2), proximal (3), and distal (4) views; transverse section through shaft (5)

HORIZON: Morrison formation

LOCALITY: ·YPM Quarry 1A (Big Canyon Quarry), Como Bluff, T. 22 N., R. 77 W., Sec. 17, Albany County, Wyo.

1. Now referred to *Apatosaurus excelsus.*
2. Now assigned to *Camarasaurus* sp.

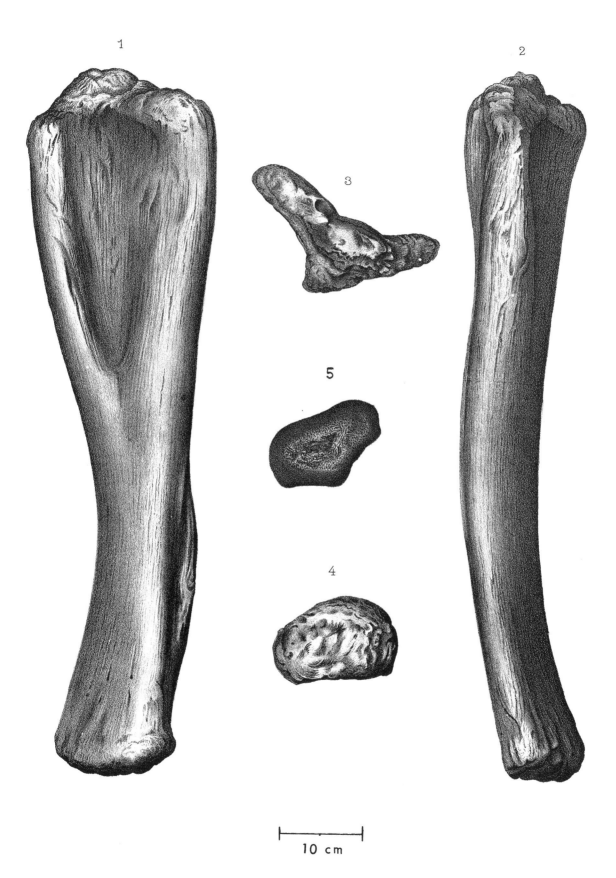

1   2   3

5

4

10 cm

PLATE 53

Morosaurus grandis[1] Marsh (1877) YPM 1901 (holotype)

Left ulna in anterior (1), distal (1a), lateral (2), posterior (3), and proximal (3a) views

HORIZON: Morrison formation

LOCALITY: YPM Quarry 1, Como Bluff, T. 22 N., R. 77 W., Sec. 10, Albany County, Wyo.

1. Now referred to *Camarasaurus grandis*.

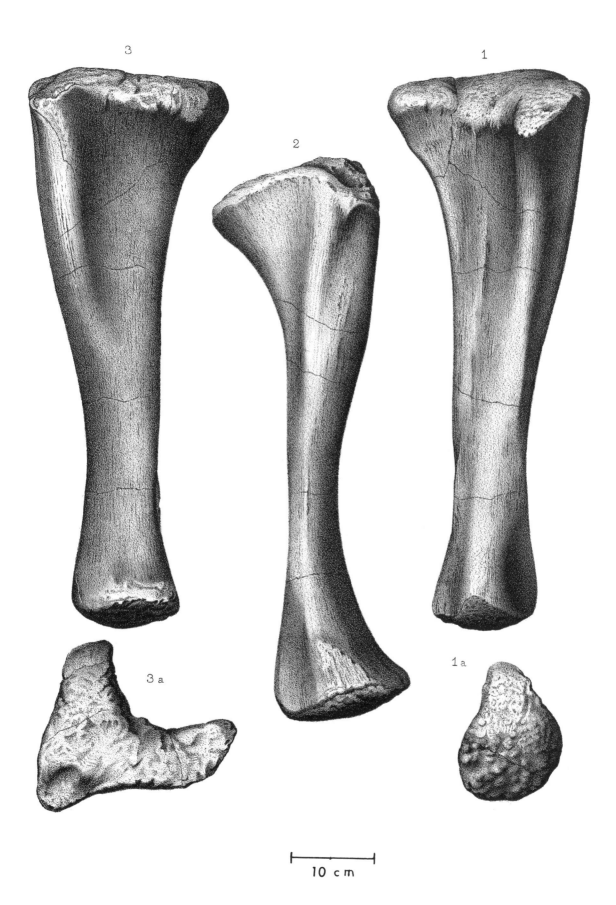

10 cm

PLATE 54

Brontosaurus excelsus[1] Marsh (1879) YPM 4633[2]
   Left radiale in proximal (1), lateral (2), and distal (3) views

   Left ulnare in proximal (4), lateral (5), and distal (6) views

   HORIZON: Morrison formation
   LOCALITY: YPM Quarry 1A (Big Canyon Quarry), Como Bluff, T. 22 N.,
            R. 77 W., Sec. 17, Albany County, Wyo.

1. Now referred to *Apatosaurus excelsus.*
2. Now assigned to *Camarasaurus* sp.

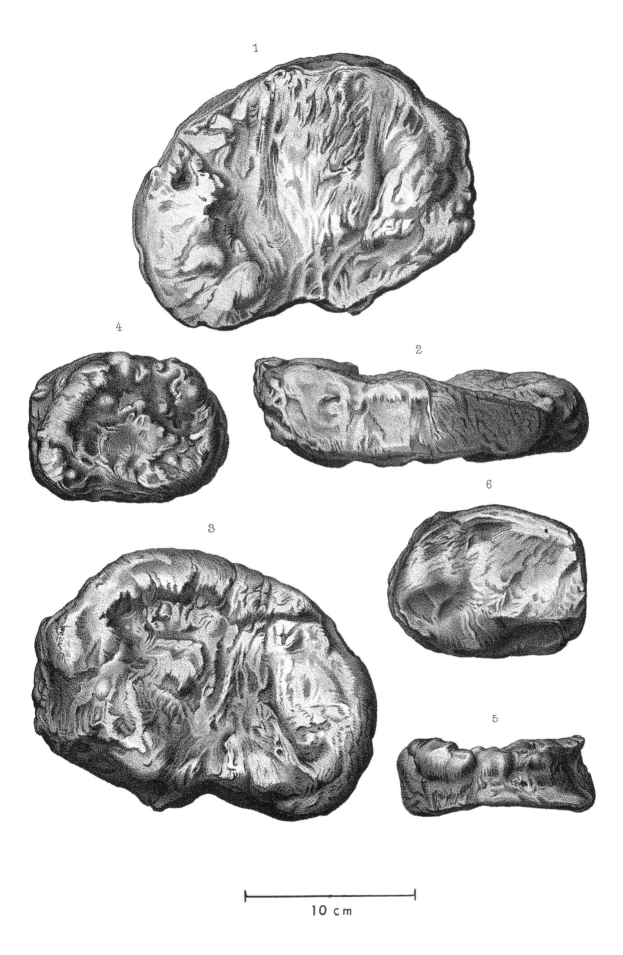

10 cm

PLATE 55

Brontosaurus excelsus[1] Marsh (1879) YPM 4633[2]

Left metacarpal I in anterior (1), medial (2), lateral (3), proximal (4), and distal (5) views

HORIZON: Morrison formation

LOCALITY: YPM Quarry 1A (Big Canyon Quarry), Como Bluff, T. 22 N., R. 77 W., Sec. 17, Albany County, Wyo.

1. Now referred to *Apatosaurus excelsus.*
2. Now assigned to *Camarasaurus* sp.

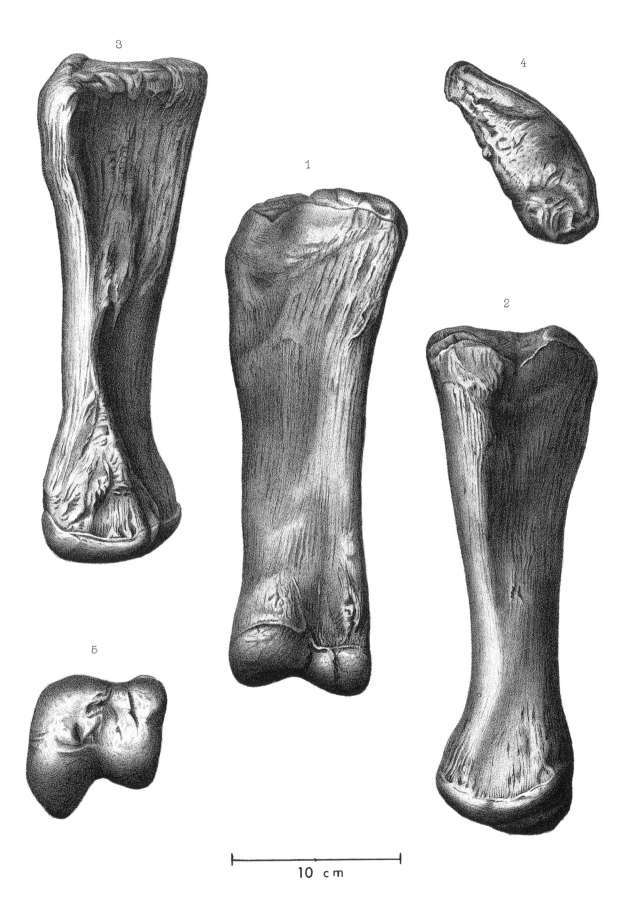

10 cm

PLATE 56

Brontosaurus excelsus[1] Marsh (1879) YPM 4633[2]
  Left metacarpal II in anterior (1), lateral (2), medial (3), proximal (4), and distal (5) views

HORIZON: Morrison formation
LOCALITY: YPM Quarry 1A (Big Canyon Quarry), Como Bluff, T. 22 N., R. 77 W., Sec. 17, Albany County, Wyo.

1. Now referred to *Apatosaurus excelsus.*
2. Now assigned to *Camarasaurus* sp.

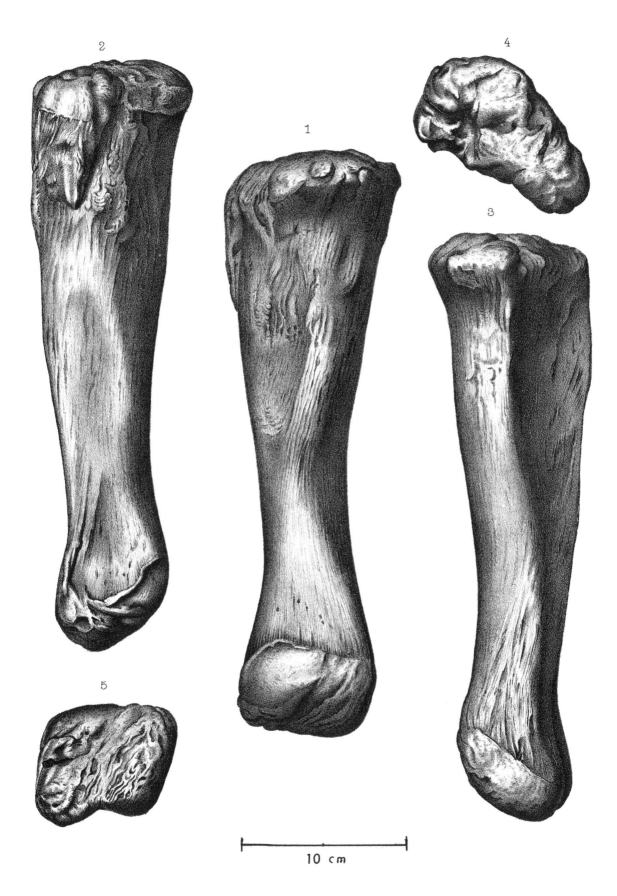

10 cm

PLATE 57

Brontosaurus excelsus[1] Marsh (1879) YPM 4633[2]
Left metacarpal III in anterior (1), lateral (2), medial (3), proximal (4), and distal (5) views

HORIZON: Morrison formation

LOCALITY: YPM Quarry 1A (Big Canyon Quarry), Como Bluff, T. 22 N., R. 77 W., Sec. 17, Albany County, Wyo.

1. Now referred to *Apatosaurus excelsus.*
2. Now assigned to *Camarasaurus* sp.

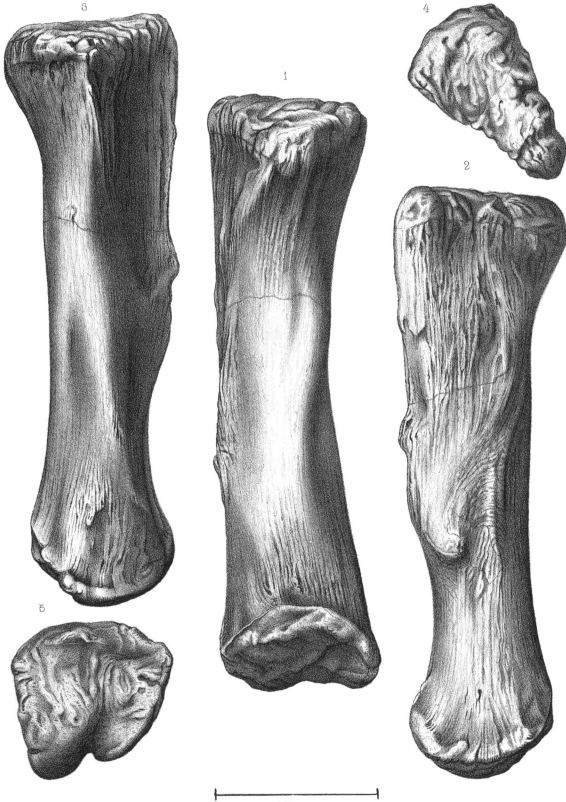

3   1   4

2

5

10 cm

PLATE 58

Brontosaurus excelsus[1] Marsh (1879) YPM 4633[2]
  Left metacarpal IV in anterior (1), lateral (2), medial (3), proximal (4), and
  distal (5) views

  HORIZON: Morrison formation
  LOCALITY: YPM Quarry 1A (Big Canyon Quarry), Como Bluff, T. 22 N.,
           R. 77 W., Sec. 17, Albany County, Wyo.

1. Now referred to *Apatosaurus excelsus.*
2. Now assigned to *Camarasaurus* sp.

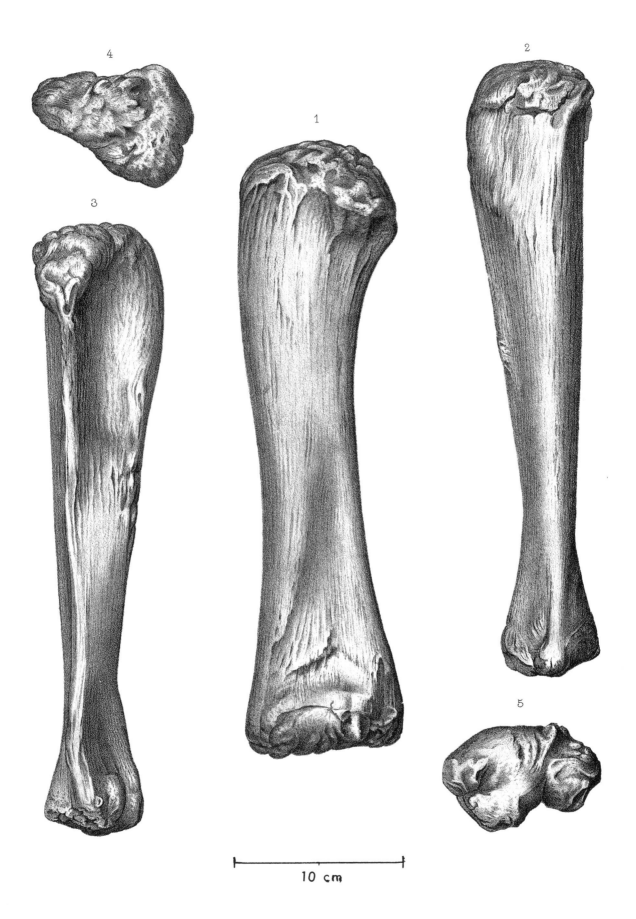

4

2

1

3

5

10 cm

PLATE 59

Brontosaurus excelsus[1] Marsh (1879) YPM 4633[2]
Left metacarpal V in anterior (1), medial (2), lateral (3), proximal (4), and distal (5) views

HORIZON: Morrison formation

LOCALITY: YPM Quarry 1A (Big Canyon Quarry), Como Bluff, T. 22 N., R. 77 W., Sec. 17, Albany County, Wyo.

1. Now referred to *Apatosaurus excelsus.*
2. Now assigned to *Camarasaurus* sp.

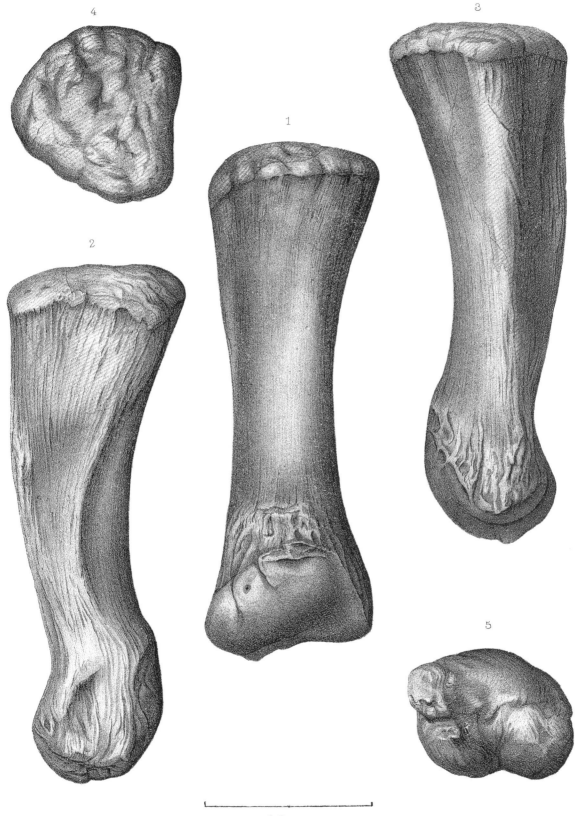

10 cm

PLATE 60

Morosaurus lentus[1] Marsh (1889) YPM 1910 (holotype)

Left metacarpal I in anterior (1), medial (2), lateral (3), proximal (4), and distal (5) views

Left metacarpal II in anterior (6), lateral (7), medial (8), proximal (9), and distal (10) views

HORIZON: Morrison formation

LOCALITY: YPM Quarry 13 West, Como Bluff, T. 22 N., R. 76 W., Sec. 4 or 5, Albany County, Wyo.

1. Now referred to *Camarasaurus lentus*.

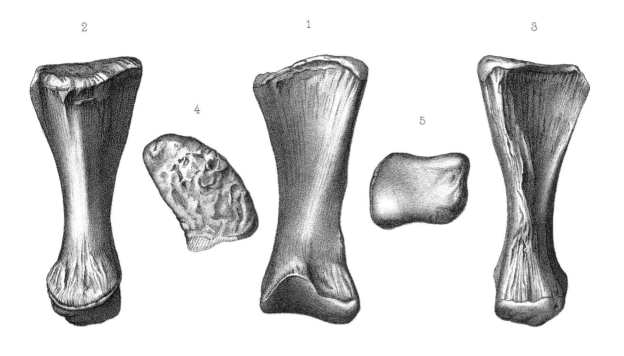

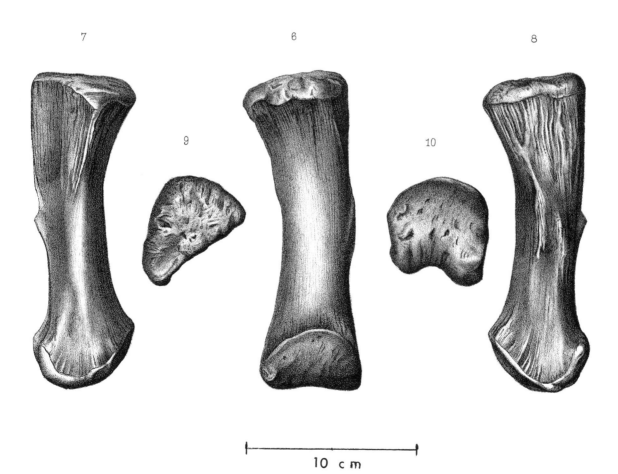

10 cm

PLATE 61

Morosaurus lentus[1] Marsh (1889) YPM 1910 (holotype)

Left metacarpal III in anterior (1), lateral (2), medial (3), proximal (4), and distal (5) views

Left metacarpal IV in anterior (6), lateral (7), medial (8), proximal (9), and distal (10) views

HORIZON: Morrison formation

LOCALITY: YPM Quarry 13 West, Como Bluff, T. 22 N., R. 76 W., Sec. 4 or 5, Albany County, Wyo.

1. Now referred to *Camarasaurus lentus.*

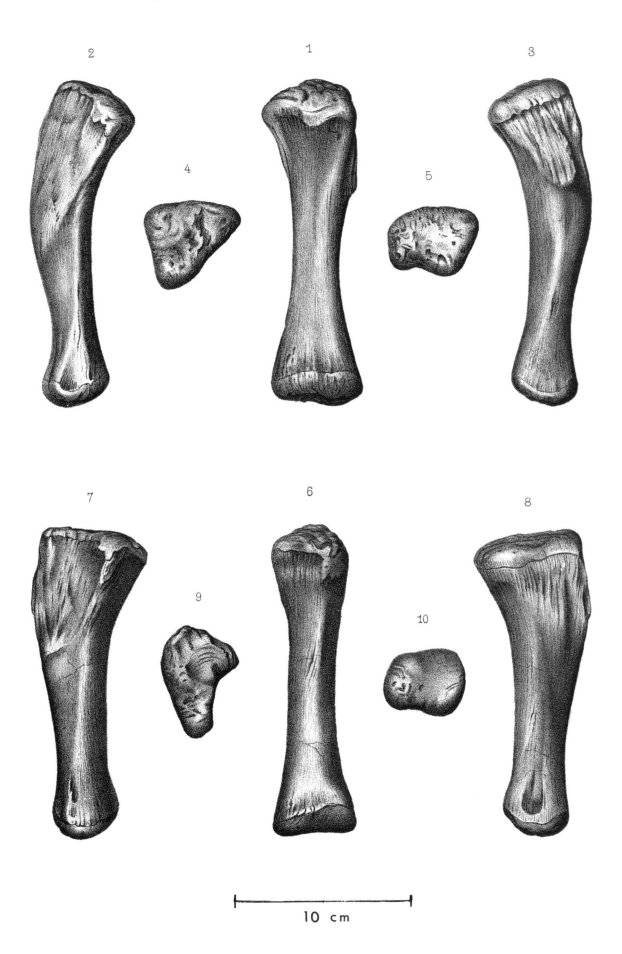

10 cm

PLATE 62

Brontosaurus excelsus[1] Marsh (1879) YPM 4633[2]

Proximal phalanx, digit I (?), in posterior (1), lateral (2), anterior (3), medial (4), proximal (5), and distal (6) views

Proximal phalanx, digit III or IV, in anterior (7), lateral (8), posterior (9), medial (10), proximal (11), and distal (12) views

HORIZON: Morrison formation

LOCALITY: YPM Quarry 1A (Big Canyon Quarry), Como Bluff, T. 22 N., R. 77 W., Sec. 17, Albany County, Wyo.

1. Now referred to *Apatosaurus excelsus.*
2. Now assigned to *Camarasaurus* sp.

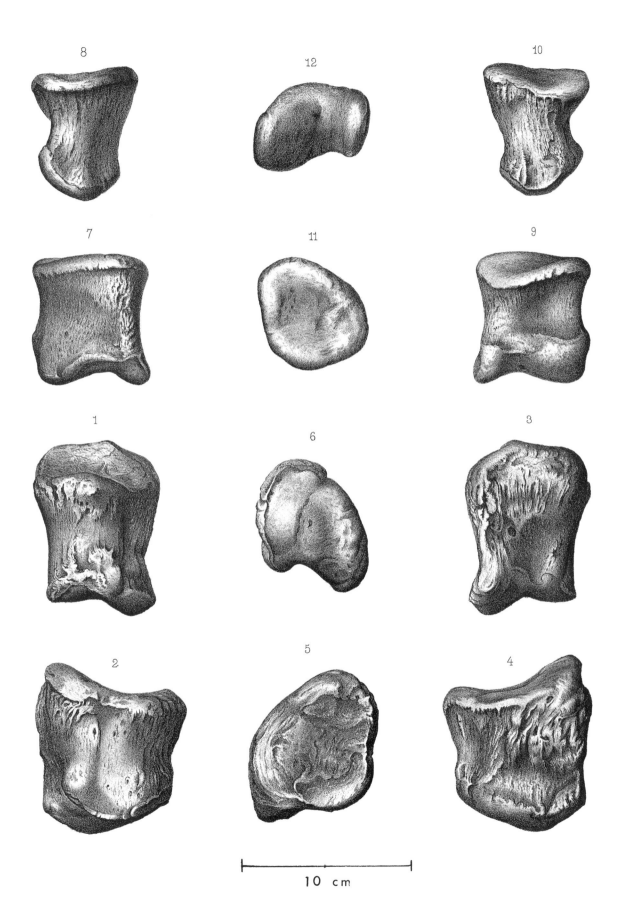

10 cm

PLATE 63

Brontosaurus excelsus[1] Marsh (1879) YPM 4633[2]

Ungual of digit I in anterior (1), lateral (2), medial (3), and proximal (4) views

Unidentifiable phalanx (5, 6, 7, 8)

HORIZON: Morrison formation

LOCALITY: YPM Quarry 1A (Big Canyon Quarry), Como Bluff, T. 22 N., R. 77 W., Sec. 17, Albany County, Wyo.

1. Now referred to *Apatosaurus excelsus*.
2. Now assigned to *Camarasaurus* sp.

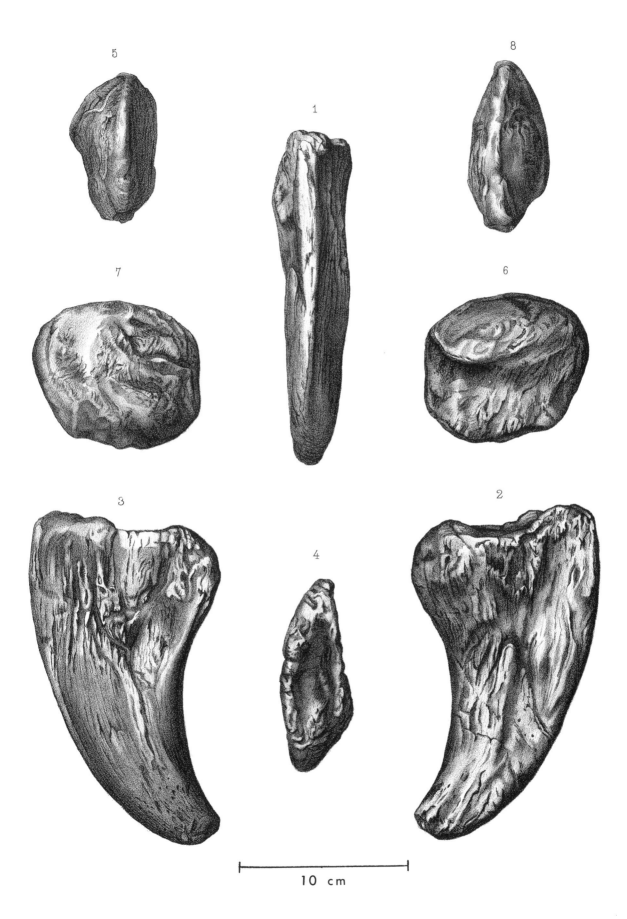

10 cm

PLATE 64

Brontosaurus amplus[1] Marsh (1881) YPM 1981 (holotype)
Left ilium in lateral view

HORIZON: Morrison formation

LOCALITY: YPM Quarry 11, Como Bluff, T. 22 N., R. 77 W., Sec. 12,
Albany County, Wyo.

ABBREVIATIONS: *a* pubic articulation
b ischial articulation
c dorsal margin of acetabulum

1. Now referred to *Apatosaurus amplus.*

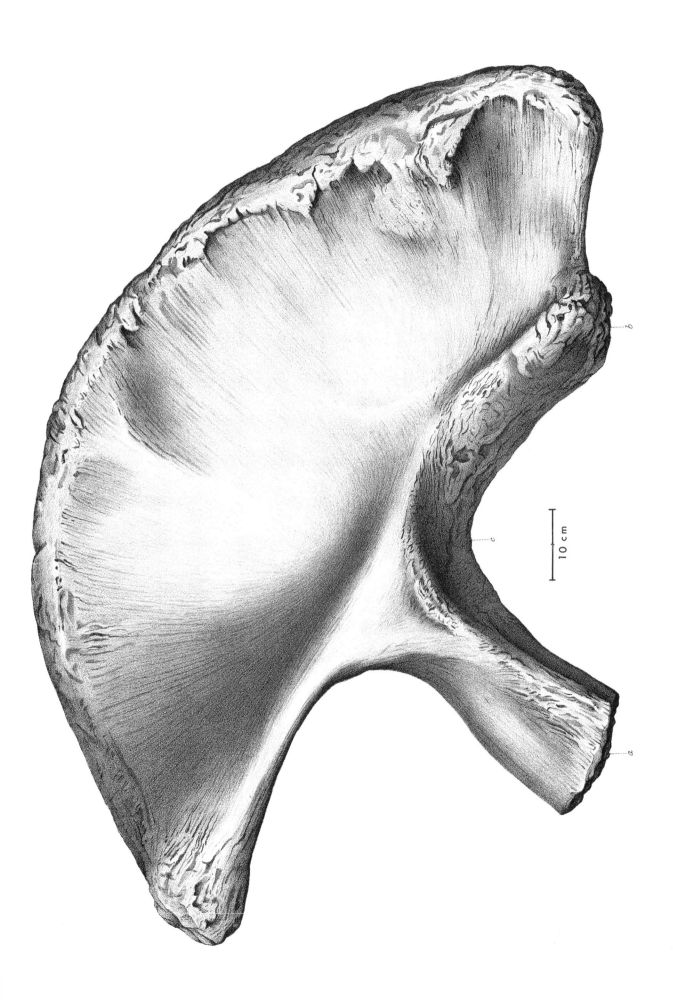

10 cm

PLATE 65

Morosaurus grandis[1] Marsh (1877) YPM 1901 (holotype)
Right ilium[2] (reversed) in lateral (1), and ventral views (2)

HORIZON: Morrison formation

LOCALITY: YPM Quarry 1, Como Bluff, T. 22 N., R. 77 W., Sec. 10, Albany County, Wyo.

ABBREVIATIONS: *a*   pubic articulation

b   ischial articulation

c   dorsal margin of acetabulum

1. Now referred to *Camarasaurus grandis.*
2. This ilium may actually belong with sacrum YPM 1900.

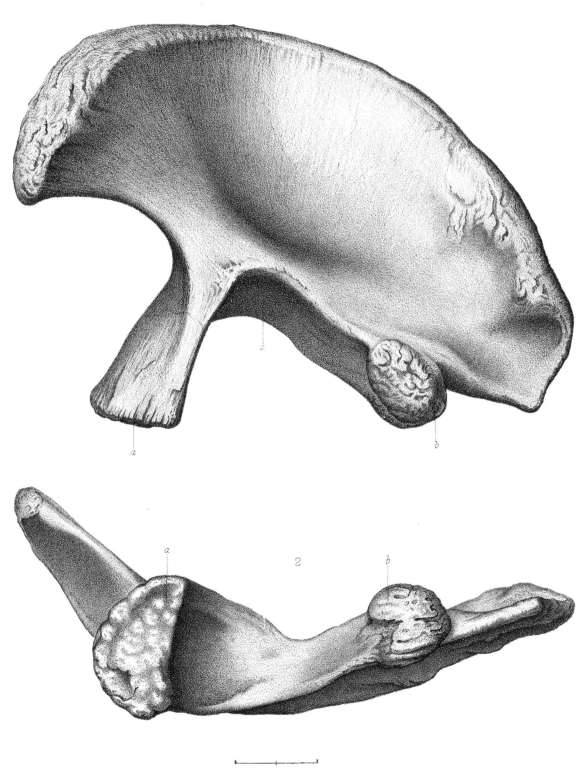

10 cm

PLATE 66

Morosaurus robustus[1] Marsh (1878) YPM 1902 (holotype)
Right ilium (reversed) in lateral (1) and ventral views (2)

HORIZON: Morrison formation

LOCALITY: YPM Quarry 1, Como Bluff, T. 22 N., R. 77 W., Sec. 10,
Albany County, Wyo.

ABBREVIATIONS: *a* pubic articulation
b ischial articulation
c dorsal margin of acetabulum

1. Now referred to *Camarasaurus grandis.*

1

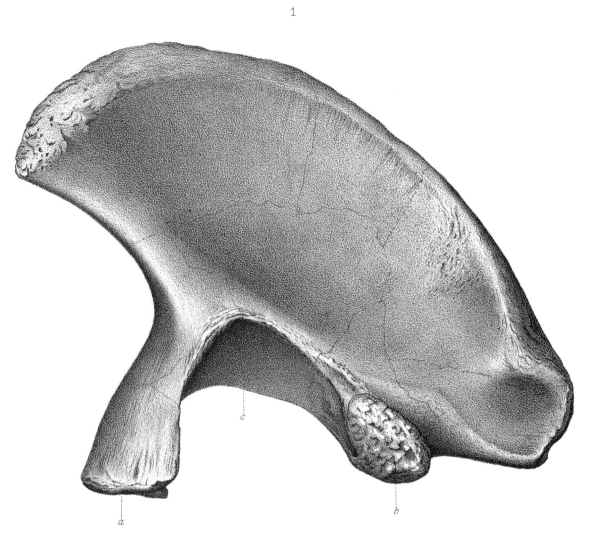

2

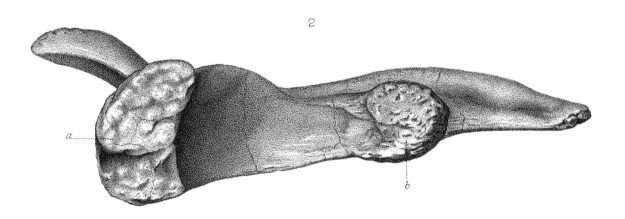

├─────┤
10 cm

PLATE 67

Brontosaurus excelsus[1] Marsh (1879) YPM 1980 (holotype)
Left ischium in lateral (1), posterior (2), proximal (3), and distal (4) views;
transverse section of shaft (5)

HORIZON: Morrison formation

LOCALITY: YPM Quarry 10, Como Bluff, T. 22 N., R. 77 W., Sec. 12,
Albany County, Wyo.

ABBREVIATIONS: *a*   acetabulum
   i   articular surface for ilium
   p   articular surface for pubis
   s   distal extremity

1. Now referred to *Apatosaurus excelsus.*

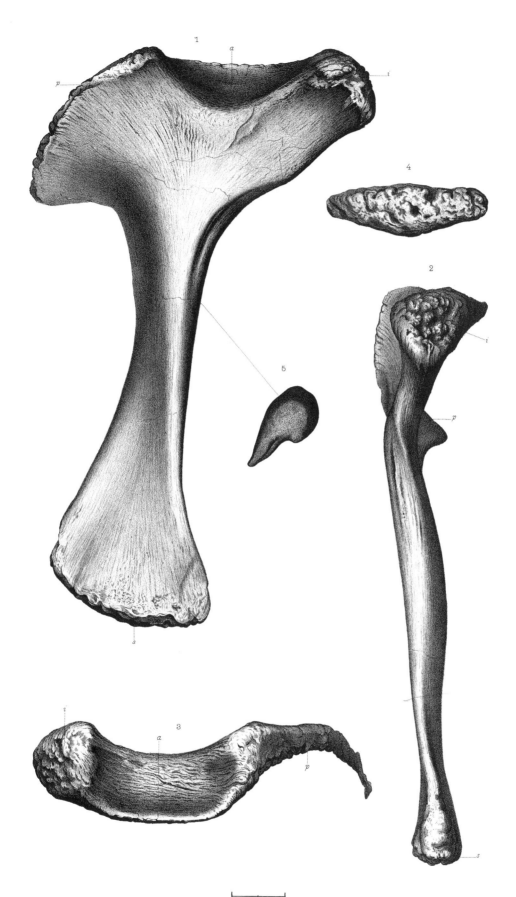

10 cm

PLATE 68

Morosaurus grandis[1] Marsh (1877) YPM 1905

Right ischium (reversed) in lateral (1), posterior (2), proximal (3), and distal (4) views; transverse section of shaft (5)

HORIZON: Morrison formation

LOCALITY: YPM Quarry 1, Como Bluff, T. 22 N., R. 77 W., Sec. 10, Albany County, Wyo.

ABBREVIATIONS: *a* acetabulum
il articular surface for ilium
n anterior notch
p articular surface for pubis
s distal extremity

1. Now referred to *Camarasaurus grandis*.

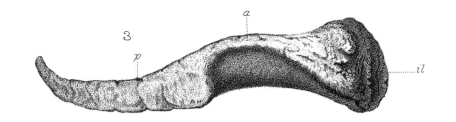

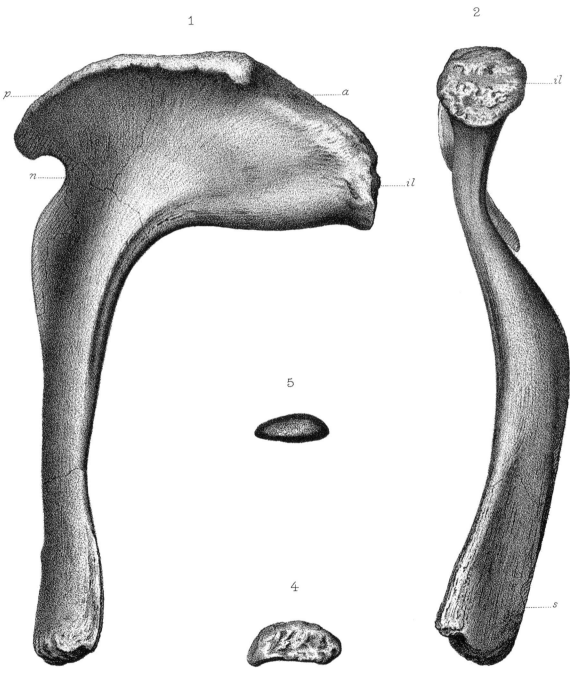

10 cm

PLATE 69

Brontosaurus excelsus[1] Marsh (1879) YPM 1980 (holotype)
  Left pubis in lateral (1), anterior (2), proximal (3), and distal (4) views

  HORIZON: Morrison formation
  LOCALITY: YPM Quarry 10, Como Bluff, T. 22 N., R. 77 W., Sec. 12,
       Albany County, Wyo.

  ABBREVIATIONS: *a*   acetabulum
            f   obturator foramen
            il articulation for ilium
            is articulation for ischium
            s   distal extremity

1. Now referred to *Apatosaurus excelsus.*

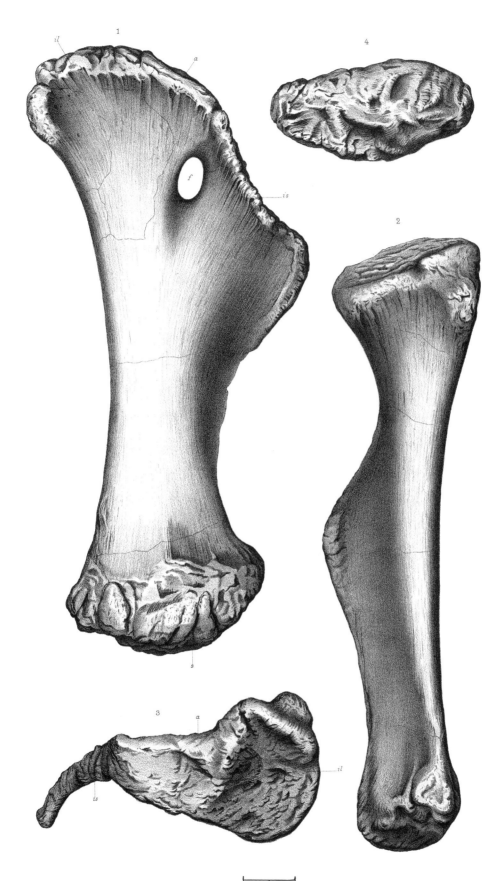

10 cm

PLATE 70

Morosaurus lentus[1] Marsh (1889) YPM 1910 (holotype)

Right pubis (reversed) in medial (1), posterior (2), lateral (3), proximal (4), and distal (5) views; transverse sections through blade (6) and shaft (7)

HORIZON: Morrison formation

LOCALITY: YPM Quarry 13 West, Como Bluff, T. 22 N., R. 76 W., Sec. 4 or 5, Albany County, Wyo.

ABBREVIATIONS:
    a   acetabulum
    f   obturator notch
    il articular surface for ilium
    is articular surface for ischium
    s   distal extremity

1. Now referred to *Camarasaurus lentus*.

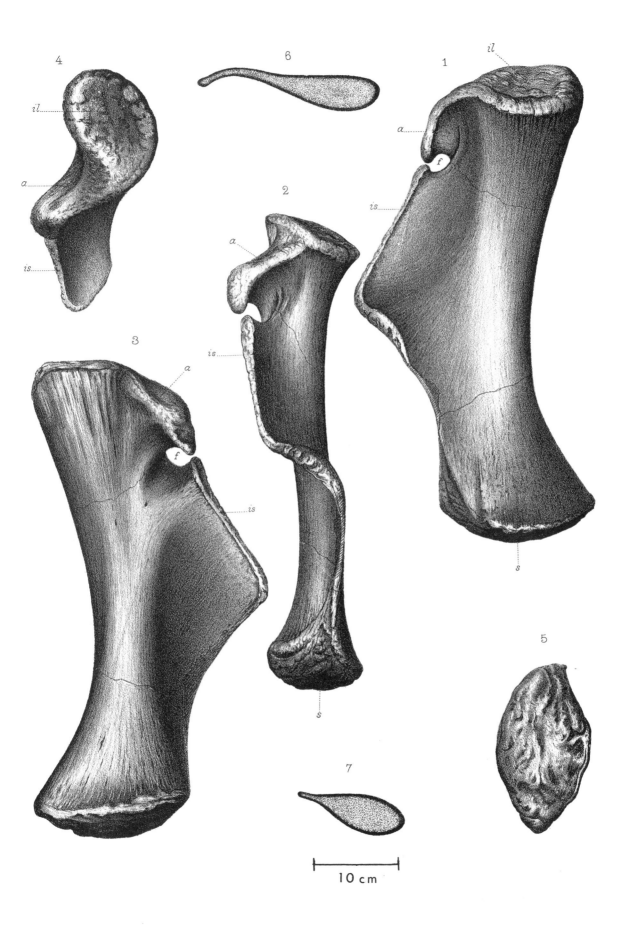

4

il

a

is

6

2

a

is

s

3

a

f

is

1

il

a

f

is

s

5

7

10 cm

PLATE 71

Brontosaurus excelsus[1] Marsh (1879) YPM 1980 (holotype)
Left femur in anterior (1) and medial (2) views

HORIZON: Morrison formation

LOCALITY: YPM Quarry 10, Como Bluff, T. 22 N., R. 77 W., Sec. 12, Albany County, Wyo.

ABBREVIATIONS:
- *c* anterior condyle
- *c'* posterior condyle
- *h* head
- *t* greater trochanter
- *t'* fourth trochanter

1. Now referred to *Apatosaurus excelsus*.

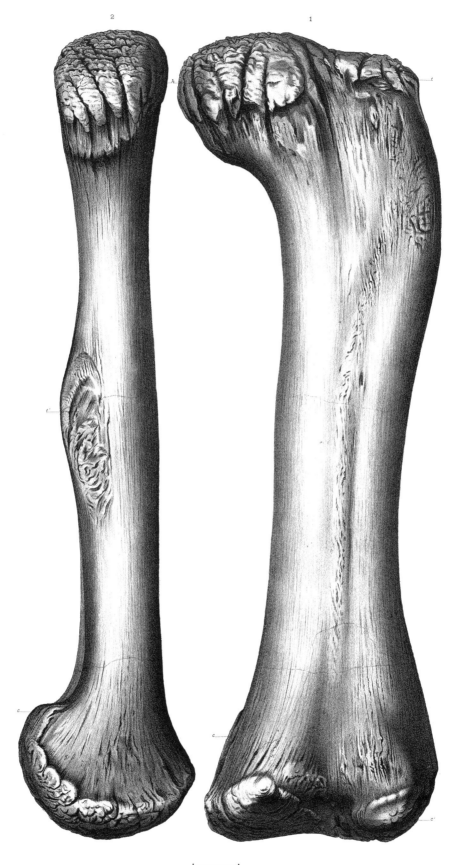

10 cm

PLATE 72

Morosaurus grandis[1] Marsh (1877) YPM 1901 (holotype)
Left femur in anterior (1), distal (1a), posterior (2), and proximal (2a) views

HORIZON: Morrison formation

LOCALITY: YPM Quarry 1, Como Bluff, T. 22 N., R. 77 W., Sec. 10, Albany County, Wyo.

ABBREVIATIONS: *c*   anterior condyle
                    c′   posterior condyle
                    f   fibular articulation
                    h   head
                    t   greater trochanter
                    t′   fourth trochanter

1. Now referred to *Camarasaurus grandis*.

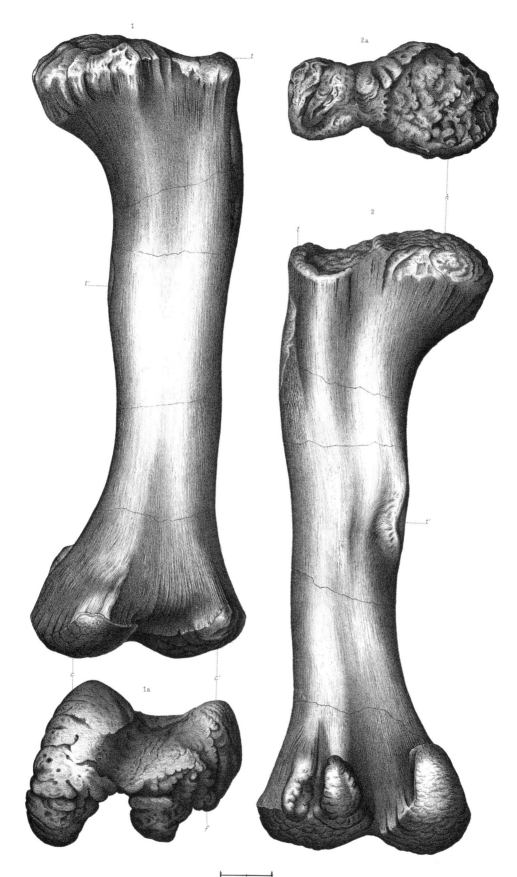

10 cm

PLATE 73

Morosaurus grandis[1] Marsh (1877) YPM 1901 (holotype)
Left femur in medial (1) and lateral (2) views; transverse section of shaft (1a)

HORIZON: Morrison formation

LOCALITY: YPM Quarry 1, Como Bluff, T. 22 N., R. 77 W., Sec. 10, Albany County, Wyo.

ABBREVIATIONS: *c*   anterior condyle
      c'   posterior condyle
      h   head
      t   greater trochanter
      t'   fourth trochanter

1. Now referred to *Camarasaurus grandis.*

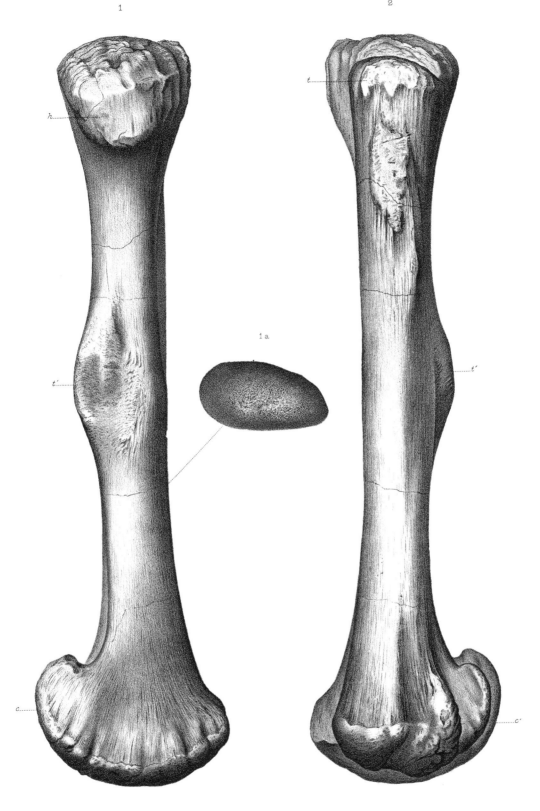

1   2

1 a

├──────┤
10 cm

PLATE 74

Brontosaurus excelsus[1] Marsh (1879) YPM 1980 (holotype)
Left tibia, fibula, and astragalus in anterior (1) and medial (2) views

HORIZON: Morrison formation

LOCALITY: YPM Quarry 10, Como Bluff, T. 22 N., R. 77 W., Sec. 12, Albany County, Wyo.

ABBREVIATIONS: *a* astragalus
c cnemial crest
f fibula
t tibia

1. Now referred to *Apatosaurus excelsus.*

1   2

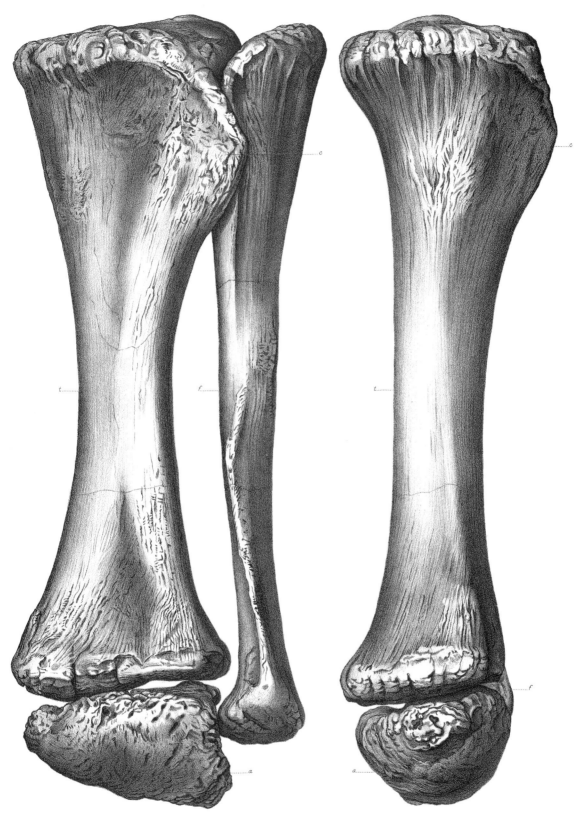

10 cm

PLATE 75

Morosaurus grandis[1] Marsh (1877) YPM 1905
   Left tibia in anterior (1), distal (1a), and medial (2) views

   HORIZON: Morrison formation
   LOCALITY: YPM Quarry 1, Como Bluff, T. 22 N., R. 77 W., Sec. 10,
      Albany County, Wyo.

   1. Now referred to *Camarasaurus grandis.*

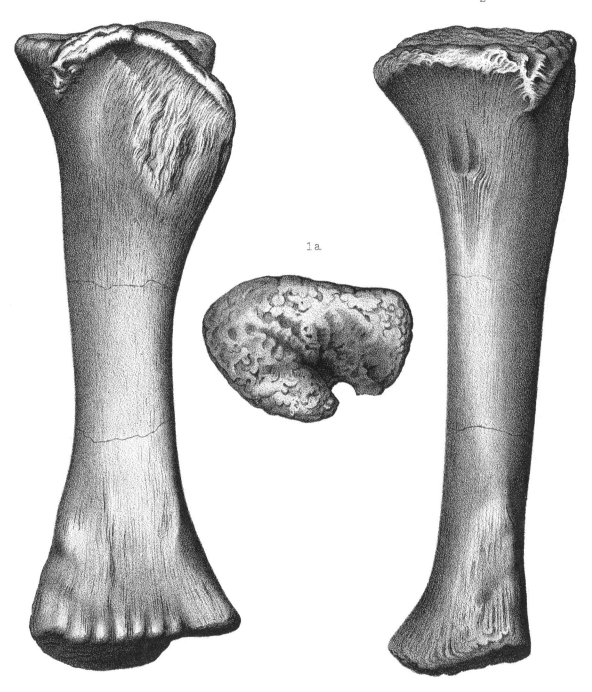

1   1a   2

|—————— 10 cm ——————|

PLATE 76

Morosaurus grandis[1] Marsh (1877) YPM 1905
Left tibia in posterior (1), proximal (1a), and lateral (2) views

HORIZON: Morrison formation

LOCALITY: YPM Quarry 1, Como Bluff, T. 22 N., R. 77 W., Sec. 10, Albany County, Wyo.

1. Now referred to *Camarasaurus grandis.*

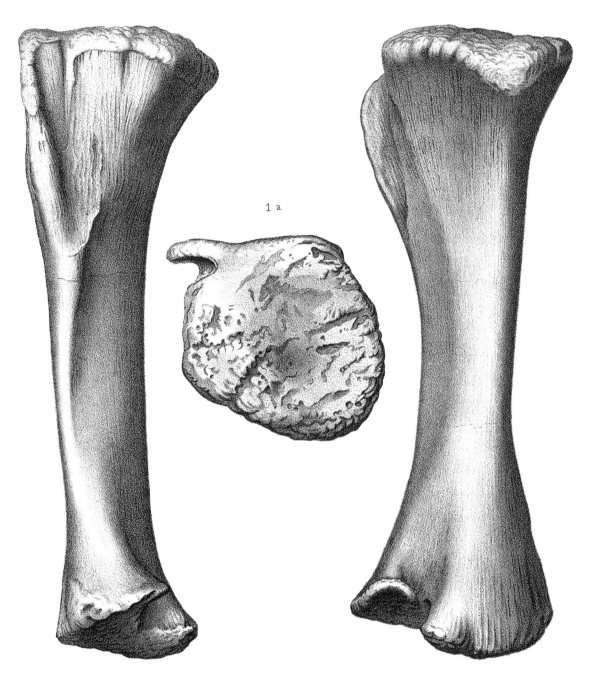

2

1

1 a

10 cm

PLATE 77

Morosaurus grandis[1] Marsh (1877) YPM 1905

Left fibula in anterior (1), medial (2), posterior (3), lateral (4), proximal (5), and distal (6) views

HORIZON: Morrison formation

LOCALITY: YPM Quarry 1, Como Bluff, T. 22 N., R. 77 W., Sec. 10, Albany County, Wyo.

ABBREVIATIONS: *a*   tibial articular surface
                b   muscle scar
                c   anterior crest

1. Now referred to *Camarasaurus grandis.*

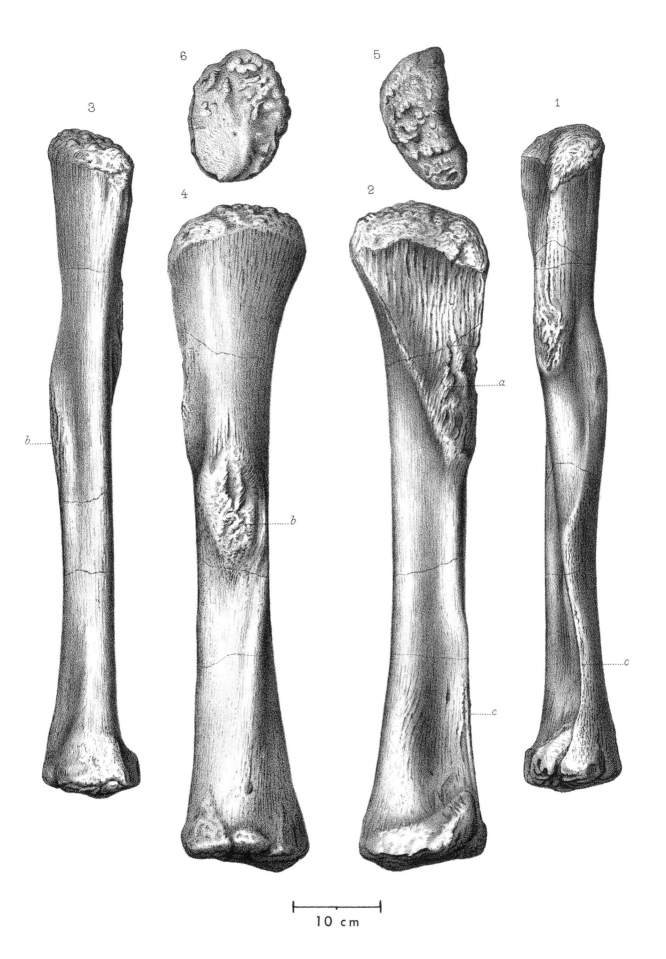

10 cm

PLATE 78

Morosaurus grandis[1] Marsh (1877) YPM 1901 or 1905
  Left astragalus in lateral (1), anterior (2), posterior (3), medial (4), proximal
  (5), and distal (6) views

  HORIZON: Morrison formation
  LOCALITY: YPM Quarry 1, Como Bluff, T. 22 N., R. 77 W., Sec. 10,
  Albany County, Wyo.

  1. Now referred to *Camarasaurus grandis.*

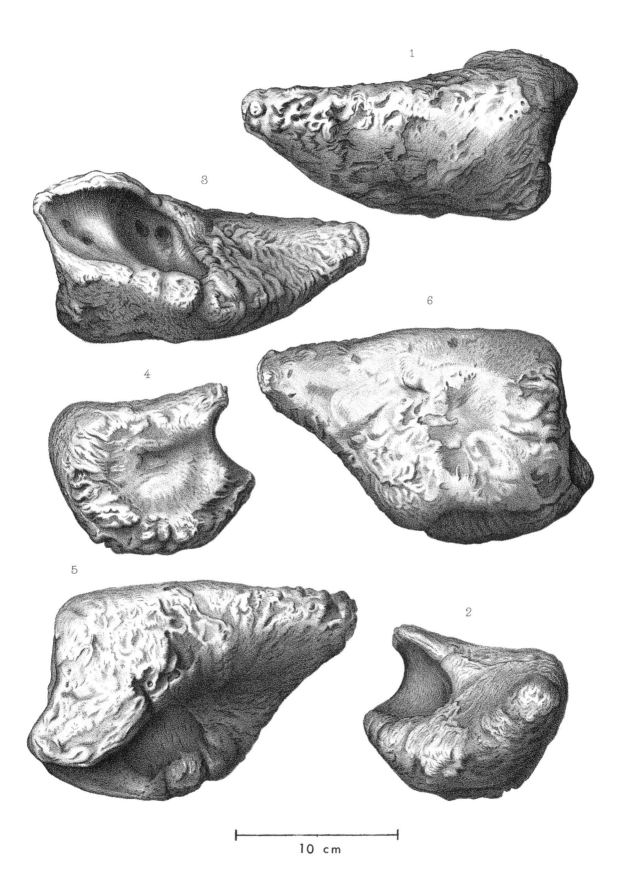

10 cm

PLATE 79

Morosaurus grandis[1] Marsh (1877) YPM 1901 or 1905

Probable carpal[2] in lateral (1), anterior (2), posterior (3), proximal (4), and distal (5) views

HORIZON: Morrison formation

LOCALITY: YPM Quarry 1, Como Bluff, T. 22 N., R. 77 W., Sec. 10, Albany County, Wyo.

Morosaurus lentus[3] Marsh (1889) YPM 1910

Probable carpal[2] in lateral (6), anterior (7), posterior (8), proximal (9), and distal (10) views

HORIZON: Morrison formation

LOCALITY: YPM Quarry 13 West, Como Bluff, T. 22 N., R. 76 W., Sec. 4 or 5, Albany County, Wyo.

1. Now referred to *Camarasaurus grandis.*
2. Marsh believed these to be calcanii.
3. Now referred to *Camarasaurus lentus.*

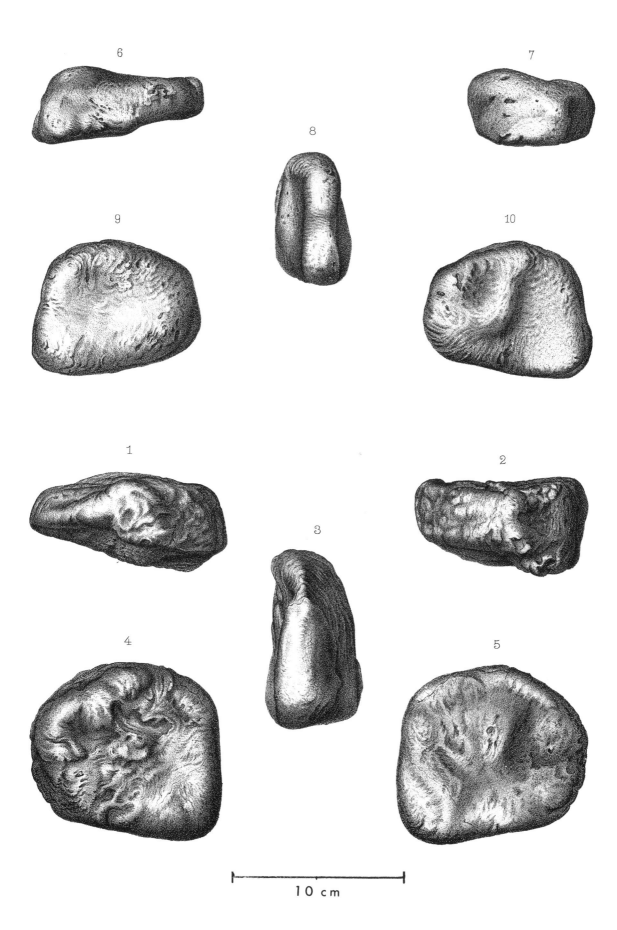

10 cm

PLATE 80

Diplodocus longus Marsh (1878) YPM 1920 (holotype?)

Right metatarsal I (?)[1] in anterior (1), lateral (2), proximal (3), and distal (4) views; transverse section (5)

HORIZON: Morrison formation

LOCALITY: Felch YPM Quarry 1, Garden Park, T. 17 S., R. 70 W., Sec. 28, Fremont County, Colo.

1. Considerable doubt exists whether this particular element actually belongs to the same individual to which YPM 1920 has been assigned.

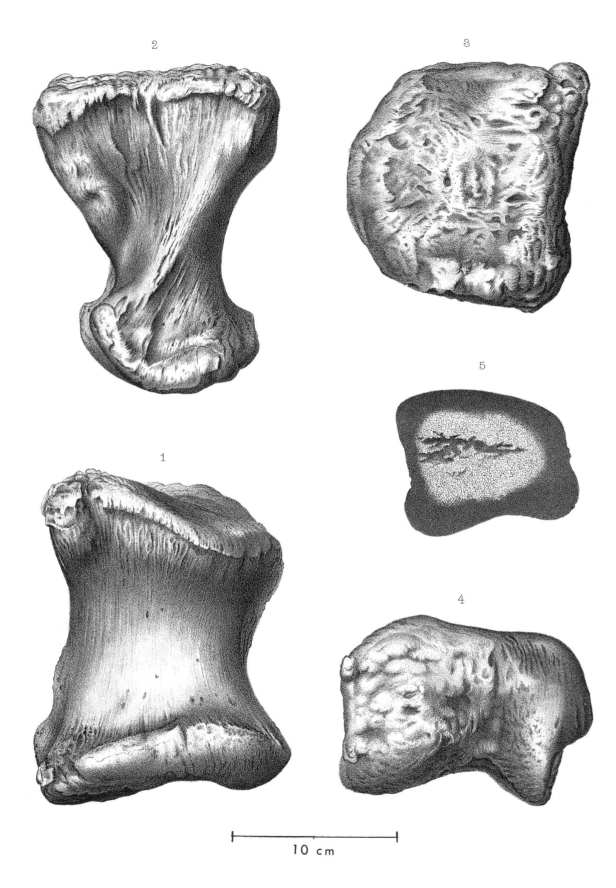

10 cm

PLATE 81

Morosaurus grandis[1] Marsh (1877) YPM 1901 or 1905
  Left metatarsal I in anterior (1), medial (2), posterior (3), lateral (4), proximal (5), and distal (6) views

  HORIZON: Morrison formation
  LOCALITY: YPM Quarry 1, Como Bluff, T. 22 N., R. 77 W., Sec. 10, Albany County, Wyo.

1. Now referred to *Camarasaurus grandis*.

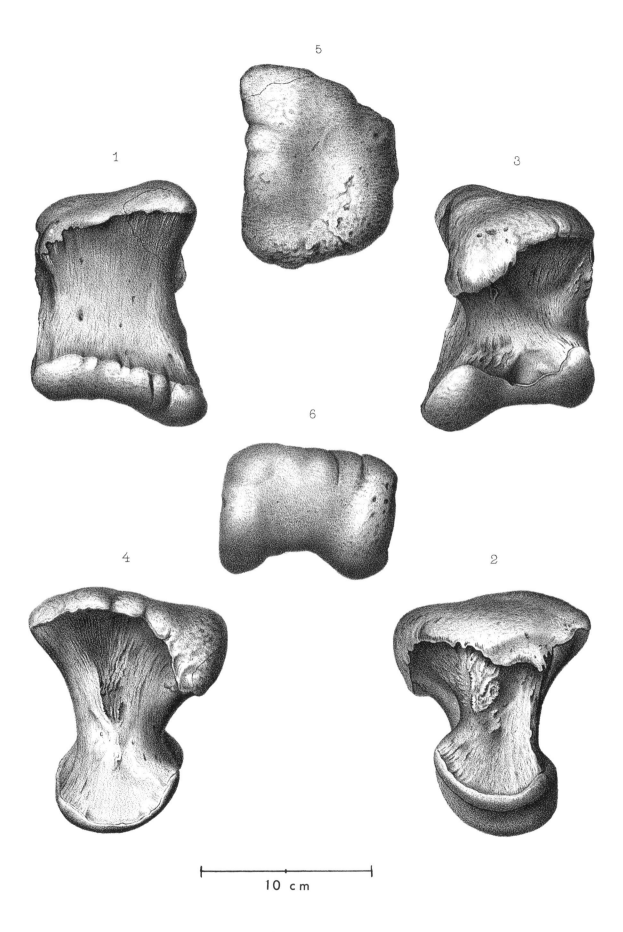

5

1

3

6

4

2

10 cm

PLATE 82

Morosaurus grandis[1] Marsh (1877) YPM 1901 or 1905
   Left metatarsal II in anterior (1), medial (2), lateral (3), posterior (4), proximal (5), and distal (6) views

   HORIZON: Morrison formation
   LOCALITY: YPM Quarry 1, Como Bluff, T. 22 N., R. 77 W., Sec. 10, Albany County, Wyo.

1. Now referred to *Camarasaurus grandis.*

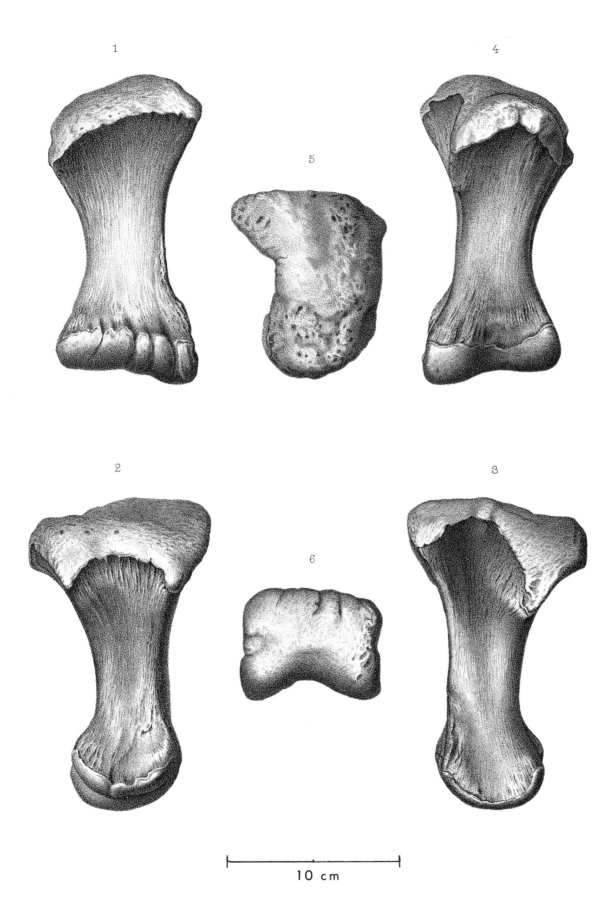

1

5

4

2

6

3

10 cm

PLATE 83

Morosaurus grandis[1] Marsh (1877) YPM 1901 or 1905

Left metatarsal III in anterior (1), medial (2), posterior (3), lateral (4), proximal (5), and distal (6) views

HORIZON: Morrison formation

LOCALITY: YPM Quarry 1, Como Bluff, T. 22 N., R. 77 W., Sec. 10, Albany County, Wyo.

1. Now referred to *Camarasaurus grandis*.

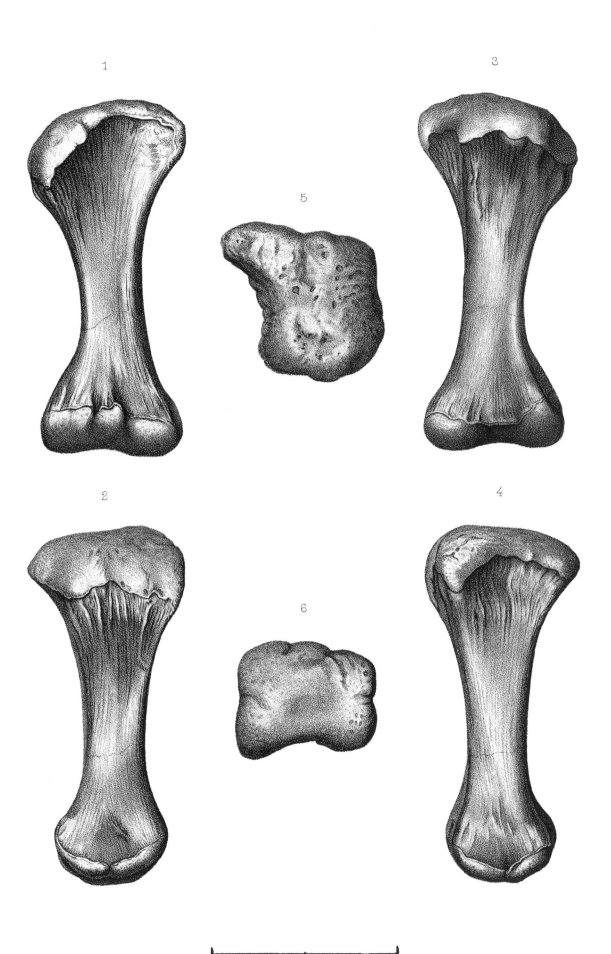

1

3

5

2

6

4

10 cm

PLATE 84

Morosaurus grandis[1] Marsh (1877) YPM 1901 or 1905
  Left metatarsal IV in anterior (1), medial (2), posterior (3), lateral (4), proximal (5), and distal (6) views

  HORIZON: Morrison formation
  LOCALITY: YPM Quarry 1, Como Bluff, T. 22 N., R. 77 W., Sec. 10, Albany County, Wyo.

1. Now referred to *Camarasaurus grandis.*

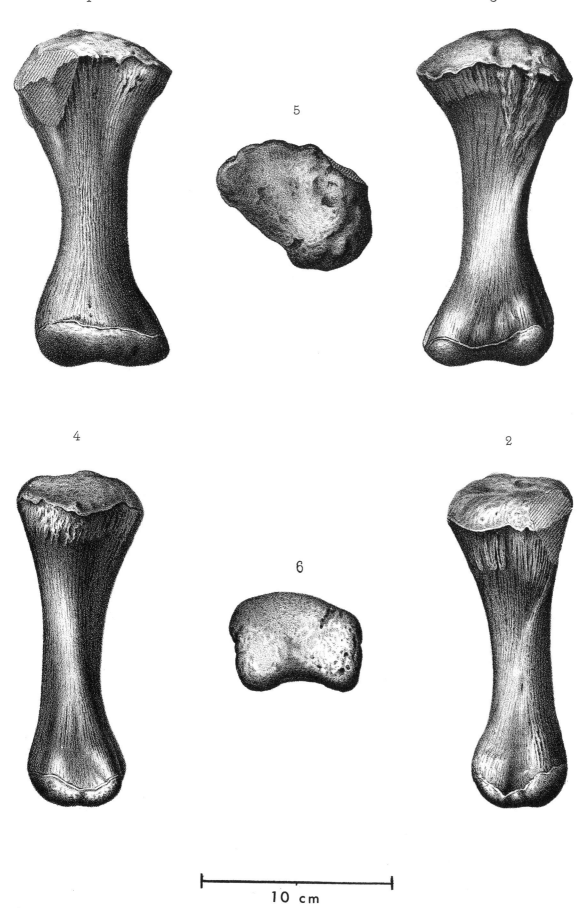

1

3

5

4

2

6

10 cm

PLATE 85

Morosaurus grandis[1] Marsh (1877) YPM 1901 or 1905
Metatarsal V in lateral (1), anterior (2), medial (3), posterior (4), proximal (5), and distal (6) views

HORIZON: Morrison formation
LOCALITY: YPM Quarry 1, Como Bluff, T. 22 N., R. 77 W., Sec. 10, Albany County, Wyo.

1. Now referred to *Camarasaurus grandis.*

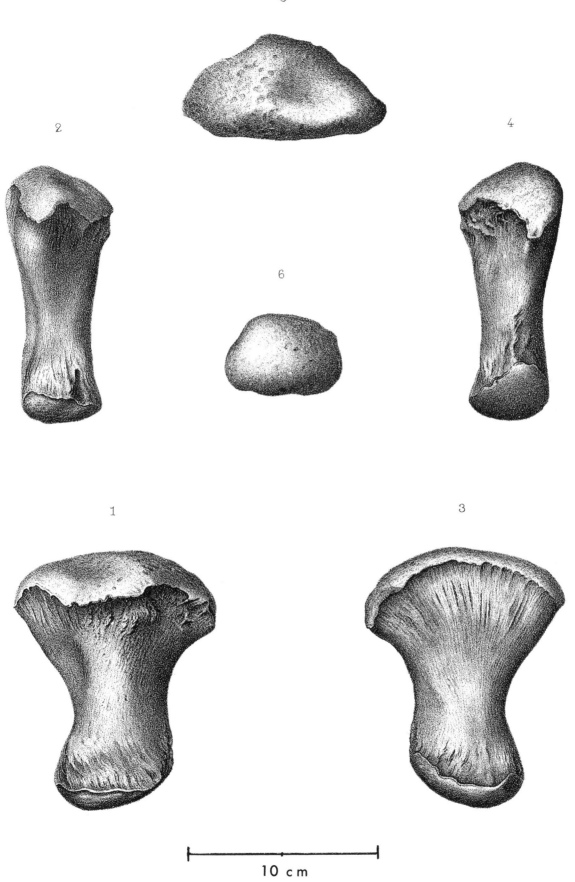

5

2

4

6

1

3

10 cm

PLATE 86

Morosaurus grandis[1] Marsh (1877) YPM 1901 or 1905

Proximal phalanx of digit III (left?) in anterior (1), posterior (2), proximal (3), and distal (4) views

Proximal phalanx of digit III (right?) in anterior (5), lateral (6), posterior (7), proximal (8), and distal (9) views

Proximal phalanx of digit II (left?) in anterior (10), lateral (11), and distal (12) views

HORIZON: Morrison formation

LOCALITY: YPM Quarry 1, Como Bluff, T. 22 N., R. 77 W., Sec. 10, Albany County, Wyo.

1. Now referred to *Camarasaurus grandis.*

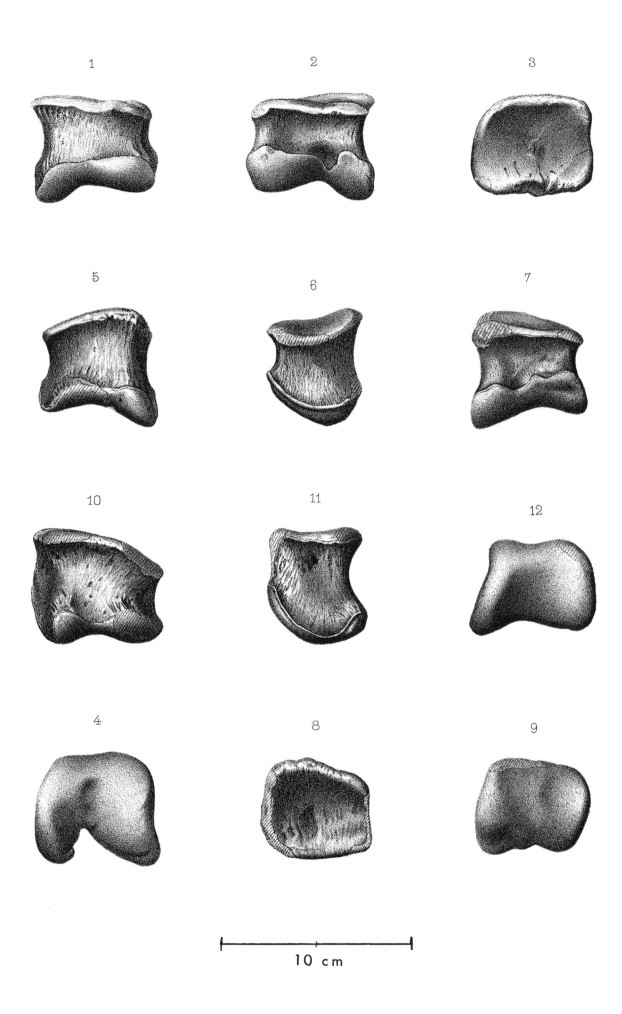

1   2   3

5   6   7

10   11   12

4   8   9

10 cm

PLATE 87

Morosaurus grandis[1] Marsh (1877) YPM 1901 or 1905
Proximal phalanx of digit IV (left?) in anterior (1), lateral (2), posterior (3), medial (4), proximal (5), and distal (6) views

Second phalanx of digit II (left?) in anterior (7), lateral (8), posterior (9), medial (10), proximal (11), and distal (12) views

HORIZON: Morrison formation
LOCALITY: YPM Quarry 1, Como Bluff, T. 22 N., R. 77 W., Sec. 10, Albany County, Wyo.

1. Now referred to *Camarasaurus grandis*.

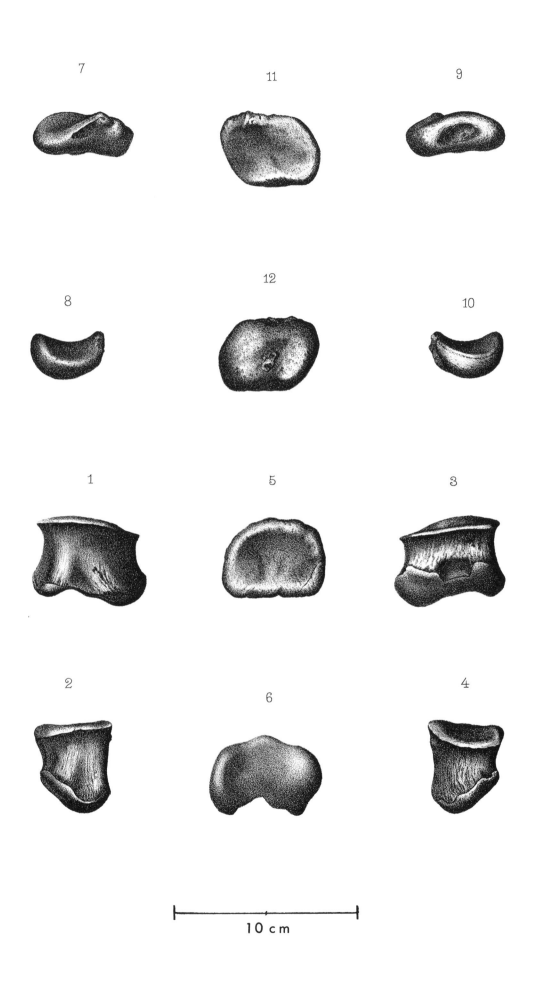

10 cm

PLATE 88

Morosaurus grandis[1] Marsh (1877) YPM 1901 or 1905

Ungual of digit I in anterior (1), medial (2), lateral (3), and proximal (4) views

Ungual of digit III in anterior (5), medial (6), lateral (7), and proximal (8) views.

HORIZON: Morrison formation

LOCALITY: YPM Quarry 1, Como Bluff, T. 22 N., R. 77 W., Sec. 10, Albany County, Wyo.

1. Now referred to *Camarasaurus grandis*.

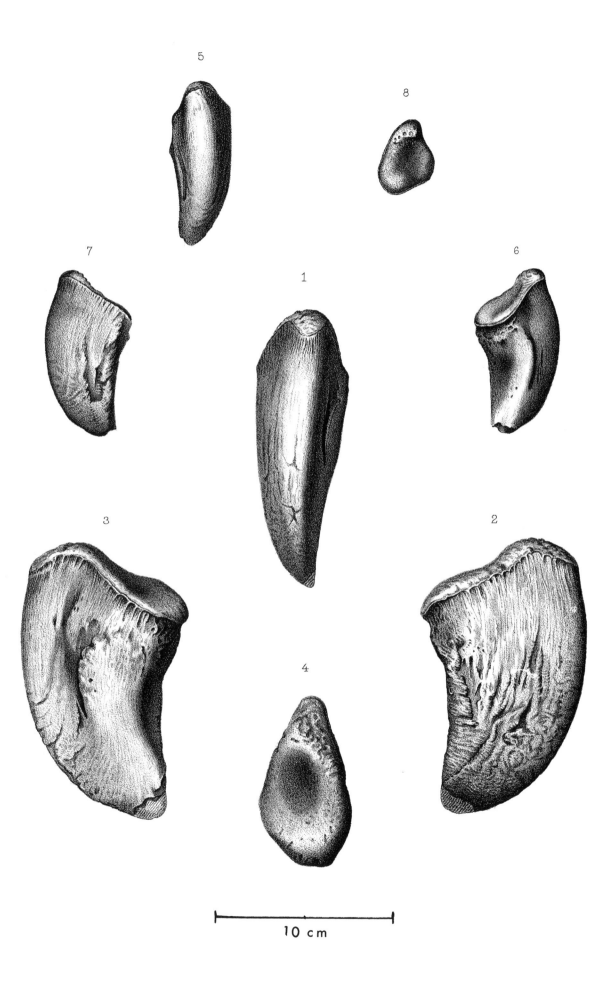

5

8

7

1

6

3

2

4

10 cm

PLATE 89

Morosaurus grandis[1] Marsh (1877)
Sacrum and pelvic girdle in anterior view

Sacrum: YPM 1900 (holotype)
Ilia: YPM 1901 or 1905
Ischia: YPM 1905
Pubes: YPM 1903

HORIZON: Morrison formation

LOCALITY: YPM Quarry 1, Como Bluff, T. 22 N., R. 77 W., Sec. 10, Albany County, Wyo.

ABBREVIATIONS:
a   anterior sacral centrum
b   anterior sacral rib
c   intervertebral fenestra
e   posterior sacral rib
il ilium
is ischium
nc neural canal
p   posterior sacral centrum
pb pubis
s   neural spine
z   prezygapophysis

1. Now referred to *Camarasaurus grandis.*

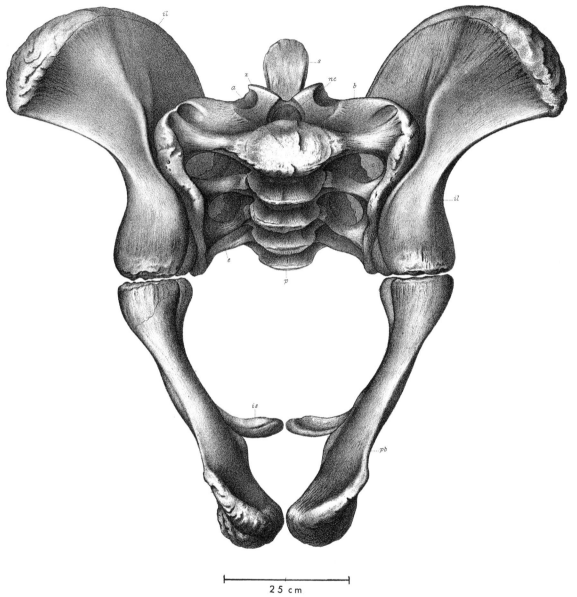

25 cm

PLATE 90

Brontosaurus excelsus[1] Marsh (1879)
  Skull[2] and jaw: USNM 5730

> HORIZON: Morrison formation
> LOCALITY: Felch YPM Quarry 1, Garden Park, T. 17 S., R. 70 W., Sec. 28, Fremont County, Colo.

Skeleton: YPM 1980 (holotype)

> HORIZON: Morrison formation
> LOCALITY: YPM Quarry 10, Como Bluff, T. 22 N., R. 77 W., Sec. 12, Albany County, Wyo.

1. Now referred to *Apatosaurus excelsus*.
2. This skull was found isolated in a quarry from which five sauropod genera have been identified. There is no evidence for referring it to *Apatosaurus* (*Brontosaurus*).

MARSH'S STEGOSAUR PLATES

PLATE 1

Stegosaurus stenops Marsh (1887) USNM 4934 (holotype)
Lateral view of restored skull

HORIZON: Morrison formation

LOCALITY: Felch YPM Quarry 1, Garden Park, T. 17 S., R. 70 W., Sec. 28, Fremont County, Colo.

ABBREVIATIONS:
a	external nares
an	angular
ar	articular
b	orbit
c	infratemporal fenestra
d	dentary
fp	postfrontal
j	jugal
l	lacrimal
m	maxilla
n	nasal
oc	occipital condyle
pd	predentary
pf	prefrontal
pm	premaxilla
po	postorbital
q	quadrate
s	splenial
sa	surangular
so	supraorbital
sq	squamosal

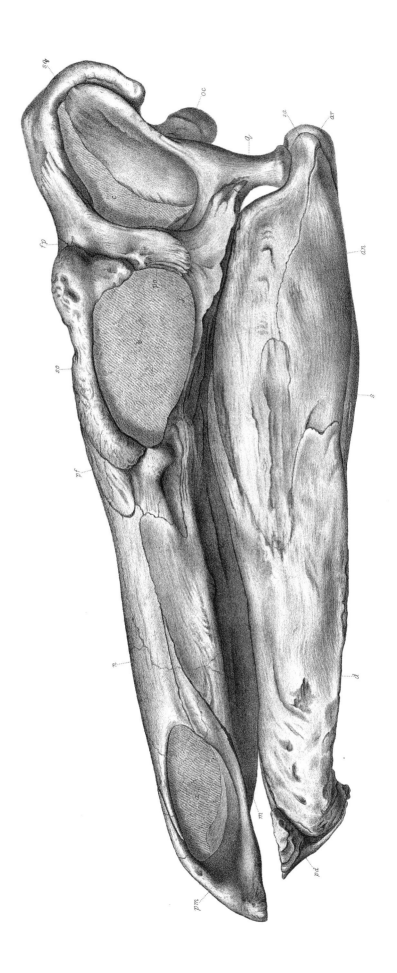

10 cm

PLATE 2

Stegosaurus stenops Marsh (1887) USNM 4934 (holotype)
Dorsal (1), anterior (2), and posterior (3) views of restored skull

HORIZON: Morrison formation

LOCALITY: Felch YPM Quarry 1, Garden Park, T. 17 S., R. 70 W., Sec. 28, Fremont County, Colo.

ABBREVIATIONS:

a	external nares
an	angular
ar	articular
b	orbit
c	infratemporal fenestra
d	dentary
e	supratemporal fenestra
f	frontal
fm	foramen magnum
fp	postfrontal
l	lacrimal
m	maxilla
n	nasal
oc	occipital condyle
os	supraoccipital
p	parietal
pd	predentary
pf	prefrontal
pm	premaxilla
po	postorbital
q	quadrate
so	supraorbital
sq	squamosal

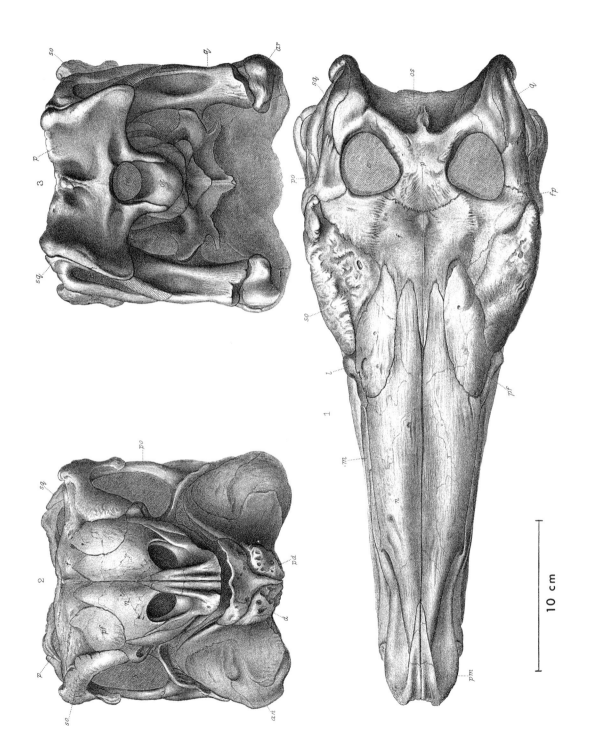

10 cm

PLATE 3

Stegosaurus stenops Marsh (1887) USNM 4934 (holotype)
Ventral (1) and mid-sagittal section (2) views of restored skull

HORIZON: Morrison formation

LOCALITY: Felch YPM Quarry 1, Garden Park, T. 17 S., R. 70 W., Sec. 28, Fremont County, Colo.

ABBREVIATIONS:

a	external nares
an	angular
ar	articular
b	orbit
d	dentary
f	frontal
fm	foramen magnum
m	maxilla
n	nasal
oc	occipital condyle
p	parietal
pd	predentary
pl	palatine
pm	premaxilla
pp	paroccipital process
pt	pterygoid
q	quadrate
s	splenial

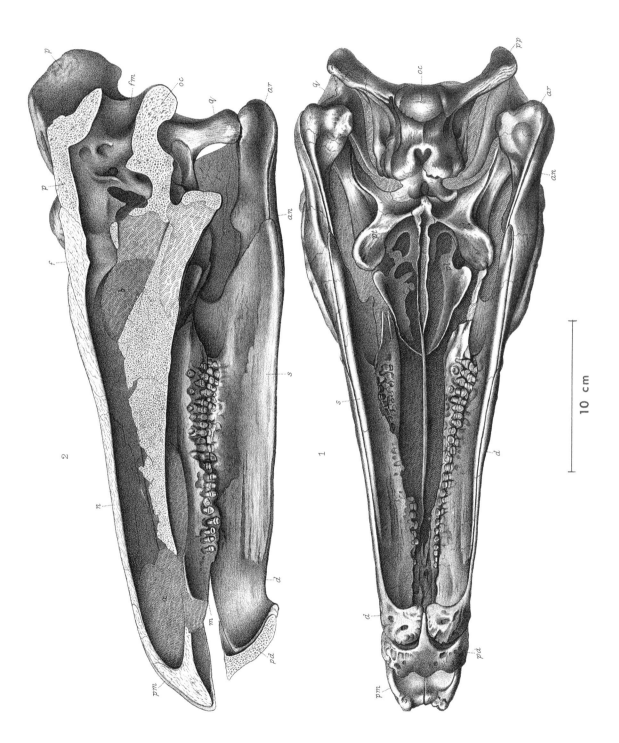

10 cm

PLATE 4

Stegosaurus armatus Marsh (1877) USNM 4936
Cranium in dorsal (1), ventral (2), and mid-sagittal section (3)

Endocranial cast in dorsal (4) and lateral (5) views

HORIZON: Morrison formation

LOCALITY: Felch YPM Quarry 1, Garden Park, T. 17 S., R. 70 W., Sec. 28, Fremont County, Colo.

ABBREVIATIONS:
b	orbit
c	cerebrum
cb	cerebellum
e	supratemporal fenestra
f	frontal
f'	foramen
fm	foramen magnum
fp	postfrontal
m	medulla
ns	nasal suture
oc	occipital condyle
of	optic foramen
ol	olfactory lobe
on	optic nerve
op	pineal organ
p	parietal
pi	pituitary fossa or body
po	postorbital
pp	paroccipital process
ps	prefrontal suture
so	supraoccipital

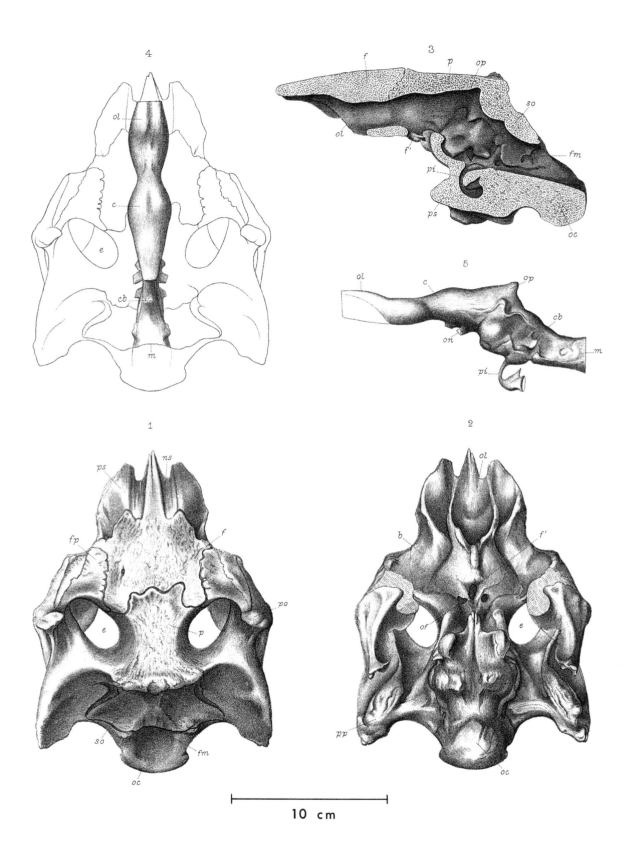

10 cm

PLATE 7[1]

Stegosaurus stenops Marsh (1887) YPM 1856

Atlas in lateral (1), dorsal (2), anterior (3), ventral (4), and posterior (5) views

Axis in lateral (6), dorsal (7), anterior (8), ventral (9), and posterior (10) views

Third cervical vertebra in lateral (11), dorsal (12), anterior (13), ventral (14), and posterior (15) views

HORIZON: Morrison formation

LOCALITY: YPM Quarry 13 West, Como Bluff, T. 22 N., R. 76 W., Sec. 4 or 5, Albany County, Wyo.

ABBREVIATIONS:
- *a*   anterior face of centrum
- *a'*   posterior face of centrum
- *d*   diapophysis
- *n*   neural canal
- *o*   odontoid process
- *p*   parapophysis
- *s*   neural spine
- *z*   prezygapophysis
- *z'*   postzygapophysis

1. Plates 5 and 6 were never completed. Plate 5 was to have illustrated the maxillae of *Diracodon laticeps* (YPM 1885) = *Stegosaurus stenops*. Plate 6 was to have illustrated the brain of *Stegosaurus*.

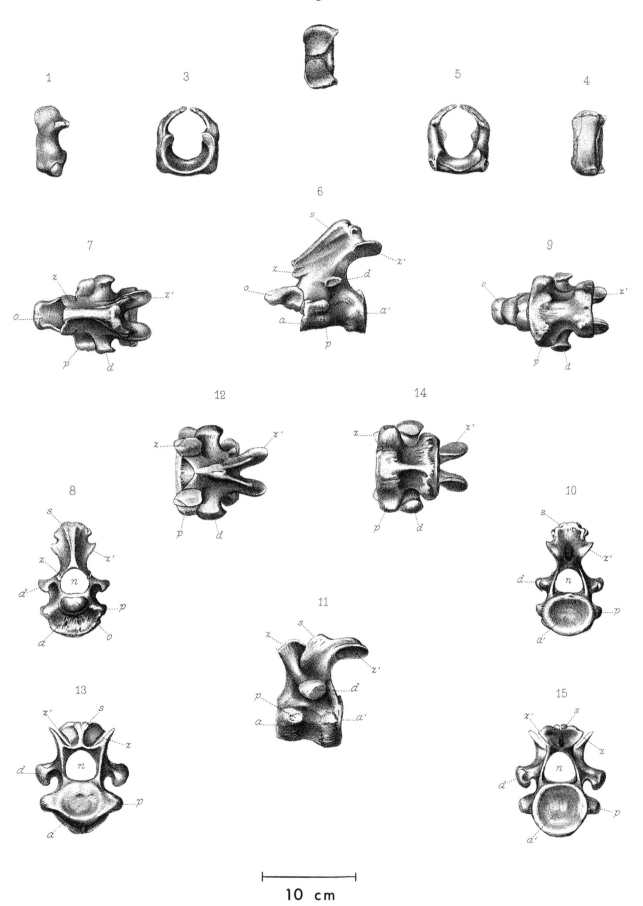

PLATE 8

Stegosaurus duplex[1] Marsh (1887) YPM 1858 (holotype)

Fourth (?) cervical vertebra in lateral (1), dorsal (2), anterior (3), ventral (4), and posterior (5) views

Fifth (?) cervical vertebra in lateral (6), dorsal (7), anterior (8), ventral (9), and posterior (10) views

HORIZON: Morrison formation

LOCALITY: YPM Quarry 11, Como Bluff, T. 22 N., R. 77 W., Sec. 12, Albany County, Wyo.

ABBREVIATIONS:
a	anterior face of centrum
a'	posterior face of centrum
d	diapophysis
n	neural canal
p	parapophysis
s	neural spine
z	prezygapophysis
z'	postzygapophysis

1. = *Stegosaurus ungulatus.*

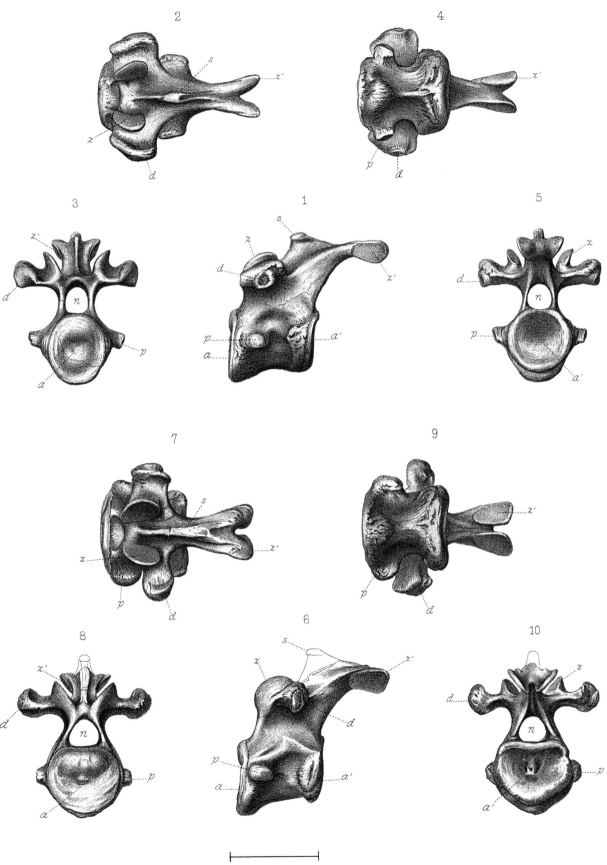

10 cm

PLATE 9

Stegosaurus stenops Marsh (1887) YPM 1856

Anterior cervical vertebra in lateral (1), dorsal (2), anterior (3), ventral (4), and posterior (5) views

Mid-cervical vertebra in lateral (6), anterior (7), ventral (8), and posterior (9) views

Posterior cervical vertebra in lateral (10), anterior (11), ventral (12), and posterior (13) views

HORIZON: Morrison formation

LOCALITY: YPM Quarry 13 West, Como Bluff, T. 22 N., R. 76 W., Sec. 4 or 5, Albany County, Wyo.

ABBREVIATIONS:
- *a*   anterior face of centrum
- *a'*   posterior face of centrum
- *d*   diapophysis
- *n*   neural canal
- *p*   parapophysis
- *s*   neural spine
- *z*   prezygapophysis
- *z'*   postzygapophysis

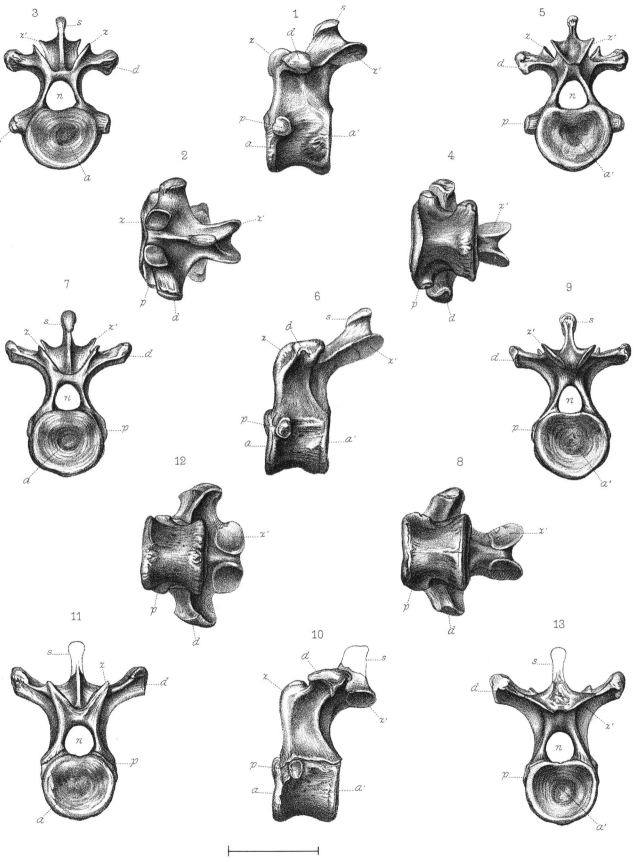

10 cm

PLATE 14[1]

Stegosaurus stenops Marsh (1887) YPM 1856
Anterior dorsal vertebrae in lateral (1, 6), dorsal (2, 7), anterior (3, 8), ventral (4, 9), and posterior (5, 10) views

HORIZON: Morrison formation

LOCALITY: YPM Quarry 13 West, Como Bluff, T. 22 N., R. 76 W., Sec. 4 or 5, Albany County, Wyo.

ABBREVIATIONS:
a	anterior face of centrum
a'	posterior face of centrum
d	diapophysis
n	neural canal
p	parapophysis
s	neural spine
z	prezygapophysis
z'	postzygapophysis

1. Plates 10, 11, 12, and 13 were never completed. Plate 10 was to have illustrated additional cervical vertebrae. Plates 11, 12, and 13 were to have illustrated dorsal vertebrae.

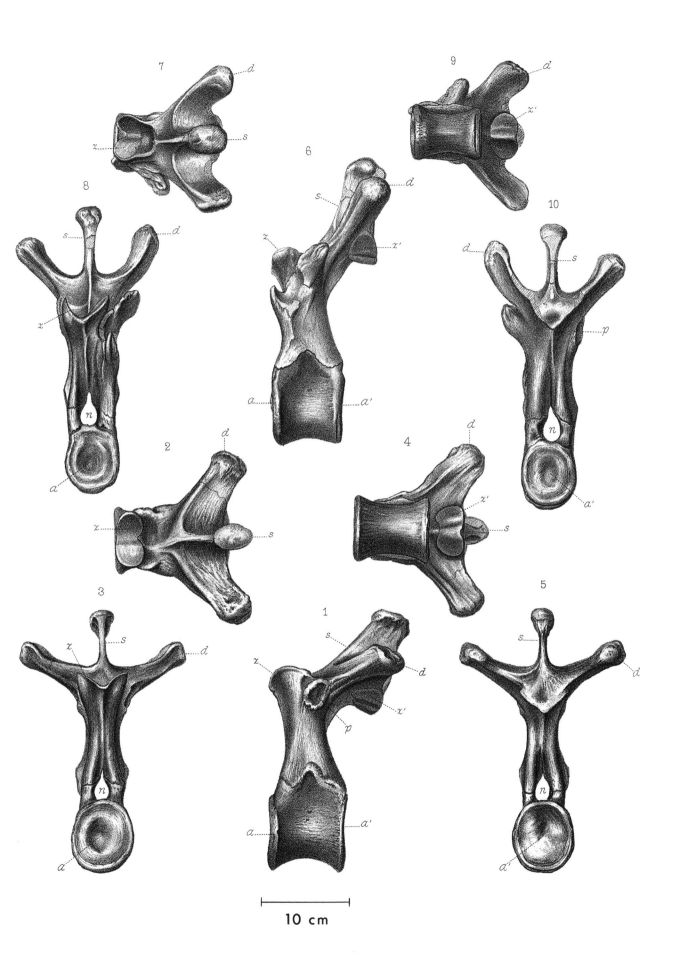

10 cm

PLATE 15

Stegosaurus ungulatus Marsh (1879) YPM 1853 (holotype)

Dorsal vertebra in lateral (1), dorsal (2), anterior (3), ventral (4), and posterior (5) views; sagittal section of centrum (6)

HORIZON: Morrison formation

LOCALITY: YPM Quarry 12, Como Bluff, T. 22 N., R. 77 W., Sec. 18, Carbon County, Wyo.

ABBREVIATIONS:
- *a*   anterior face of centrum
- *a'*   posterior face of centrum
- *d*   diapophysis
- *n*   neural canal
- *p*   parapophysis
- *s*   neural spine
- *s'*   line of section (6)
- *z*   prezygapophysis
- *z'*   postzygapophysis

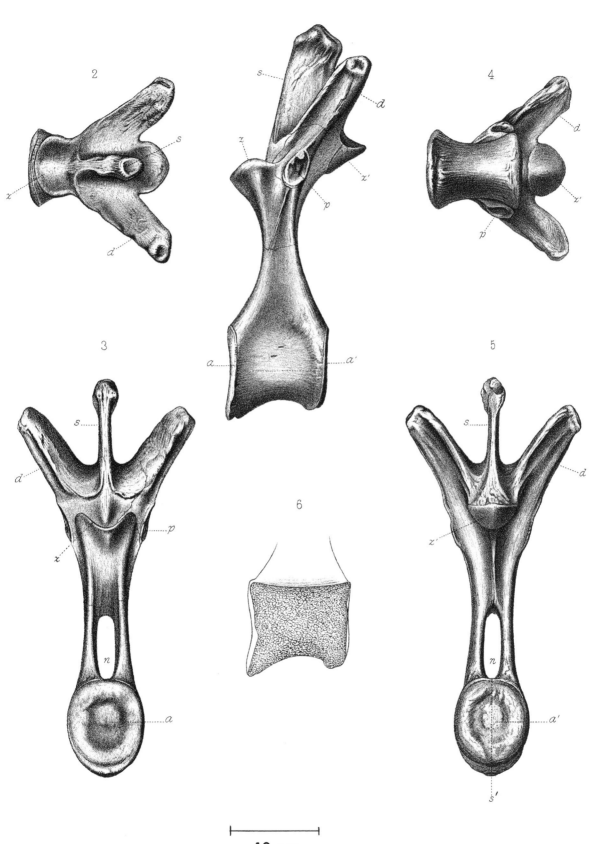

10 cm

PLATE 16

Stegosaurus ungulatus Marsh (1879) YPM 1853 (holotype)
Dorsal vertebra in lateral (1), dorsal (2), anterior (3), ventral (4), and posterior (5) views; transverse section of the centrum (6)

HORIZON: Morrison formation

LOCALITY: YPM Quarry 12, Como Bluff, T. 22 N., R. 77 W., Sec. 18, Carbon County, Wyo.

ABBREVIATIONS:
- *a*   anterior face of centrum
- *a'*   posterior face of centrum
- *d*   diapophysis
- *n*   neural canal
- *p*   parapophysis
- *s*   neural spine
- *s'*   line of section (6)
- *z*   prezygapophysis
- *z'*   postzygapophysis

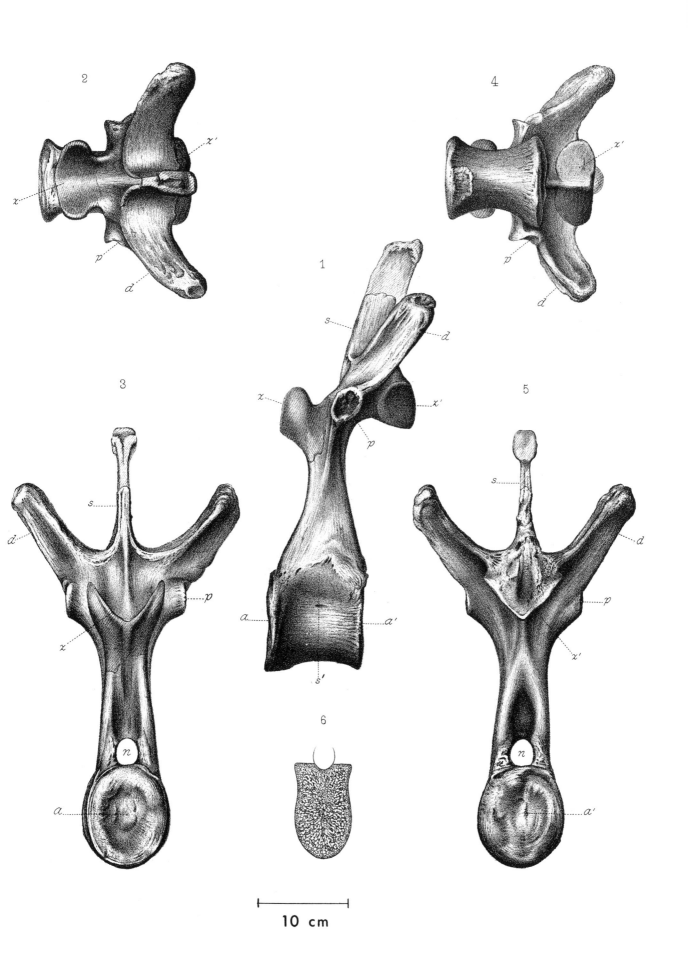

10 cm

PLATE 17

Stegosaurus duplex[1] Marsh (1887) YPM 1858 (holotype)

Dorsal vertebra in lateral (1), dorsal (2), anterior (3), ventral (4), and posterior (5) views; horizontal transverse section of centrum (6)

HORIZON: Morrison formation

LOCALITY: YPM Quarry 11, Como Bluff, T. 22 N., R. 77 W., Sec. 12, Albany County, Wyo.

ABBREVIATIONS:
- *a* anterior face of centrum
- *a'* posterior face of centrum
- *d* diapophysis
- *n* neural canal
- *p* parapophysis
- *s* neural spine
- *s'* line of section (6)
- *z* prezygapophysis
- *z'* postzygapophysis

1. = *Stegosaurus ungulatus.*

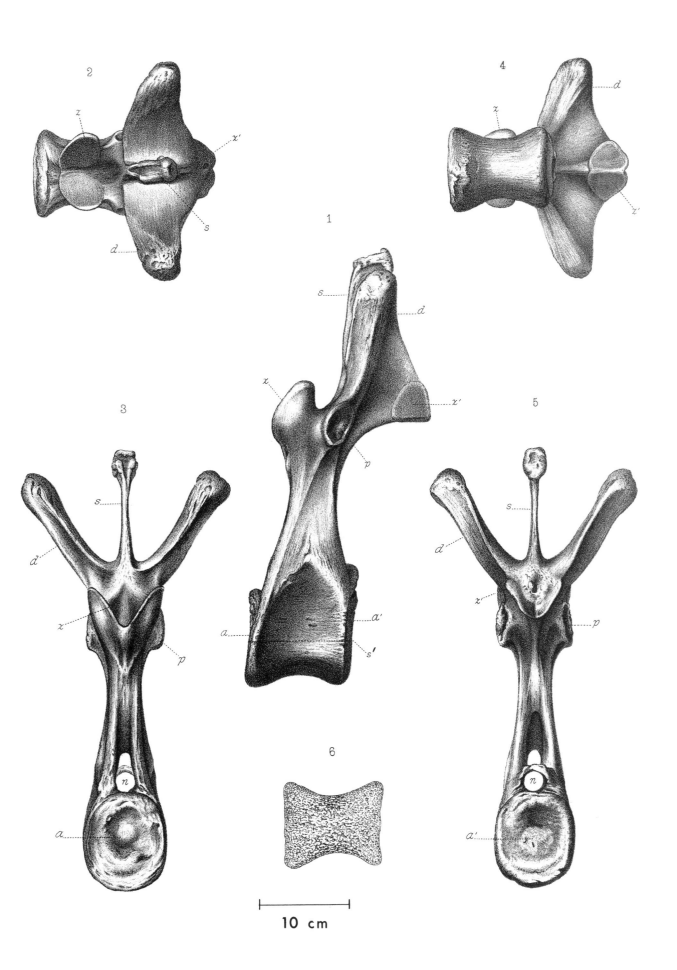

10 cm

PLATE 18

Stegosaurus duplex[1] Marsh (1887) YPM 1858 (holotype)
Dorsal vertebra in lateral (1), dorsal (2), anterior (3), ventral (4), and posterior (5) views; horizontal transverse section of centrum (6)

HORIZON: Morrison formation

LOCALITY: YPM Quarry 11, Como Bluff, T. 22 N., R. 77 W., Sec. 12, Albany County, Wyo.

ABBREVIATIONS:
a anterior face of centrum
a' posterior face of centrum
d diapophysis
n neural canal
p parapophysis
s neural spine
s' line of section (6)
z prezygapophysis
z' postzygapophysis

1. = *Stegosaurus ungulatus.*

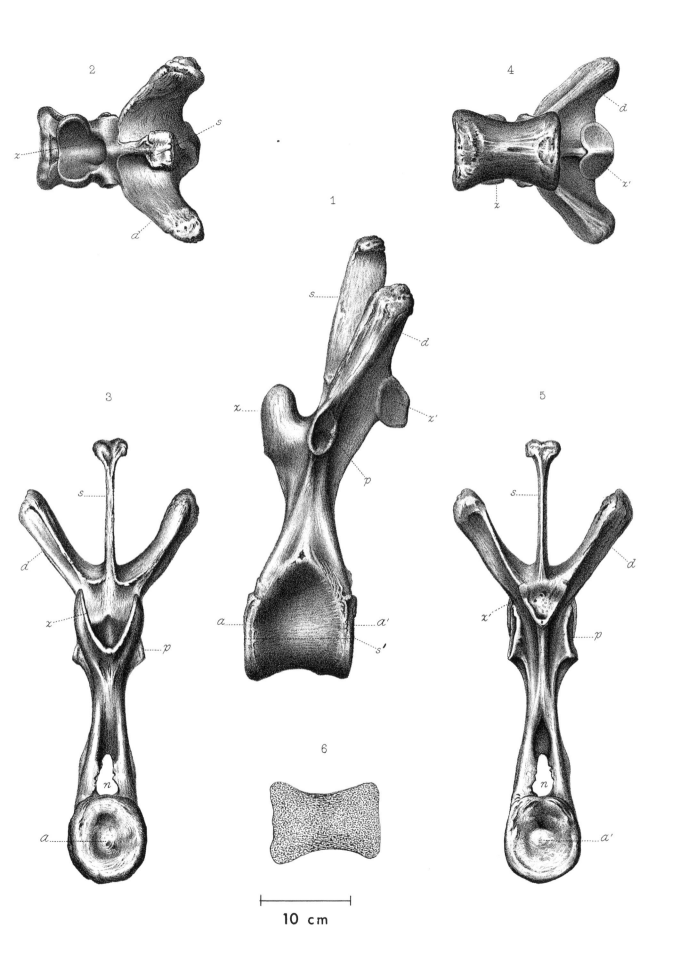

10 cm

PLATE 20[1]

Stegosaurus duplex[2] Marsh (1887) YPM 1858 (holotype)
Thoracic rib in anterior (1), posterior (2), medial (3), and dorsal (4) views

HORIZON: Morrison formation

LOCALITY: YPM Quarry 11, Como Bluff, T. 22 N., R. 77 W., Sec. 12, Albany County, Wyo.

ABBREVIATIONS: *h* capitulum

t tuberculum

1. Plate 19 was never completed. Marsh planned to illustrate the sternum of *Stegosaurus* in Plate 19.
2. = *Stegosaurus ungulatus.*

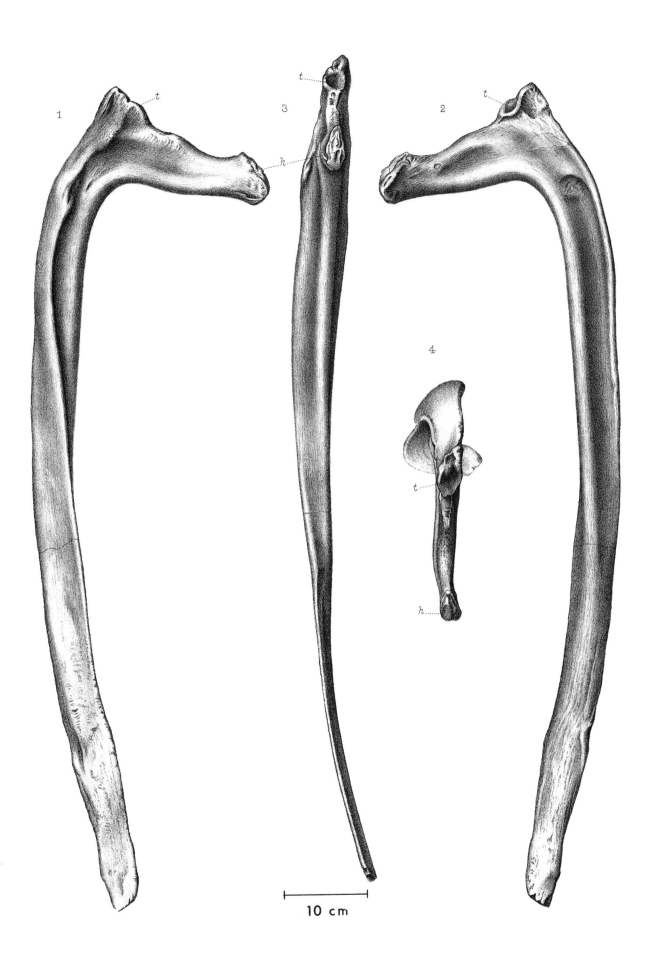

10 cm

PLATE 21

Stegosaurus duplex[1] Marsh (1887) YPM 1858 (holotype)

Sacrum and ilia in ventral view (1) and posterior view of sacrum (2)

Cast of sacral cavity in lateral view (3)

HORIZON: Morrison formation

LOCALITY: YPM Quarry 11, Como Bluff, T. 22 N., R. 77 W., Sec. 12, Albany County, Wyo.

ABBREVIATIONS:

ac	acetabulum
b	first sacral rib
e	last sacral rib
f, f', f''	intervertebral fenestrae
i, i', i'', i'''	sacrospinal nerves
il	ilium
l, l'	"lumbar" vertebrae
n	neural canal
p	posterior face of centrum
s	neural spine
v, v', v'', v'''	vertebral segments of sacral neural canal
z'	postzygapophysis

1. = *Stegosaurus ungulatus.*

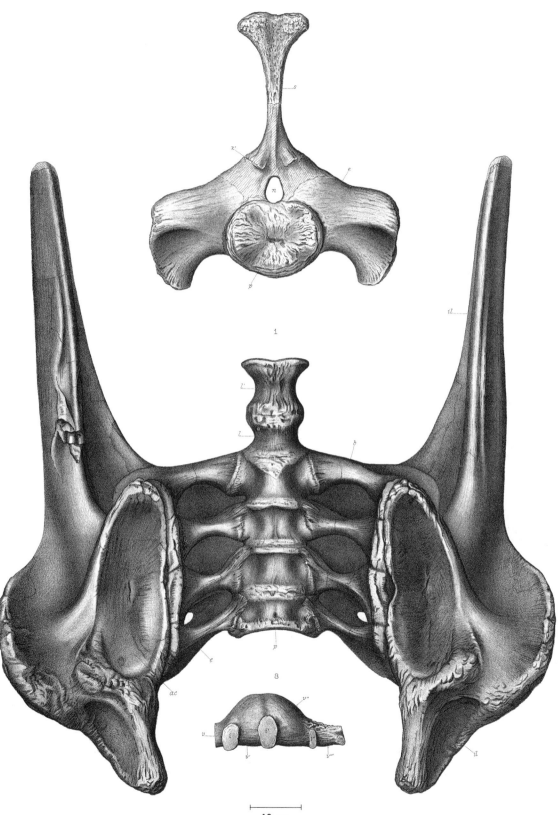

10 cm

PLATE 22

Stegosaurus ungulatus Marsh (1879) YPM 1857
  Sacrum in ventral view

    HORIZON: Morrison formation

    LOCALITY: YPM Quarry 13 East, Como Bluff, T. 22 N., R. 76 W., Sec.
    4 or 5, Albany County, Wyo.

    ABBREVIATIONS:
a	anterior face of first sacral vertebra
b	first sacral rib
c	second sacral rib
d	third sacral rib
f, f′, f″	intervertebral fenestrae
p	postsacral vertebra

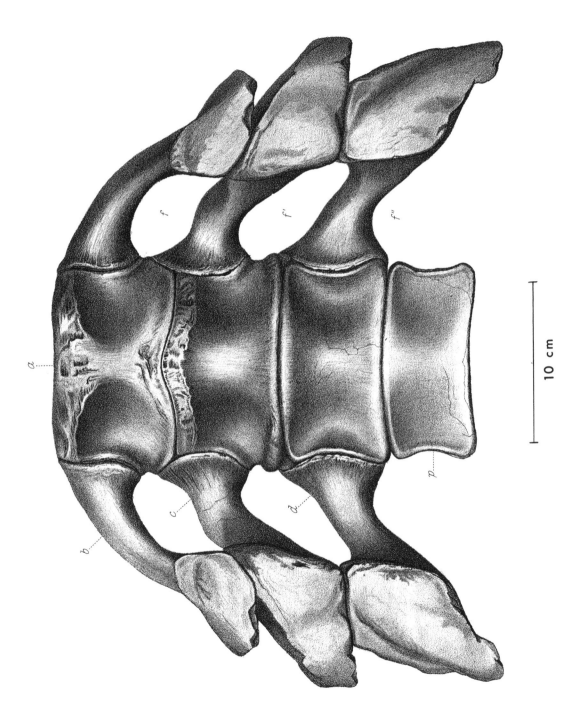

10 cm

PLATE 23

Stegosaurus ungulatus Marsh (1879) YPM 1857
  Endosacral cast in lateral (1), dorsal (2), and ventral (3) views

  HORIZON: Morrison formation
  LOCALITY: YPM Quarry 13 East, Como Bluff, T. 22 N., R. 76 W., Sec.
             4 or 5, Albany County, Wyo.
  ABBREVIATIONS: i, i'', i''' sacrospinal nerves
                  v, v', v'', v''' vertebral segments of sacral neural canal

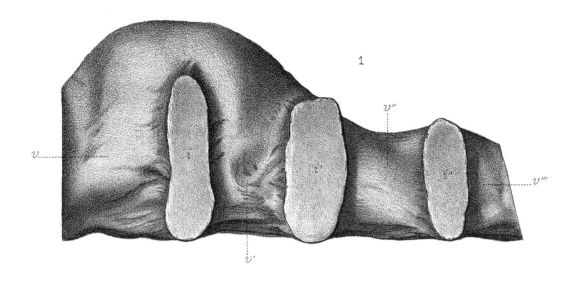

1

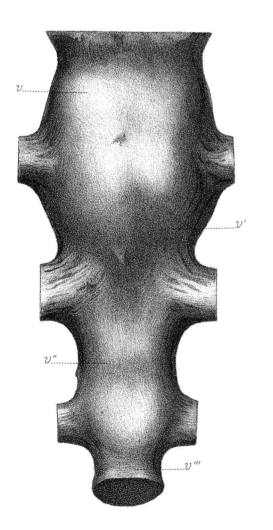

2

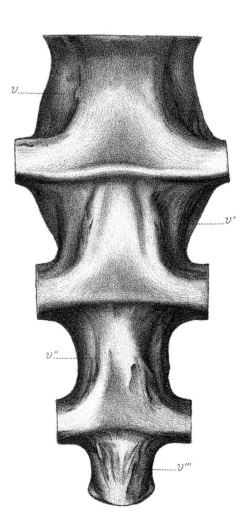

3

10 cm

PLATE 24

Stegosaurus stenops Marsh (1887) YPM 4834

Sacrum in dorsal view (1); sacral neural arches in lateral (2) and ventral (3) views; endosacral cast in lateral (4) and dorsal (5) views

HORIZON: Morrison formation

LOCALITY: YPM Quarry 13 West, Como Bluff, T. 22 N., R. 76 W., Sec. 4 or 5, Albany County, Wyo.

ABBREVIATIONS:

a	first sacral vertebra
b	first sacral rib
c	second sacral rib
d	third sacral rib
e	fourth sacral rib
f, f', f''	intervertebral fenestrae
i, i', i'', i'''	sacrospinal nerve canals
l	last "lumbar" vertebra
p	posterior face of last sacral centrum
v, v', v'', v'''	vertebral segments of sacral neural canal

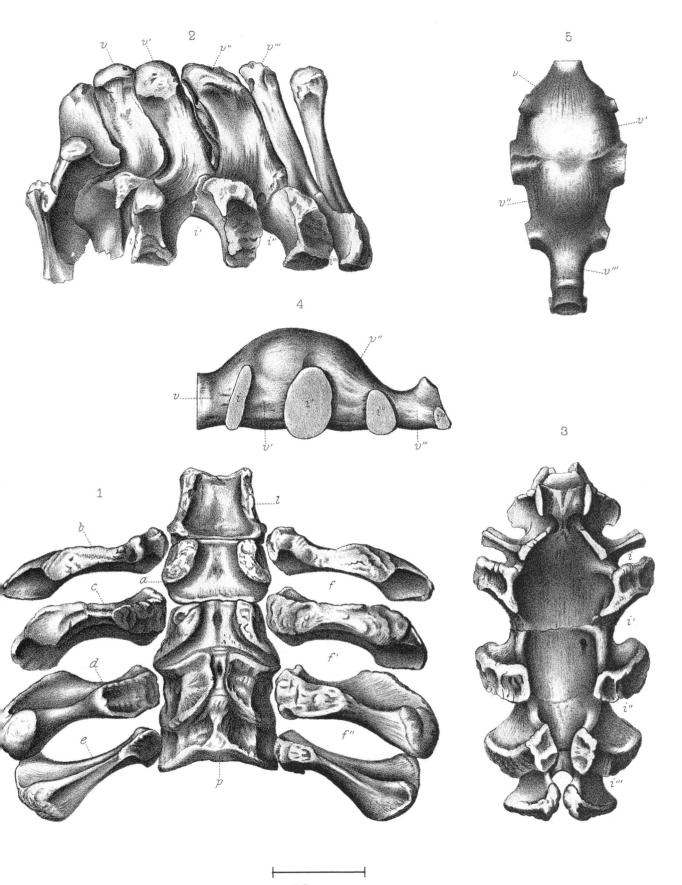

10 cm

PLATE 25

Stegosaurus ungulatus Marsh (1879) YPM 1853 (holotype)
Third caudal vertebra in lateral (1), anterior (2), and ventral (3) views

HORIZON: Morrison formation

LOCALITY: YPM Quarry 12, Como Bluff, T. 22 N., R. 77 W., Sec. 18,
Carbon County, Wyo.

ABBREVIATIONS:
- *a*   anterior face of centrum
- *a′*   posterior face of centrum
- *n*   neural canal
- *s*   neural spine
- *t*   transverse process
- *z*   prezygapophysis
- *z′*   postzygapophysis

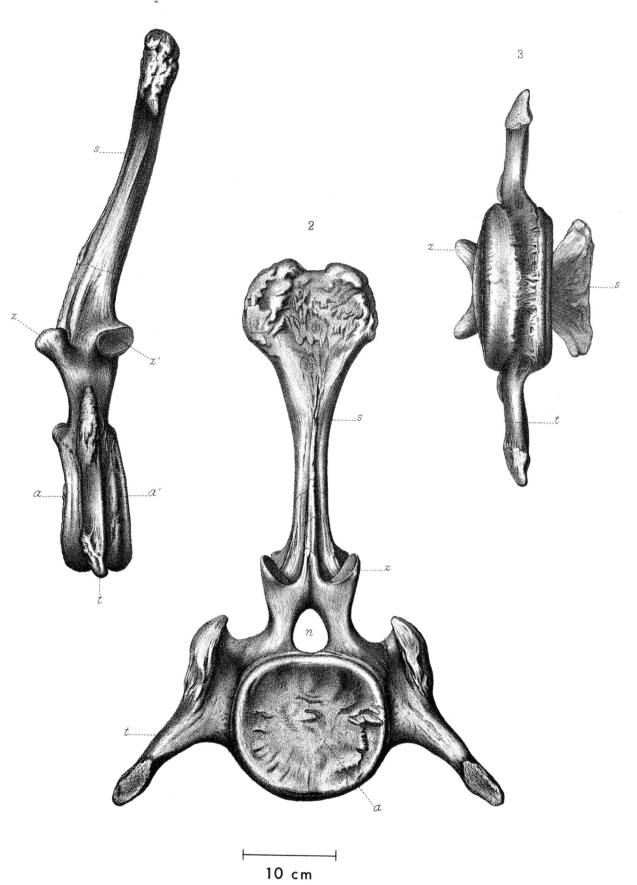

10 cm

PLATE 26

Stegosaurus ungulatus Marsh (1879) YPM 1853 (holotype)

Fifth caudal vertebra in lateral (1), dorsal (2), anterior (3), ventral (4), and posterior (5) views

HORIZON: Morrison formation

LOCALITY: YPM Quarry 12, Como Bluff, T. 22 N., R. 77 W., Sec. 18, Carbon County, Wyo.

ABBREVIATIONS:
- *n*   neural canal
- *s*   neural spine
- *t*   transverse process
- *z*   prezygapophysis
- *z′*   postzygapophysis

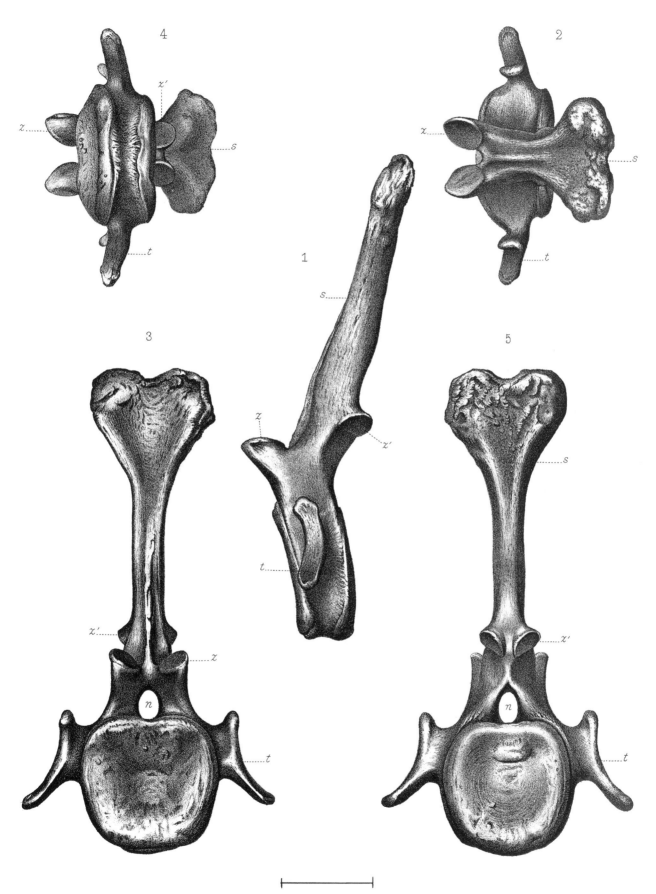

10 cm

PLATE 27

Stegosaurus ungulatus Marsh (1879) YPM 1853 (holotype)

Caudal vertebra in lateral (1), anterior (2), and posterior (3) views, and chevron in lateral (4), anterior (5), and posterior (6) views

HORIZON: Morrison formation

LOCALITY: YPM Quarry 12, Como Bluff, T. 22 N., R. 77 W., Sec. 18, Carbon County, Wyo.

ABBREVIATIONS:
a articular facet of chevron
c' articular facet for chevron
h haemal canal
n neural canal
s neural spine
t transverse process
z prezygapophysis
z' postzygapophysis

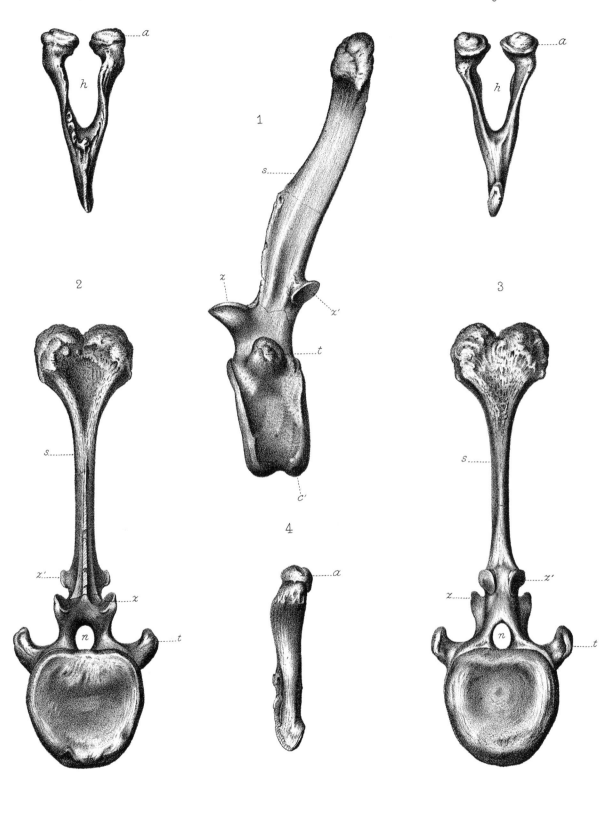

10 cm

PLATE 28

Stegosaurus duplex[1] Marsh (1887) YPM 1858 (holotype)

Caudal vertebrae in lateral (1, 6), dorsal (2, 7), anterior (3, 8), ventral (4, 9), and posterior (5, 10) views

HORIZON: Morrison formation

LOCALITY: YPM Quarry 11, Como Bluff, T. 22 N., R. 77 W., Sec. 12, Albany County, Wyo.

ABBREVIATIONS:
c' articular facet for chevron
n neural canal
s neural spine
z prezygapophysis
z' postzygapophysis

1. $=$ *Stegosaurus ungulatus.*

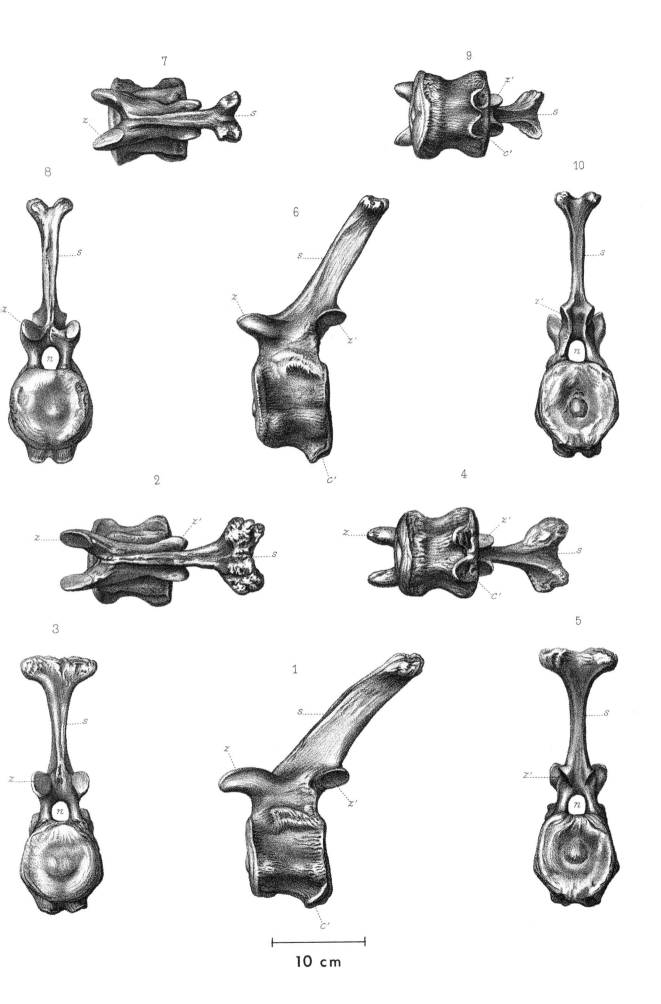

10 cm

PLATE 29

Stegosaurus ungulatus Marsh (1879) YPM 1853 (holotype)
Caudal vertebrae in lateral (1, 6), dorsal (2, 7), anterior (3, 8), ventral (4, 9), and posterior (5, 10) views

HORIZON: Morrison formation
LOCALITY: YPM Quarry 12, Como Bluff, T. 22 N., R. 77 W., Sec. 18, Carbon County, Wyo.
ABBREVIATIONS: c anterior articular facet for chevron
c' posterior articular facet for chevron
n neural canal
s neural spine
z prezygapophysis
z' postzygapophysis

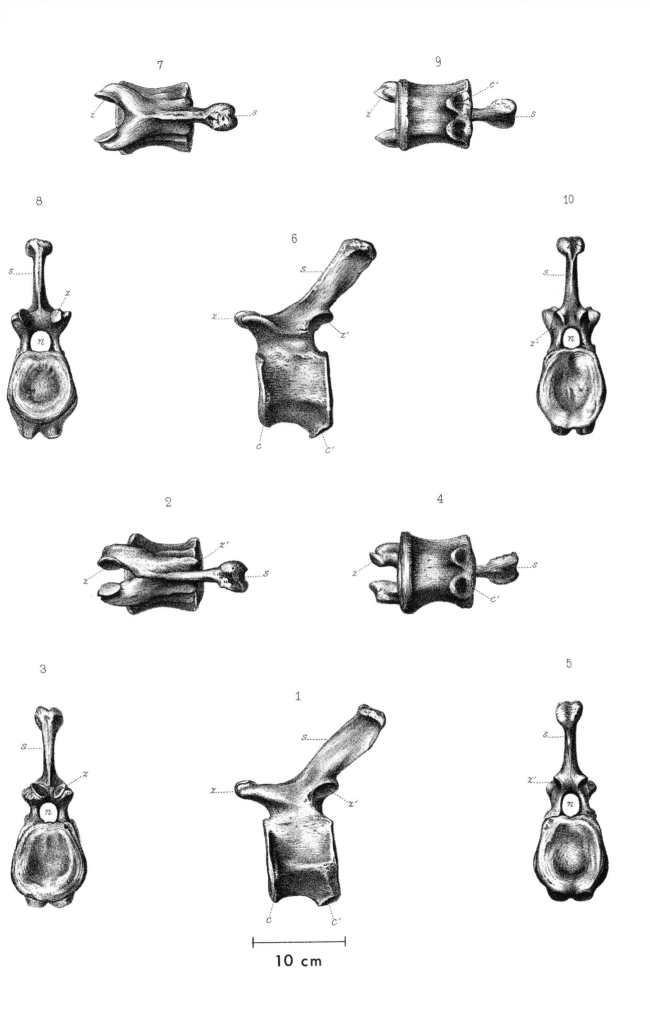

10 cm

PLATE 30

Stegosaurus stenops Marsh (1887) YPM 1856
    First caudal vertebra in lateral (1), dorsal (2), anterior (3), ventral (4), and posterior (5) views

       HORIZON: Morrison formation

       LOCALITY: YPM Quarry 13 West, Como Bluff, T. 22 N., R. 76 W., Sec. 4 or 5, Albany County, Wyo.

       ABBREVIATIONS: *a*   anterior face of centrum
                     a'   posterior face of centrum
                     n   neural canal
                     s   neural spine
                     t   transverse process
                     z   prezygapophysis
                     z'   postzygapophysis

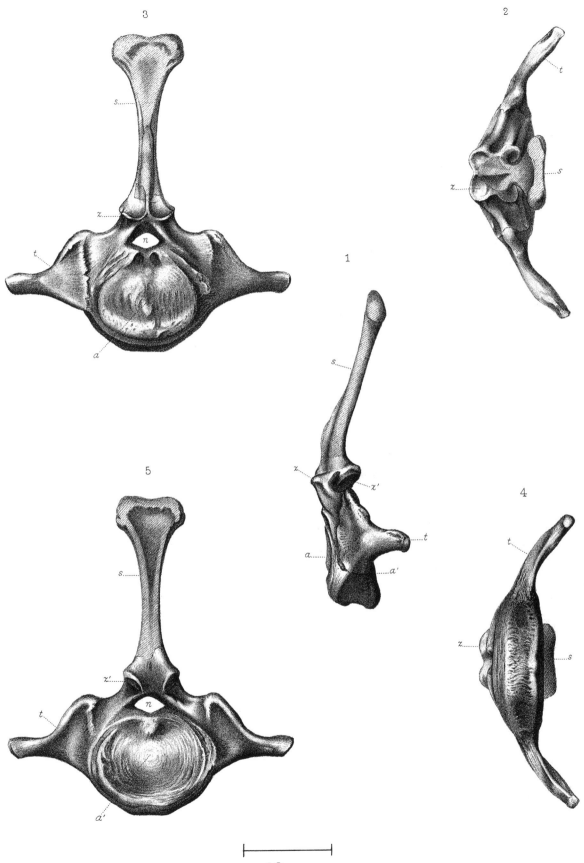

10 cm

PLATE 31

Stegosaurus stenops Marsh (1887) YPM 1856

Second caudal vertebra in lateral (1), dorsal (2), anterior (3), ventral (4), and posterior (5) views

HORIZON: Morrison formation

LOCALITY: YPM Quarry 13 West, Como Bluff, T. 22 N., R. 76 W., Sec. 4 or 5, Albany County, Wyo.

ABBREVIATIONS:
a anterior facet of centrum
a' posterior facet of centrum
n neural canal
s neural spine
t transverse process
z prezygapophysis
z' postzygapophysis

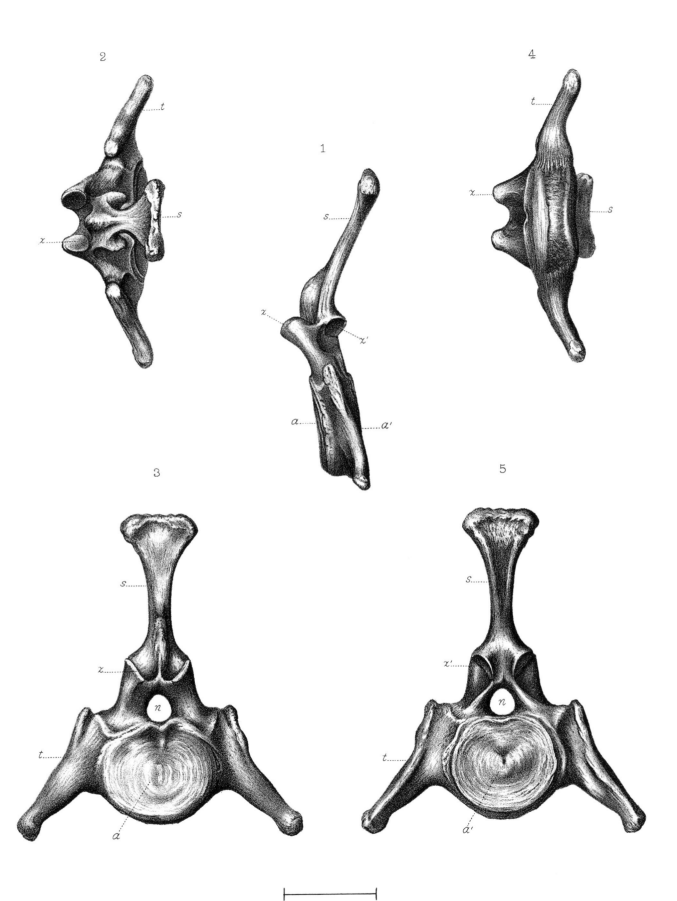

10 cm

PLATE 32

Stegosaurus sulcatus Marsh (1887) YPM 1854
  Scapula-coracoid in lateral (1) and ventral (2) views

HORIZON: Morrison formation
LOCALITY: YPM Quarry 13 East, Como Bluff, T. 22 N., R. 76 W., Sec. 4 or 5, Albany County, Wyo.

ABBREVIATIONS:
a	scapular portion of glenoid
a'	coracoid portion of glenoid
b	articulation for coracoid
b'	articulation for scapula
c	dorsal process
d	dorsoposterior end
n	coracoid notch

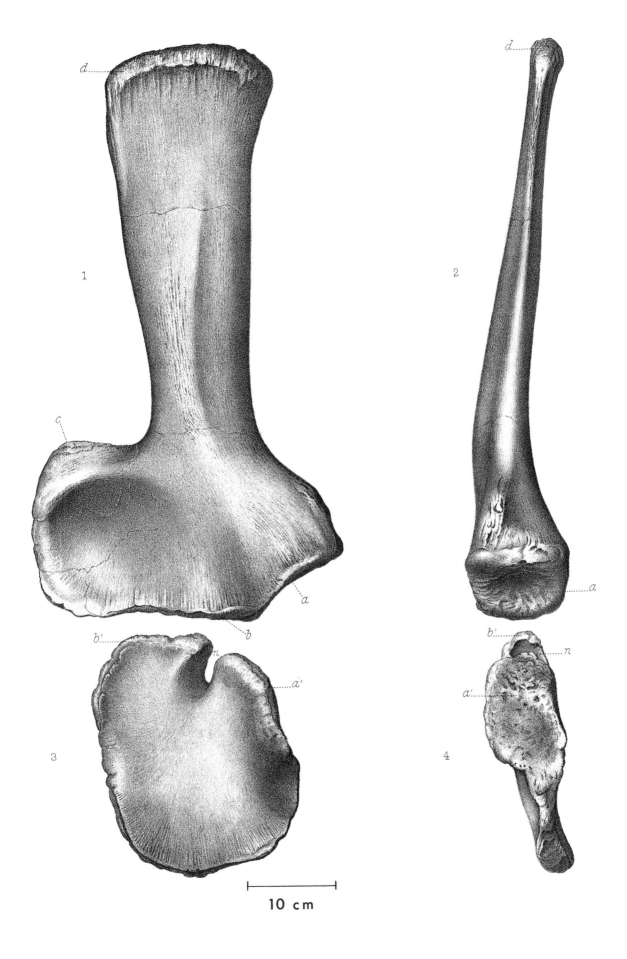

10 cm

PLATE 33

Stegosaurus ungulatus Marsh (1887) YPM 1853 (holotype)
Right humerus in anterior (1), distal (1a), lateral (2), posterior (3), and proximal (3a) views

HORIZON: Morrison formation

LOCALITY: YPM Quarry 12, Como Bluff, T. 22 N., R. 77 W., Sec. 18, Carbon County, Wyo.

ABBREVIATIONS: *h* head
r deltopectoral crest
r' radial condyle
t internal tuberosity
u external tuberosity
u' ulnar condyle

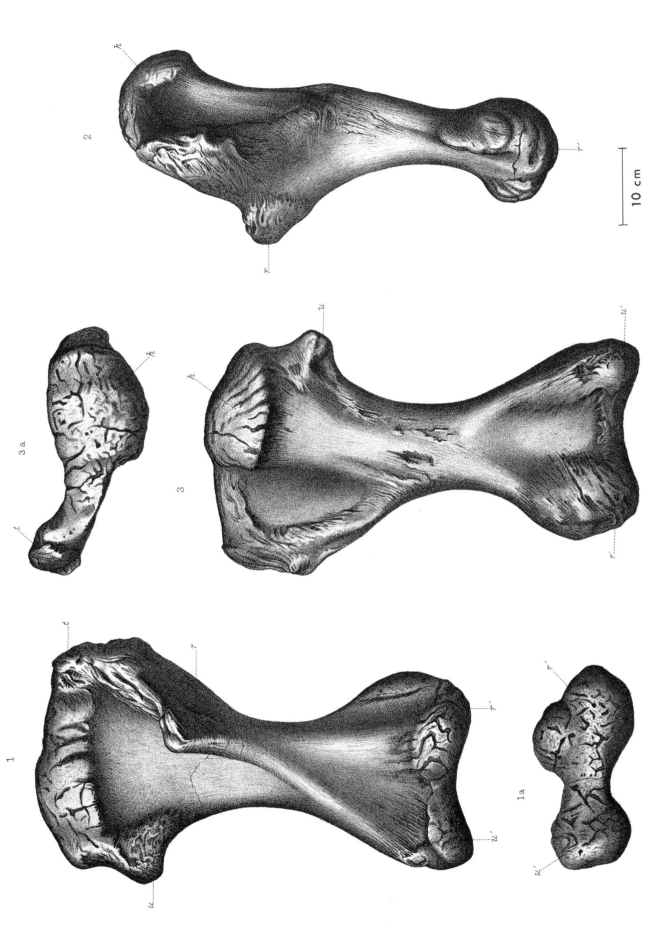

10 cm

PLATE 34

Stegosaurus sulcatus Marsh (1887) YPM 4835
    Left radius in anterior (1), lateral (2), posterior (3), medial (4), proximal (5), and distal (6) views; section of shaft (7)

    HORIZON: Morrison formation
    LOCALITY: YPM Quarry 13 West, Como Bluff, T. 22 N., R. 76 W., Sec.
            4 or 5, Albany County, Wyo.

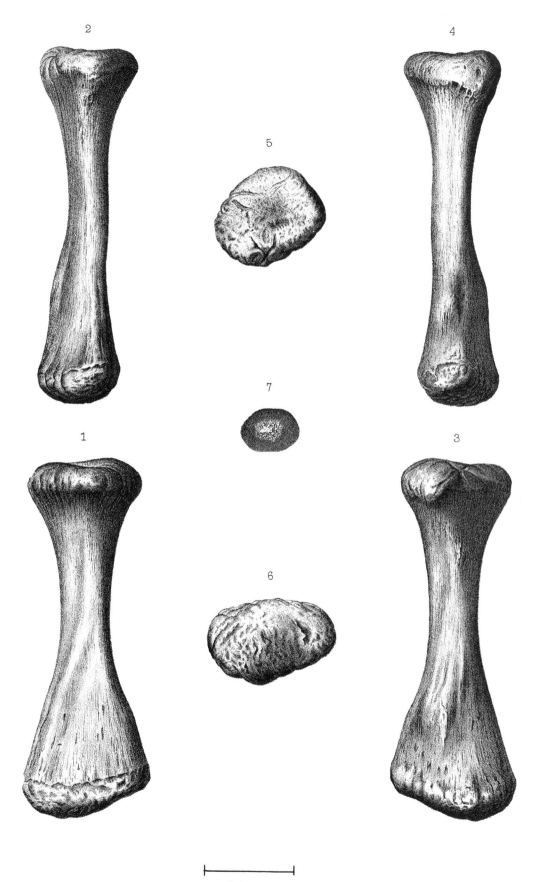

10 cm

PLATE 35

Stegosaurus sulcatus Marsh (1887) YPM 1854
  Left ulna in medial (1), posterior (2), anterior (3), proximal (4), and distal
  (5) views; cross section of shaft (6)

  HORIZON: Morrison formation
  LOCALITY: YPM Quarry 13 East, Como Bluff, T. 22 N., R. 76 W., Sec.
    4 or 5, Albany County, Wyo.

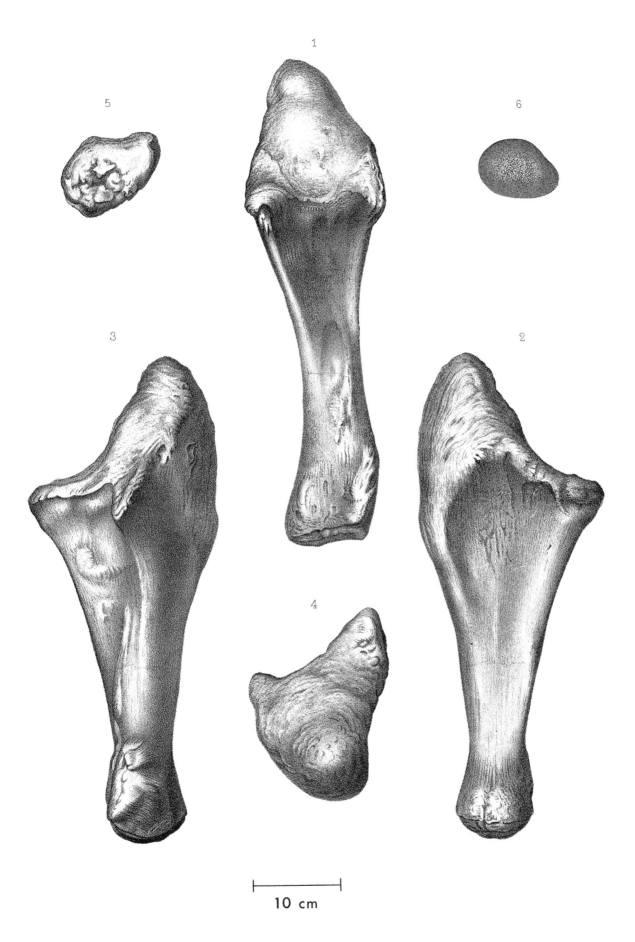

10 cm

PLATE 36

Stegosaurus sulcatus Marsh (1887) YPM 1859

Ulnare in anterior (1), posterior (2), proximal (3), and distal (4) views

Radiale in anterior (5), posterior (6), proximal (7), and distal (8) views

Pisiform in anterior (9), proximal (10), and distal (11) views

HORIZON: Morrison formation

LOCALITY: YPM Quarry 13 West, Como Bluff, T. 22 N., R. 76 W., Sec. 4 or 5, Albany County, Wyo.

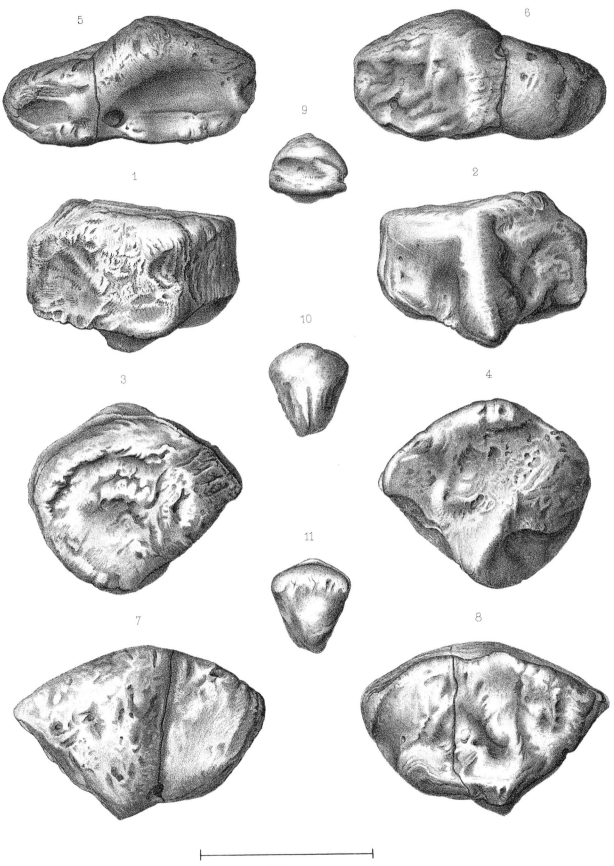

10 cm

PLATE 37

Stegosaurus sulcatus Marsh (1887) YPM 1859

Metacarpal I in anterior (1), lateral (2), posterior (3), medial (4), proximal (5), and distal (6) views

Metacarpal II in anterior (7), lateral (8), posterior (9), medial (10), proximal (11), and distal (12) views

HORIZON: Morrison formation

LOCALITY: YPM Quarry 13 West, Como Bluff, T. 22 N., R. 76 W., Sec. 4 or 5, Albany County, Wyo.

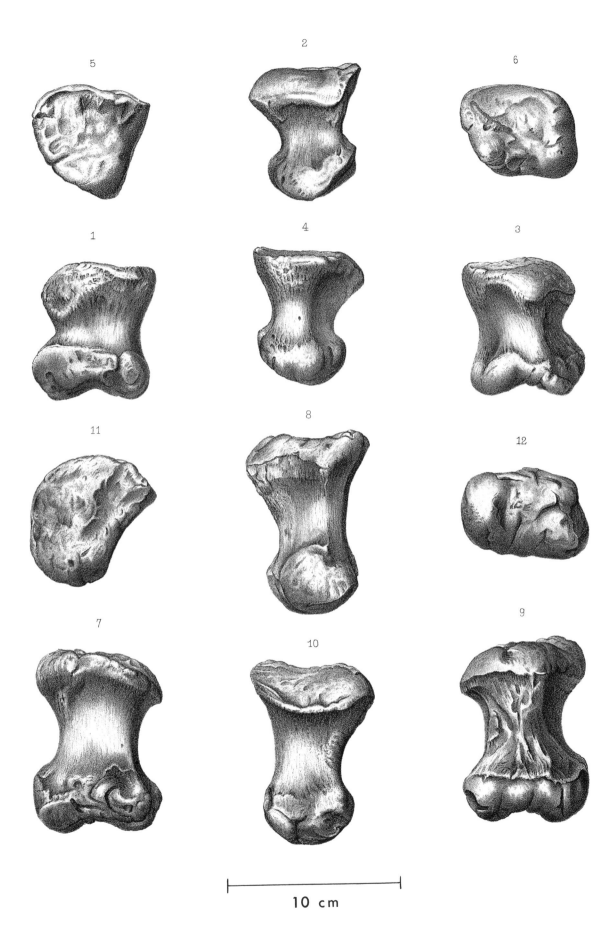

5   2   6

1   4   3

11   8   12

7   10   9

10 cm

PLATE 38

Stegosaurus sulcatus Marsh (1887) YPM 1859
  Metacarpal III in anterior (1), lateral (2), posterior (3), medial (4), proximal (5), and distal (6) views

Cross section of shaft (7)

Metacarpal IV in anterior (8), proximal (9), and distal (10) views

  HORIZON: Morrison formation
  LOCALITY: YPM Quarry 13 West, Como Bluff, T. 22 N., R. 76 W., Sec. 4 or 5, Albany County, Wyo.

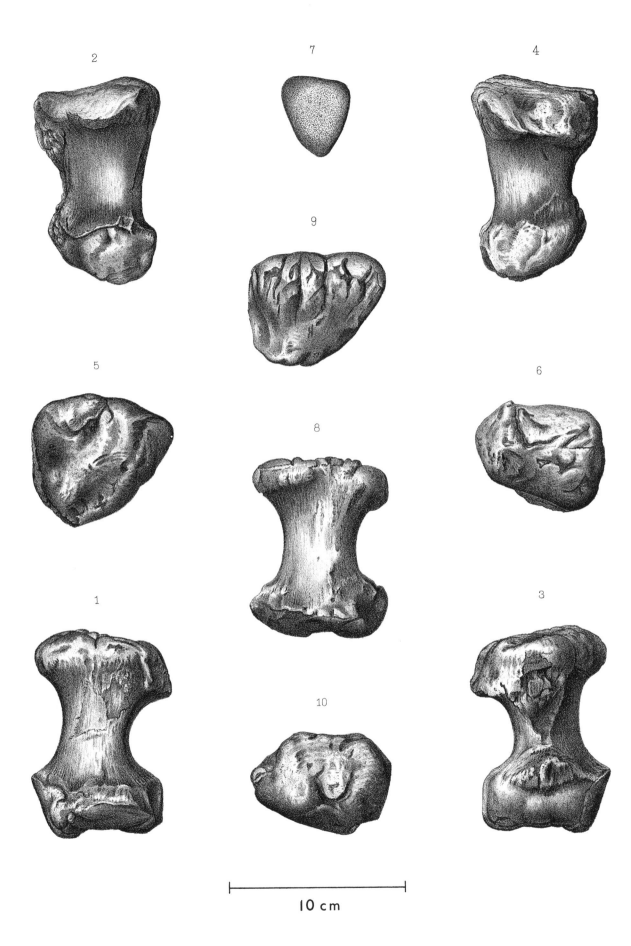

PLATE 39

Stegosaurus sulcatus Marsh (1887) YPM 1859

Metacarpal IV in lateral (1), posterior (2), medial (3), and cross-sectional (4) views

Metacarpal V in anterior (5), lateral (6), posterior (7), medial (8), proximal (9), distal (10), and cross-sectional (11) views

HORIZON: Morrison formation

LOCALITY: YPM Quarry 13 West, Como Bluff, T. 22 N., R. 76 W., Sec. 4 or 5, Albany County, Wyo.

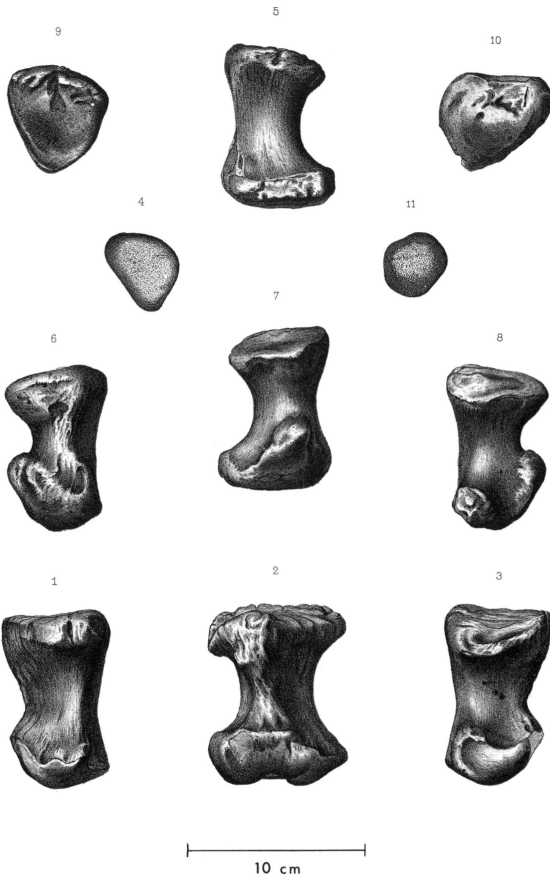

9 5 10

4 11

7

6 7 8

1 2 3

10 cm

PLATE 40

Stegosaurus sulcatus Marsh (1887) YPM 1959
  Phalangeal elements in anterior (1, 7, 13, 19, 25), lateral (2, 8, 14, 20, 26),
  posterior (3, 9, 15, 21, 27), medial (4, 10, 16, 22, 28), dorsal (5, 11, 17, 23,
  29), and ventral (6, 12, 18, 24, 30) views

    HORIZON: Morrison formation
    LOCALITY: YPM Quarry 13 West, Como Bluff, T. 22 N., R. 76 W., Sec.
        4 or 5, Albany County, Wyo.

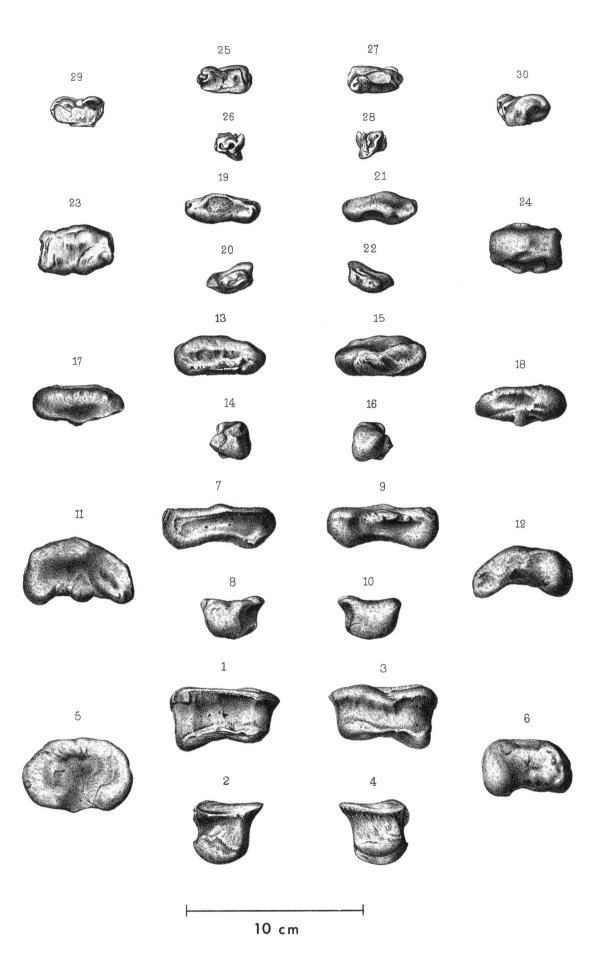

10 cm

PLATE 41

Stegosaurus sulcatus Marsh (1887) YPM 1859

Unguals in anterior (1, 5), posterior (2, 6), lateral (3, 7), and proximal (4, 8) views

Indeterminate ossicles in various views (9–13) and (14–18)

HORIZON: Morrison formation

LOCALITY: YPM Quarry 13 West, Como Bluff, T. 22 N., R. 76 W., Sec. 4 or 5, Albany County, Wyo.

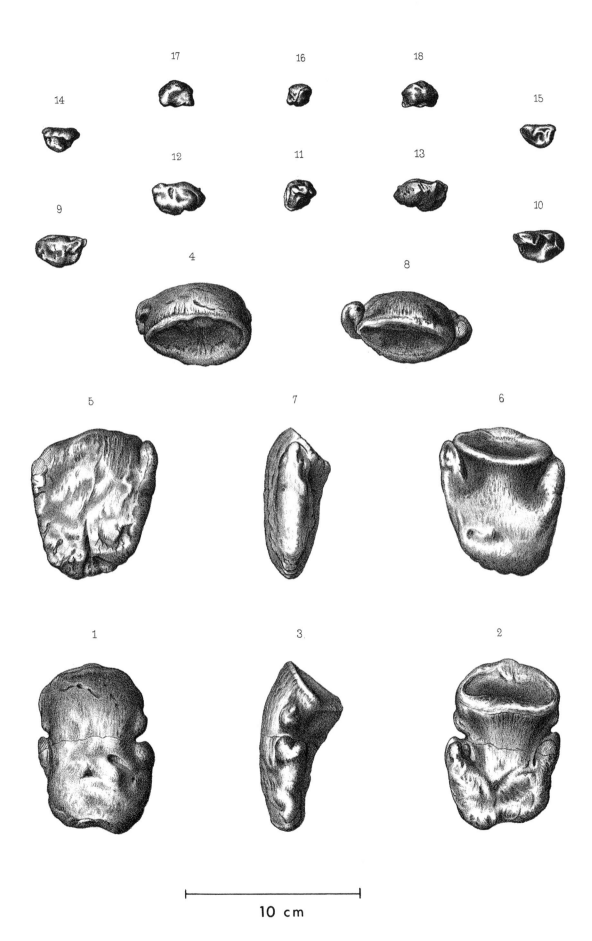

10 cm

PLATE 42

Stegosaurus duplex[1] Marsh (1887) YPM 1858 (holotype)
Left ilium in lateral (1) and medial (2) views

HORIZON: Morrison formation

LOCALITY: YPM Quarry 11, Como Bluff, T. 22 N., R. 77 W., Sec. 12,
Albany County, Wyo.

ABBREVIATIONS:
a   anterior blade of ilium
ac   acetabulum
is   ischial peduncle
p   posterior blade of ilium
pb   pubic peduncle
s   sacral suture

1. = *Stegosaurus ungulatus.*

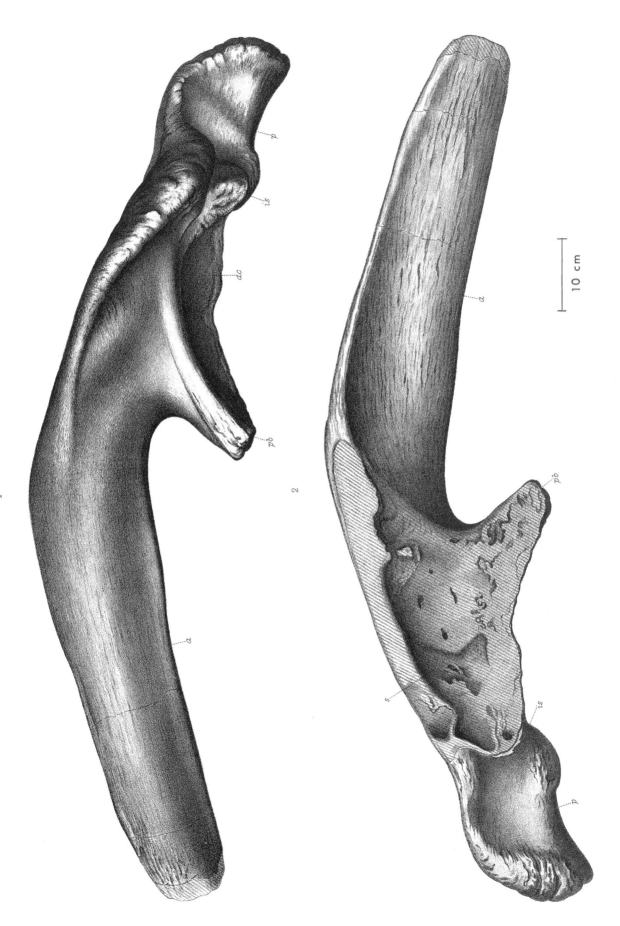

10 cm

PLATE 43

Stegosaurus ungulatus Marsh (1879) YPM 1853 (holotype)
Left ischium in medial (1), lateral (2), dorsal (3), and anterior (4) views

HORIZON: Morrison formation

LOCALITY: YPM Quarry 12, Como Bluff, T. 22 N., R. 77 W., Sec. 18, Carbon County, Wyo.

ABBREVIATIONS: *a* acetabulum
il iliac peduncle
p pubic peduncle
s ischial symphysis

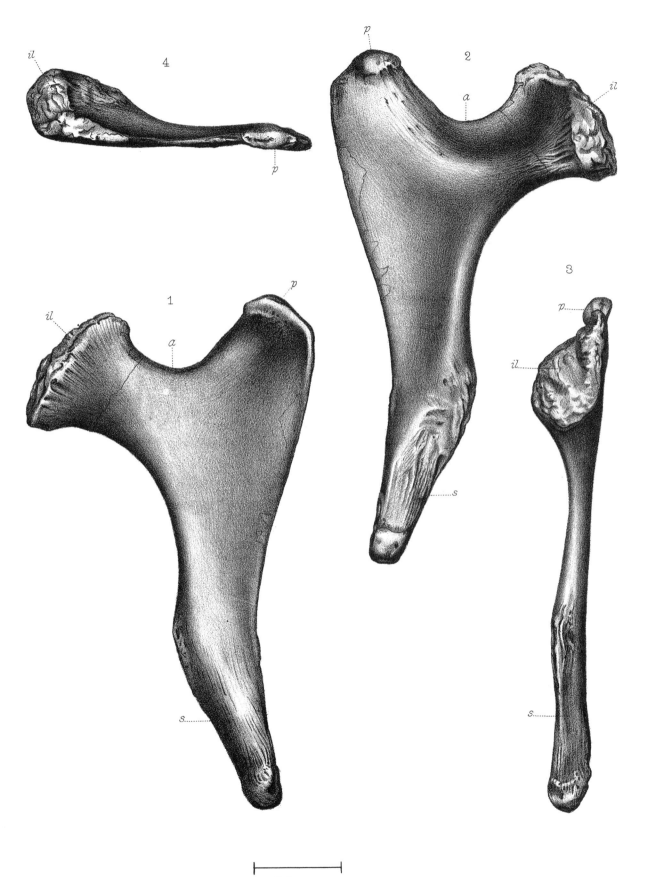

10 cm

PLATE 44

Stegosaurus stenops Marsh (1887) YPM 1856
Right pubis in lateral (1), dorsal (2), medial (3), ventral (4), anterior (5), and posterior (6) views

HORIZON: Morrison formation

LOCALITY: YPM Quarry 13 West, Como Bluff, T. 22 N., R. 76 W., Sec. 4 or 5, Albany County, Wyo.

ABBREVIATIONS: *a*   anterior process
il   iliac suture
is   ischiac suture
n   obturator notch
p   posterior process—(postpubis)

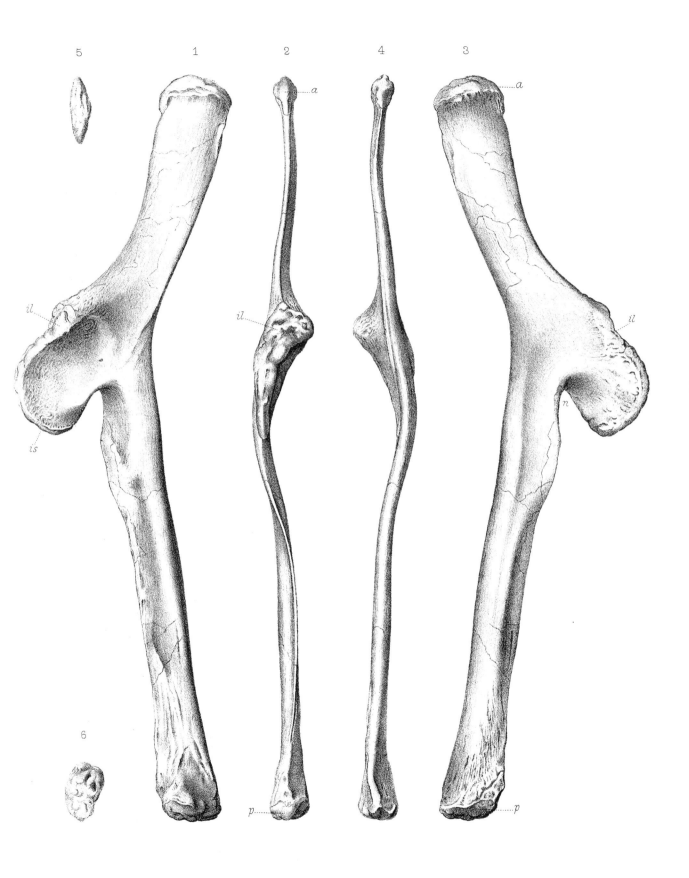

5   1   2   4   3

a

a

il

il

il

is

n

6

p

p

10 cm

PLATE 45

Stegosaurus duplex[1] Marsh (1887) YPM 1858 (holotype)
  Sacrum and pelves in anterior view

HORIZON: Morrison formation

LOCALITY: YPM Quarry 11, Como Bluff, T. 22 N., R. 77 W., Sec. 12, Albany County, Wyo.

ABBREVIATIONS:

ac	acetabulum
b	first sacral rib
e	last sacral rib
f, f′	intervertebral fenestrae
il	ilium
is	ischium
l, l′	transverse processes
p	posterior sacral vertebra
pb	pubis
pb′	posterior pubic process
s	neural spine
z	prezygapophysis

1. = *Stegosaurus ungulatus.*

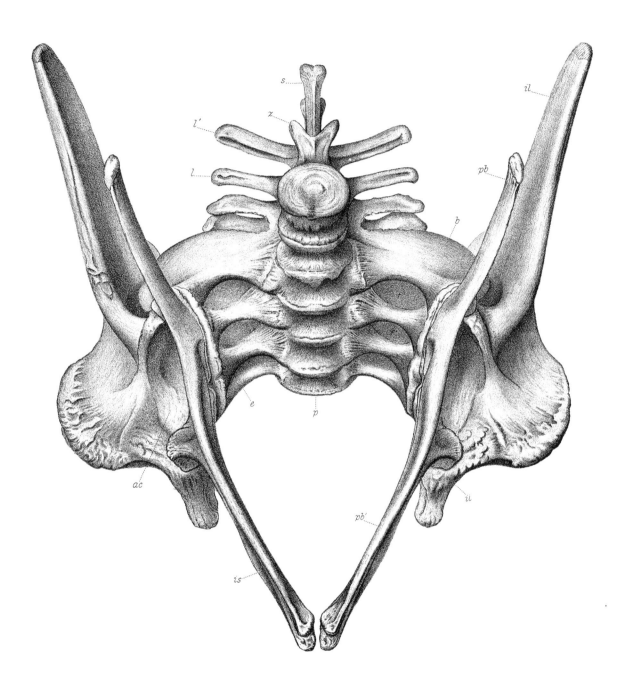

10 cm

PLATE 46

Stegosaurus ungulatus Marsh (1879) YPM 1853 (holotype)
Left femur in anterior (1), posterior (2), proximal (3), and distal (4) views

HORIZON: Morrison formation

LOCALITY: YPM Quarry 12, Como Bluff, T. 22 N., R. 77 W., Sec. 18,
Carbon County, Wyo.

ABBREVIATIONS: *c* anterior condyle
h head
t greater trochanter

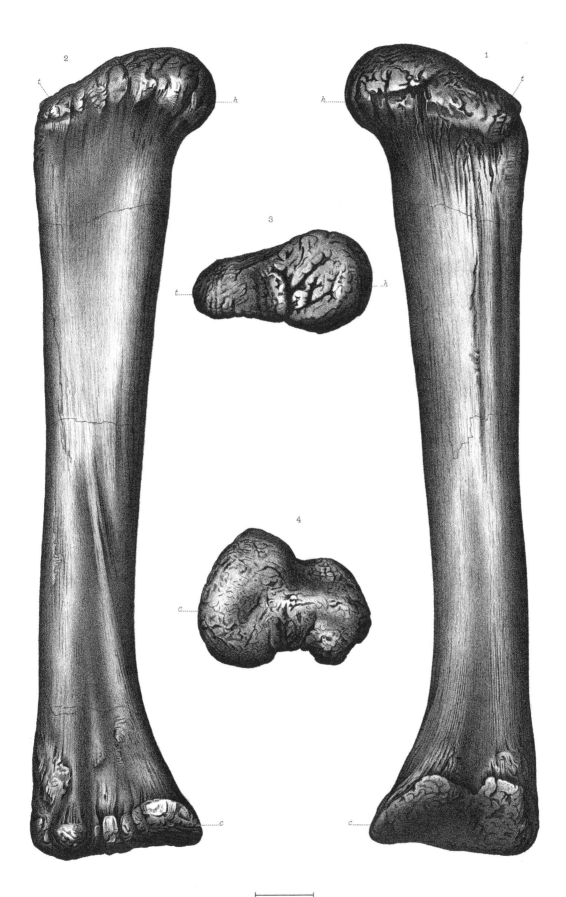

10 cm

PLATE 47

Stegosaurus duplex[1] Marsh (1887) YPM 1858 (holotype)

Left femur in anterior (1), medial (2), proximal (3), distal (4), and cross-sectional (5) views

HORIZON: Morrison formation

LOCALITY: YPM Quarry 11, Como Bluff, T. 22 N., R. 77 W., Sec. 12, Albany County, Wyo.

ABBREVIATIONS: *c* anterior condyle

h head

t greater trochanter

1. = *Stegosaurus ungulatus.*

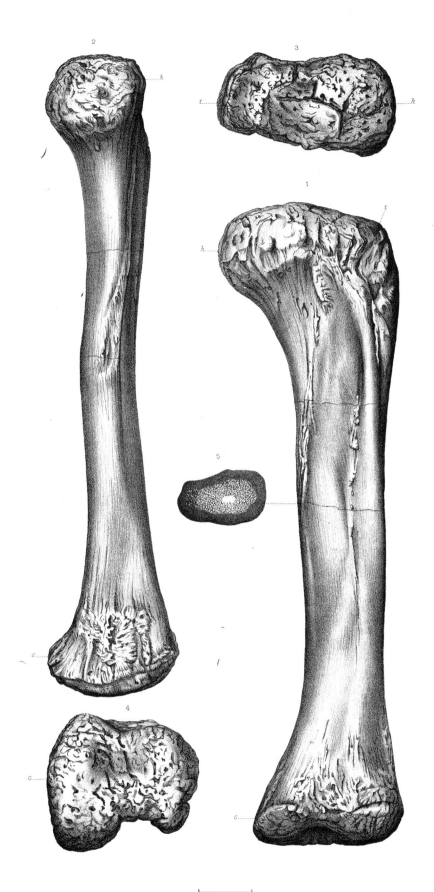

10 cm

PLATE 48

Stegosaurus ungulatus Marsh (1879) YPM 1853 (holotype)
Left tibia, fibula, astragalus, and calcaneum in anterior (1), posterior (2), lateral (3), distal (1a), and proximal (2a) views

HORIZON: Morrison formation

LOCALITY: YPM Quarry 12, Como Bluff, T. 22 N., R. 77 W., Sec. 18, Carbon County, Wyo.

ABBREVIATIONS: *a* astragalus
c calcaneum
f fibula
t tibia

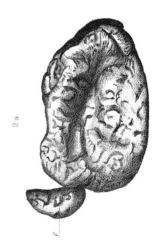

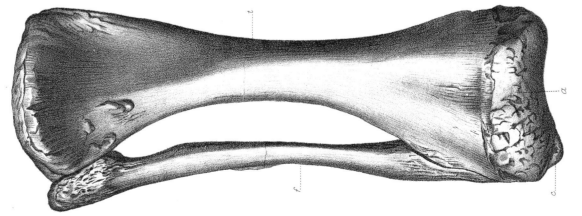

10 cm

PLATE 49

Stegosaurus duplex[1] Marsh (1887) YPM 1858 (holotype)

Left tibia, fibula, astragalus, and calcaneum in anterior (1), posterior (2), lateral (3), distal (1a), and proximal (2a) views

Cross section of tibia shaft (4) and fibula shaft (5)

HORIZON: Morrison formation

LOCALITY: YPM Quarry 11, Como Bluff, T. 22 N., R. 77 W., Sec. 12, Albany County, Wyo.

ABBREVIATIONS: *a* astragalus
c calcaneum
f fibula
s line of sections (4 and 5)
t tibia

1. = *Stegosaurus ungulatus.*

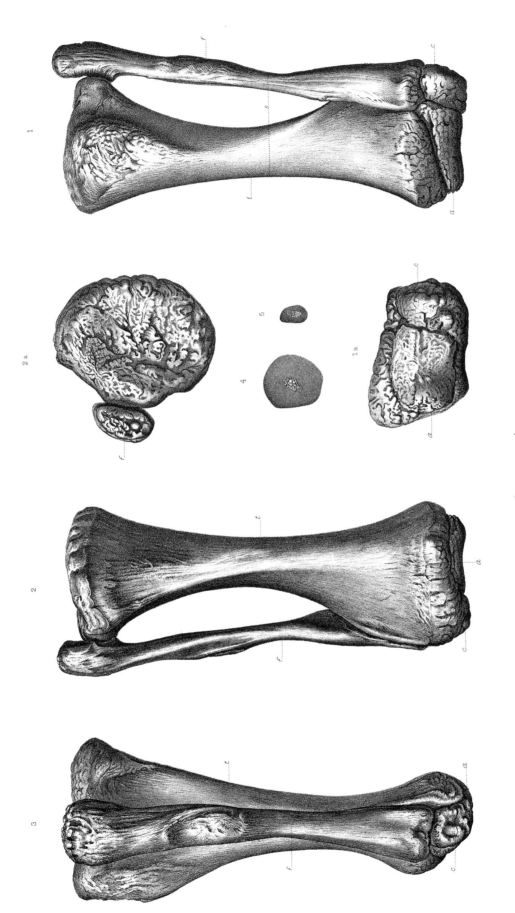

10 cm

PLATE 50

Stegosaurus stenops Marsh (1887) YPM 1856
Tibia and astragalus in medial (1) and distal (2) views; calcaneum (3–8).

HORIZON: Morrison formation

LOCALITY: YPM Quarry 13 West, Como Bluff, T. 22 N., R. 76 W., Sec. 4 or 5, Albany County, Wyo.

ABBREVIATIONS: *a* astragalus
        t tibia

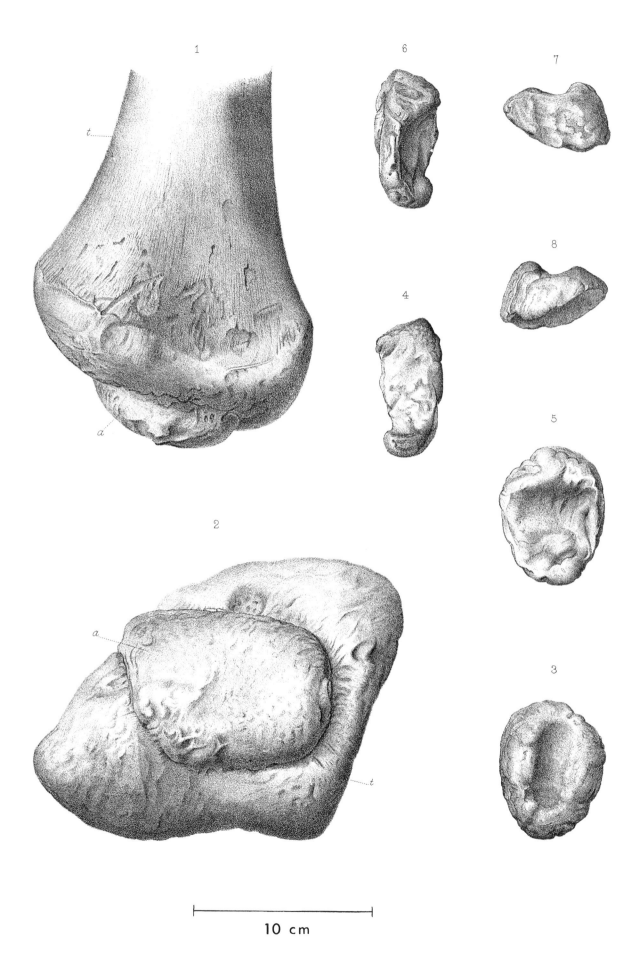

10 cm

PLATE 51

Stegosaurus sulcatus Marsh (1887) YPM 4836
Metatarsal I (or II) in anterior (1), medial (2), posterior (3), lateral (4), proximal (5), and distal (6) views

HORIZON: Morrison formation
LOCALITY: YPM Quarry 13 West, Como Bluff, T. 22 N., R. 76 W., Sec. 4 or 5, Albany County, Wyo.

6

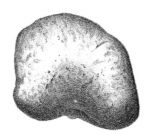

1

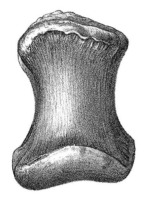

3

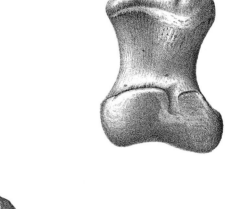

5

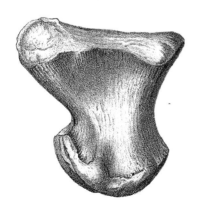

2

4

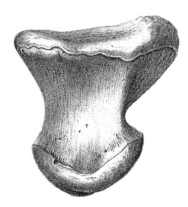

|———————————|
10 cm

PLATE 52

Stegosaurus sulcatus Marsh (1887) YPM 4836

Metatarsal II (or III) in anterior (1), medial (2), posterior (3), lateral (4), proximal (5), and distal (6) views

HORIZON: Morrison formation

LOCALITY: YPM Quarry 13 West, Como Bluff, T. 22 N., R. 76 W., Sec. 4 or 5, Albany County, Wyo.

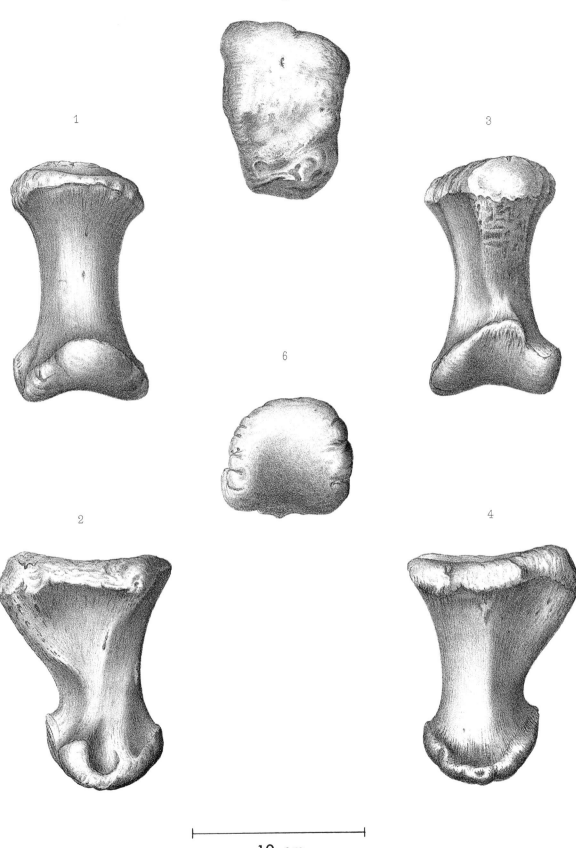

5

1   3

6

2   4

|—————————————|
10 cm

PLATE 53

Stegosaurus sulcatus Marsh (1887) YPM 4836
    Metatarsal III (or IV) in anterior (1), medial (2), posterior (3), lateral (4),
    proximal (5), and distal (6) views; transverse section of shaft (7)

    HORIZON: Morrison formation
    LOCALITY: YPM Quarry 13 West, Como Bluff, T. 22 N., R. 76 W., Sec.
        4 or 5, Albany County, Wyo.

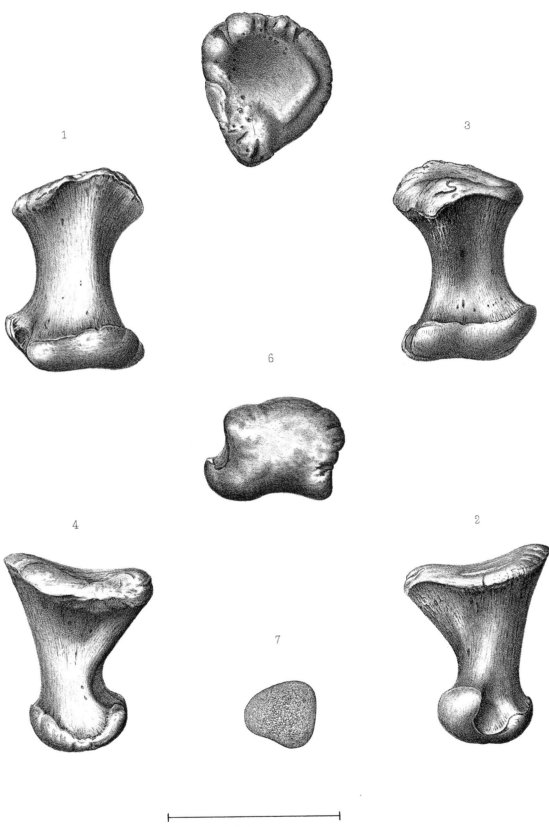

5

1

3

6

4

2

7

10 cm

PLATE 54

Stegosaurus stenops Marsh (1887) USNM 4714
    Caudal vertebrae and set of tail spines

      HORIZON: Morrison formation
      LOCALITY: YPM Quarry 13 (dg. 5), Como Bluff, T. 22 N., R. 77 W.,
              Sec. 4 or 5, Albany County, Wyo.
      ABBREVIATIONS: *a, a′*   anterior spines
                    c   chevron
                    p, p′   posterior spines
                    v   vertebra

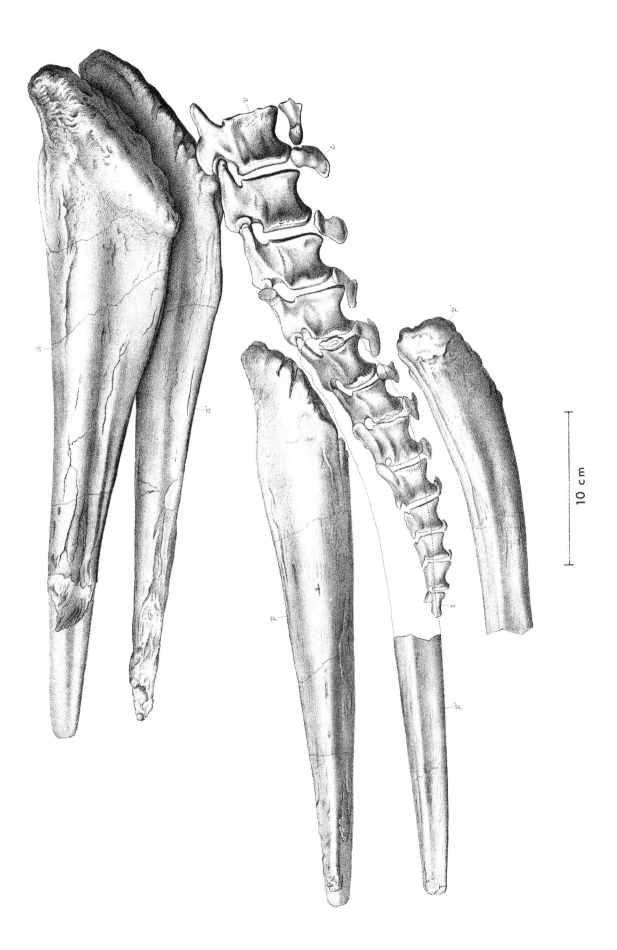

10 cm

PLATE 55

Stegosaurus ungulatus Marsh (1879) YPM 1853 (holotype)
Caudal spine in lateral (1), proximal (2), and cross-sectional (3 and 4) views

HORIZON: Morrison formation
LOCALITY: YPM Quarry 12, Como Bluff, T. 22 N., R. 77 W., Sec. 18, Carbon County, Wyo.
ABBREVIATION: *s* spine

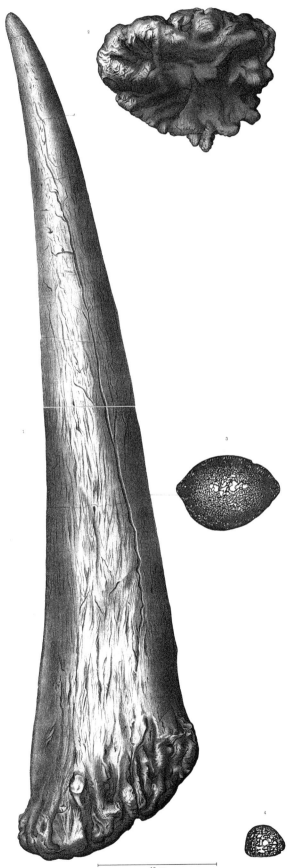

10 cm

PLATE 56

Stegosaurus ungulatus Marsh (1879) YPM 1853 (holotype)

Caudal spines in lateral (1), anterior (2), ventral (3), posterior (4), lateral (5), and ventral (6) views; cross-sectional views (1a and 4a)

HORIZON: Morrison formation

LOCALITY: YPM Quarry 12, Como Bluff, T. 22 N., R. 77 W., Sec. 18, Carbon County, Wyo.

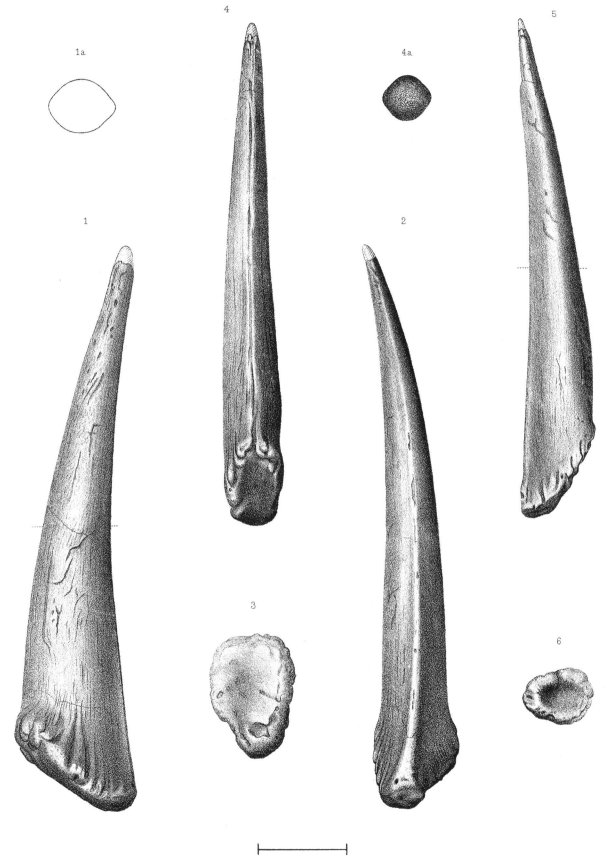

1a   4   4a   5

1   2

3   6

10 cm

PLATE 57

Stegosaurus stenops Marsh (1887) USNM 6135
Caudal spine in lateral (1, 2) and posterior (3) views

HORIZON: Morrison formation
LOCALITY: YPM Quarry 13 (dg. 5), Como Bluff, T. 22 N., R. 76 W.,
Sec. 4 or 5, Albany County, Wyo.

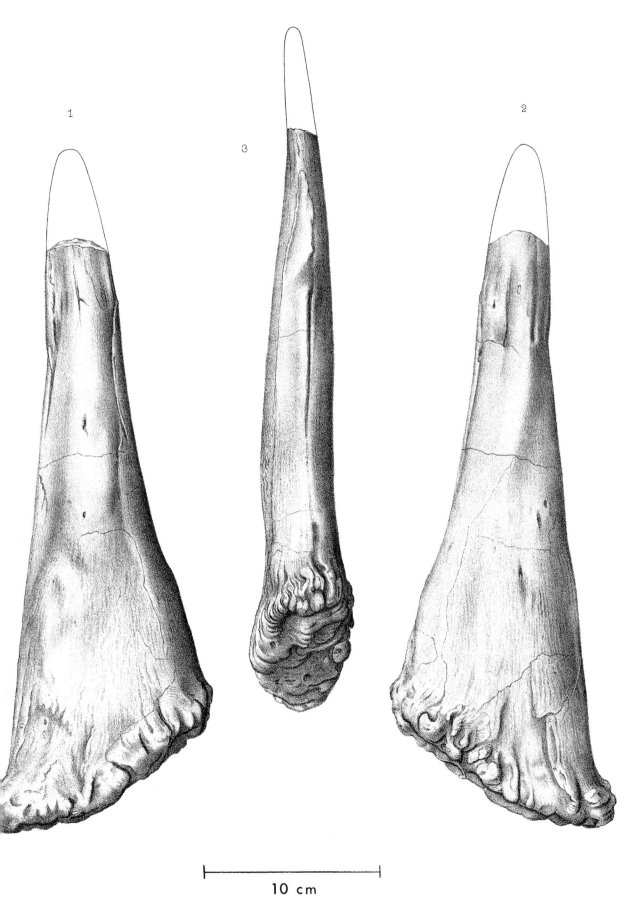

1   3   2

10 cm

PLATE 58

Stegosaurus sulcatus Marsh (1887) USNM 4937 (holotype)
Caudal spine in lateral (1, 2) and posterior (3) views; cross sections (4 and 5)

HORIZON: Morrison formation

LOCALITY: YPM Quarry 13 (middle), Como Bluff, T. 22 N., R. 76 W.,
Sec. 4 or 5, Albany County, Wyo.

ABBREVIATIONS: *a*   lateral groove
 b   base
 p   medial groove
 r   posterior ridge
 s   suture

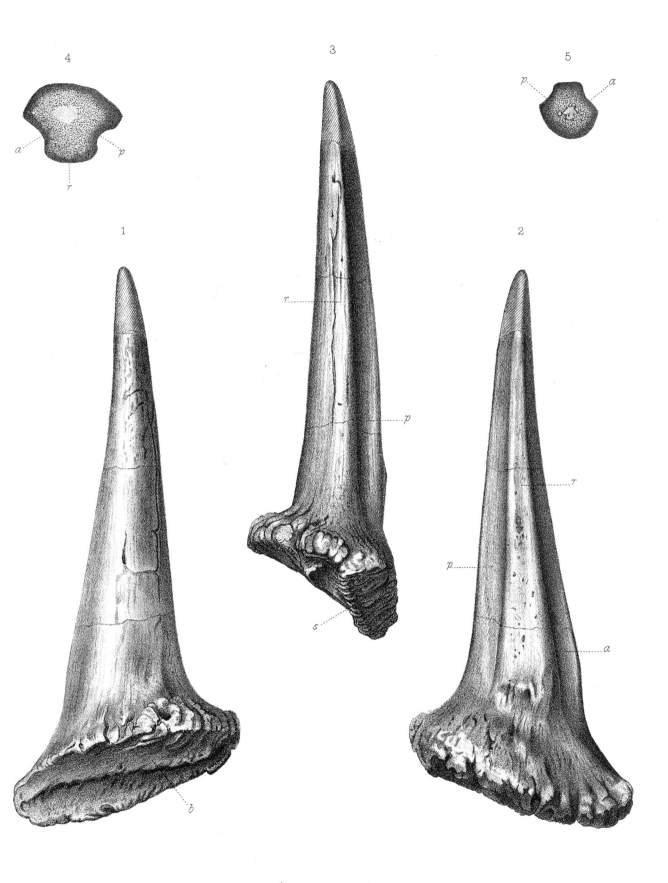

10 cm

PLATE 59

Stegosaurus ungulatus Marsh (1879) YPM 1853 (holotype)
  Dermal plates in lateral (1, 4, 6), posterior (2, 5, 8), and anterior (3, 7) views; basal views (5a, 8a)

  HORIZON: Morrison formation
  LOCALITY: YPM Quarry 12, Como Bluff, T. 22 N., R. 77 W., Sec. 18, Carbon County, Wyo.

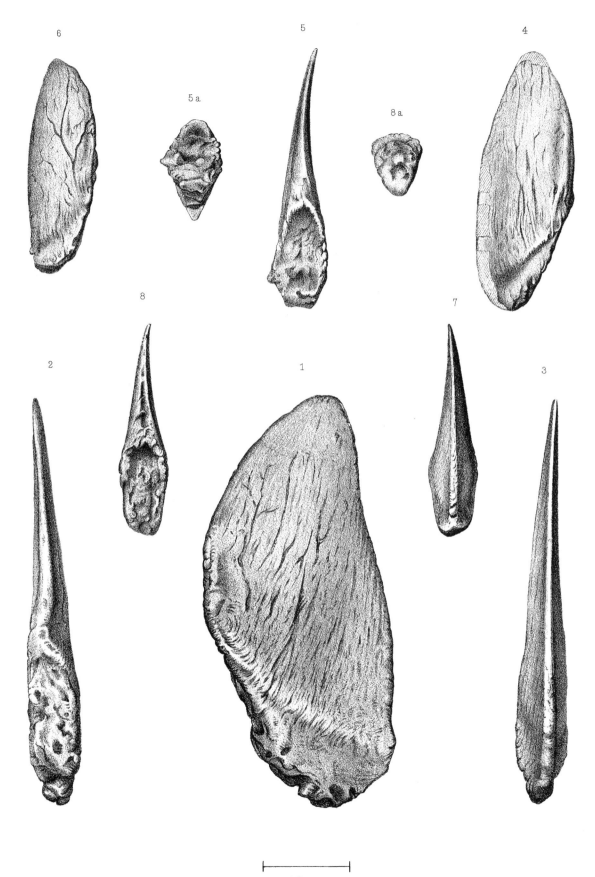

10 cm

PLATE 60

Stegosaurus ungulatus Marsh (1879) YPM 1853 (holotype)
  Dermal plate in lateral view

  HORIZON: Morrison formation
  LOCALITY: YPM Quarry 12, Como Bluff, T. 22 N., R. 77 W., Sec. 18,
    Carbon County, Wyo.
  ABBREVIATIONS: *a* anterior margin
    b posterior margin
    c base

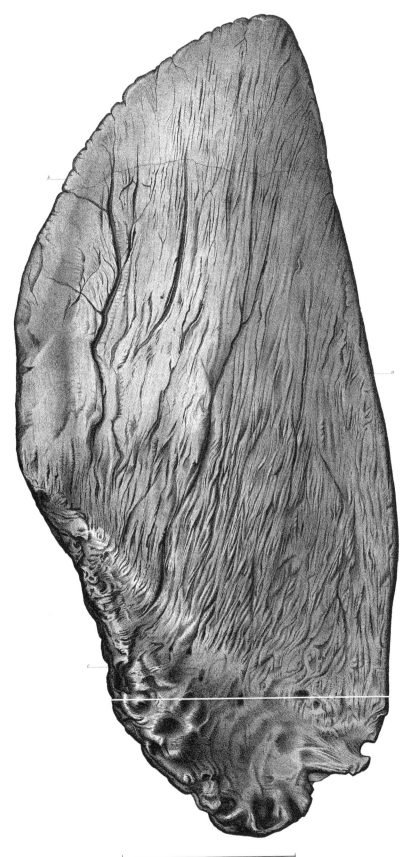

10 cm

PLATE 61

Stegosaurus stenops Marsh (1887) USNM 4714
Dermal plate in lateral (1) and ventral (2) views

HORIZON: Morrison formation

LOCALITY: YPM Quarry 13 (dg. 5), Como Bluff, T. 22 N., R. 76 W., Sec. 4 or 5, Albany County, Wyo.

ABBREVIATIONS: *a* anterior margin
p posterior margin

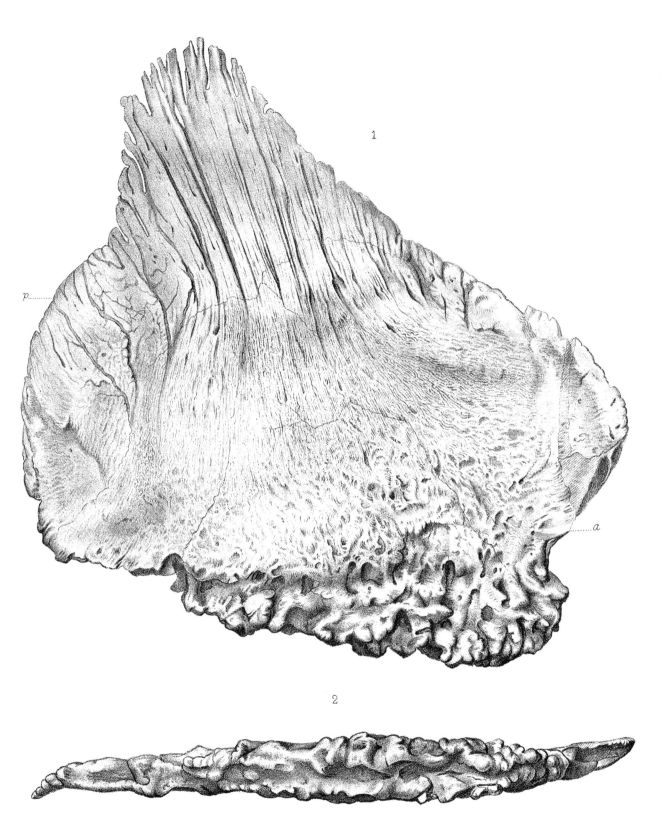

1

p

a

2

10 cm

PLATE 62

Stegosaurus ungulatus Marsh (1879) YPM 1853 (holotype)
  Dermal plate in lateral (1, 3) and ventral (2) views

    HORIZON: Morrison formation

    LOCALITY: YPM Quarry 12, Como Bluff, T. 22 N., R. 77 W., Sec. 18,
                 Carbon County, Wyo.

    ABBREVIATIONS: *a*   base
                       b   dorsal margin

1

a

b

2

a

3

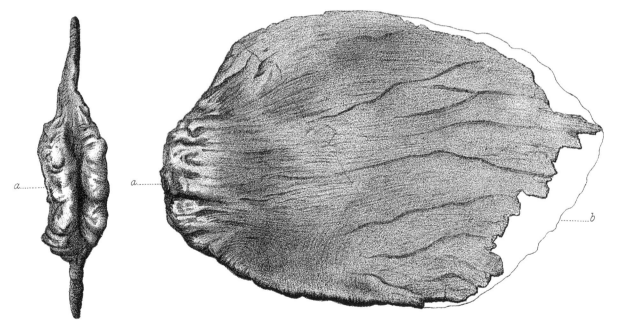

a

b

10 cm

PLATE 63

Stegosaurus ungulatus Marsh (1879) YPM 1853 (holotype)
Dermal plate in lateral (1, 3) and ventral (2) views

HORIZON: Morrison formation

LOCALITY: YPM Quarry 12, Como Bluff, T. 22 N., R. 77 W., Sec. 18,
Carbon County, Wyo.

ABBREVIATIONS: *a*   base
b   dorsal margin

1

2

3

a.

a.

b.

b.

10 cm

PLATE 64

Stegosaurus stenops Marsh (1887) USNM 4714
Dermal plate in lateral (1) and ventral (2) views

HORIZON: Morrison formation
LOCALITY: YPM Quarry 13 (dg. 5), Como Bluff, T. 22 N., R. 76 W.,
Sec. 3 or 4, Albany County, Wyo.
ABBREVIATIONS: *a* anterior margin
p posterior margin

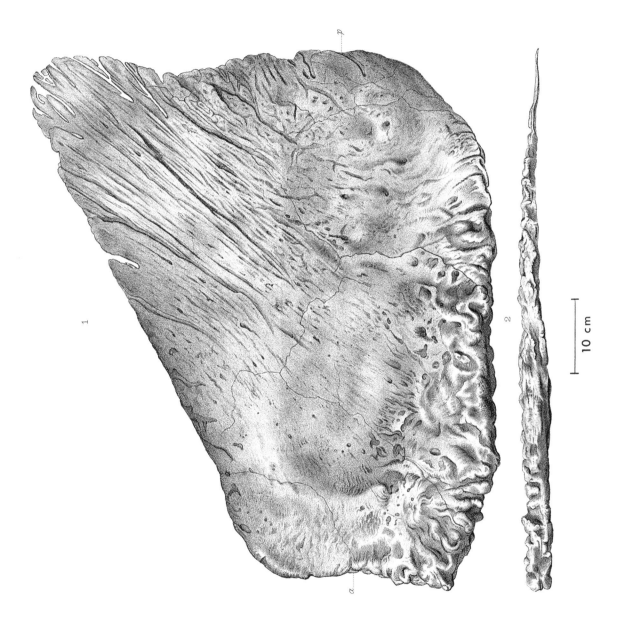

10 cm

PLATE 65[1]

Stegosaurus ungulatus Marsh (1879) composite skeleton
Lateral view of restored skeleton

HORIZON: Morrison formation

LOCALITY: Como Bluff, Wyo., various quarries

1. Plate 65 was never completed as a lithograph. Marsh planned to duplicate Plate 52 from his *Dinosaurs of North America*. For this reason, the latter plate is included here.

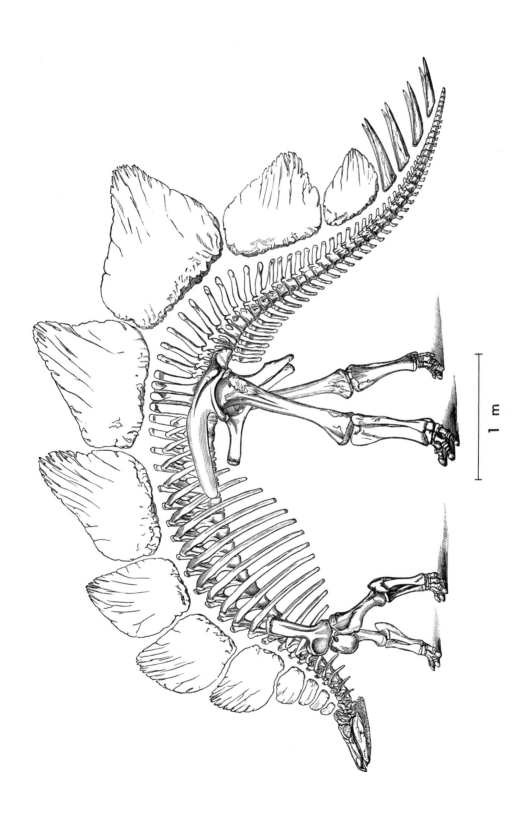

1 m

ANNOTATED BIBLIOGRAPHY OF FOSSIL VERTEBRATES
FROM COMO BLUFF

The following bibliography is not intended to include every reference to Como specimens, but rather to include papers in which descriptions and illustrations of material are given. The generic and specific names are those assigned by the author of the paper in question. New species are starred; figured specimens are daggered.[1]

Butler, P. M.
1939 The teeth of the Jurassic mammals. *Proc. Zool. Soc. London, 109,* 329–56.

† *Archaeotrigon brevimaxillus* (YPM 13775), fig. 3d
Archaeotrigon brevimaxillus (YPM 13776)
† *Archaeotrigon distagmus* (YPM 13641), fig. 3e
† *Docodon striatus* (YPM 11823), fig. 2a
† *Docodon superus* (YPM 13769), fig. 1a,b
† *Docodon superus* (YPM 13770), fig. 1c,d
Docodon victor (YPM 10647)
† *Docodon* sp. (YPM 13737), fig. 2b
† *Docodon* sp. (YPM 13767), fig. 2c,d
† *Laolestes eminens* (YPM 13725), fig. 6a,b,g,h
† *Laolestes eminens* (YPM 13726), fig. 6c
† *Laolestes eminens* (YPM 13720), fig. 6d
† *Laolestes eminens* (YPM 10660), fig. 6e,f
† *Melanodon arcuatus* (YPM 13743), fig. 4d
† *Melanodon goodrichi* (YPM 13750), fig. 5
† *Melanodon oweni* (YPM 10663), fig. 4b,c,g,h
† *Priacodon* sp. (YPM 10339), fig. 8c
† *Tathiodon agilis* (YPM 13649), fig. 3a–c
† *Tinodon lepidus?* (YPM 13645), fig. 7h–k
† *Triconodon bisulcus* (YPM 10345), fig. 8d

---

1. Each figured specimen from Como is identified by its catalogue number. Confusion frequently arises because Marsh often referred to a particular specimen by one name in the text and in a figure by another. Prime examples are: (1) sacrum YPM 1900 is referred to in the text as *Morosaurus impar,* but always in figures as *Morosaurus grandis;* (2) YPM 1858 is sometimes referred to *Stegosaurus duplex* (of which it is the type) and *Stegosaurus ungulatus* in the same papers; (3) YPM 4677 was transferred from *Stegosaurus armatus* to *Diplodocus lacustrus* in reference 34 but then in figures as *Diplodocus longus.*

Cope, E. D.

    1879 New Jurassic Dinosauria. *Amer. Naturalist, 13,* 402–04.

      * *Hypsirhophus seeleyanus* (?AMNH 5754) (Cope Q1?)[2]

Gidley, James Williams

    1906 Evidence bearing on tooth cusp development. *Proc. Washington Acad. Sci., 8,* 91–110.

      † *Dicrocynodon* sp. (USNM 2715), pl. 5 figs. 4, 4a

      † *Dryolestes* sp. (USNM 2845), pl. 5 figs. 2, 2a,b

      † *Dryolestes* sp. (USNM 2839), pl. 5 fig. 3

      † *Paurodon* sp. (USNM 2733), pl. 5 figs. 5, 5a–c

      † *Triconodon bisulcus* (USNM 2698), pl. 5 figs. 1, 1a

Gilmore, C. W.

    1909 Osteology of the Jurassic reptile *Camptosaurus. Proc. U.S. Nat. Museum, 36,* 197–332.

      † *Camptosaurus amplus* (YPM 1879) (Q1A), fig. 38; pl. 17

     †* *Camptosaurus browni* (USNM 4282) (Q13W), figs. 4–19, 21, 23–27, 30; pl. 14 fig. 3

      † *Camptosaurus depressus* (USNM 5820) (Q13 Middle), fig. 47

      † *Camptosaurus dispar* (USNM 5473) (Q13 Middle), figs. 4, 5, 11, 12, 22, 29; pls. 10–12, 14 fig. 1

      † *Camptosaurus dispar* (USNM 5819) (Q13 Middle), fig. 10

      † *Camptosaurus dispar* (USNM 5818) (Q13 Middle), figs. 20, 33, 34

      † *Camptosaurus dispar* (USNM 4277) (Q13 Middle), figs. 28, 35

      † *Camptosaurus dispar* (YPM 1878) (Q13E), figs. 32, 36; pl. 15

      † *Camptosaurus dispar* (YPM 1877) (Q13E), fig. 37(1,2); pl. 18

      † *Camptosaurus dispar* (YPM 1877a) (Q13E), fig. 37(3); pl. 13

      † *Camptosaurus medius* (YPM 1880) (Q13W), figs. 6, 9, 31; pl. 16

      † *Camptosaurus nanus* (USNM 2210) (Q13 Middle), figs. 39–42; pl. 14 fig. 2

      † *Camptosaurus* sp. (YPM 1886) (Q13), figs. 7, 8

    1909 A new rhynchocephalian reptile from the Jurassic of Wyoming, with notes on the fauna of Quarry 9. *Proc. U.S. Nat. Museum, 27,* 36–52.

      † *Coelurus fragilis* (YPM 1992) (Q9), fig. 3

      † *Laosaurus gracilis* (USNM 5808) (Q9), fig. 2

     †* *Opisthias rarus* (USNM 2860) (Q9), fig. 1

---

2. Quarry site of each specimen is listed (Q13E, dg 4 = Quarry 13 east, diagram 4; SQ4 = *Sauranodon* Quarry 4, etc.) except for a few American Museum specimens collected for Cope. Where no quarry is indicated for the cited specimen, it is from Quarry 9.

1914 Osteology of the armored Dinosauria in the United States National Museum with special reference to the genus *Stegosaurus*. *Bull. U.S. Nat. Museum, 89,* 1–143.

† *Stegosaurus stenops?* (USNM 2274) (Q13 dg5), fig. 4

† *Stegosaurus stenops?* (USNM 6645) (Q13 dg13), figs. 5–7, 13

† *Stegosaurus stenops* (USNM 4714) (Q13 dg5), fig. 18; pls. 12, 13, 15, 23 fig. 6; pl. 24

† *Stegosaurus stenops* (USNM 4288) (Q13 dg7), pl. 16

† *Stegosaurus stenops* (USNM 6135) (Q13 dg5), pl. 17

† *Stegosaurus stenops* (USNM 7411) (Q13 dg11,13), pl. 20 fig. 1

† *Stegosaurus stenops* (USNM 4929) (Q13 dg4,8), pl. 20 fig. 2

† *Stegosaurus stenops* (USNM 7371) (Q13 dg5), pl. 21 fig. 3

† *Stegosaurus stenops* (USNM 7615) (Q13 dg4), pl. 22 fig. 2; pl. 23 figs. 2, 3

† *Stegosaurus stenops* (USNM 7584) (Q13 dg4), pl. 23 figs. 4, 5

† *Stegosaurus stenops* (USNM 6629) (Q13 dg11,13), pl. 25 figs. 1, 2

† *Stegosaurus sulcatus* (USNM 4937) (Q13 Middle), figs. 38, 39, 41(2), 57, 60b, 65; pl. 18; pl. 20 figs. 3, 4; pl. 21 fig. 2; pl. 23 fig. 1; pl. 25 fig. 3

† *Stegosaurus ungulatus* (YPM 1938 (Q9), fig. 10

† *Stegosaurus ungulatus* (YPM 1853) (Q12), figs. 15, 21, 25, 27, 28, 30, 44, 45(1), 46, 47, 51, 54, 55, 59

† *Stegosaurus ungulatus?* (USNM 7348) (Q13 dg4), fig. 17

† *Stegosaurus ungulatus* (YPM 1858) (Q11), figs. 22, 24, 43

† *Stegosaurus ungulatus* (USNM 6646) (Q13 dg12,13), fig. 26

† *Stegosaurus ungulatus* (YPM 1854) (Q13E), fig. 35

† *Stegosaurus ungulatus* (YPM 1854) (Q13E), fig. 56

† *Stegosaurus ungulatus* (USNM 6099) (Q13 dg4), figs. 60–63

† *Stegosaurus* sp. (USNM 4935) (Q13 dg4), figs. 8, 9, 14

† *Stegosaurus* sp. (USNM 6531) (Q13 dg11,13), figs. 18–20, 29

Stegosaurus sp. (USNM 7620) (Q13 dg7)

† *Stegosaurus* sp. (USNM 7403) (Q13 dg7), fig. 31

† *Stegosaurus* sp. (USNM 7401) (Q13 dg7), figs. 39, 41(3)

† *Stegosaurus* sp. (USNM 7419) (Q13 dg7), figs. 41(1), 53

† *Stegosaurus* sp. (USNM 7387) (Q13 dg7), figs. 48, 49

† *Stegosaurus* sp. (USNM 7367) (Q13 dg5), fig. 50

† *Stegosaurus* sp. (USNM 4280) (Q13 dg5), fig. 52; pl. 21 fig. 1

† *Stegosaurus* sp. (USNM 7386) (Q13 dg7), pl. 19 fig. 2

† *Stegosaurus* sp. (USNM 7389) (Q13 dg7), pl. 25 fig. 5

1920 Osteology of the carnivorous Dinosauria in the United States National

Gilmore, C. W. (*cont'd*)

Museum with special reference to the genera *Antrodemus* (*Allosaurus*) and *Ceratosaurus*. *Bull. U.S. Nat. Museum, 110,* 1–159.

† *Antrodemus valens* (USNM 8367) (QC), figs. 18, 21–29, 32, 36, 38

† *Antrodemus valens* (USNM 2323) (Q9), pls. 12, 14

Antrodemus valens (USNM 8405) (QD)

Antrodemus valens (USNM 8302) (Q9)

† *Antrodemus valens* (YPM 1931) [type of *Labrosaurus lucaris*] (Q3), pl. 6

† *Antrodemus* sp. (YPM 1890) (Q1) fig. 11

† *Antrodemus* sp. (AMNH 5753) (Cope Q3), fig. 16; pl. 16 fig. 1

† *Antrodemus* sp. (YPM 1894) (Q4), fig. 58 (humerus only)

† *Antrodemus* sp. (YPM 1894) (Q4), pl. 11

† *Coelurus agilis* (YPM 2010) (Q13E), pl. 34 figs. 5, 6

Coelurus fragilis (USNM 5809, 5810, 6624, 6625, 6626, 6627, 6628) (Q9)

† *Coelurus fragilis* (YPM 1991) (Q13E), pl. 34 figs. 7, 8

1928 Fossil lizards of North America. *Mem. Nat. Acad. Sci., 22,* 1–201.

†**Cteniogenys antiquus* (USNM 6134) (Q9), pl. 20 fig. 12

† *Cteniogenys antiquus* (YPM 1068) (Q9), pl. 20 fig. 13

Hecht, M. K., and R. Estes

1960 Fossil amphibians from Quarry Nine. *Yale Peabody Museum, Postilla,* No. 46, 1–19.

†**Comobatrachus aenigmatis* (YPM 1863) (Q9), pl. 1 figs. 2, 4, 6; pl. 2 fig. 2

†**Comonecturoides marshi* (YPM 3919) (Q9), pl. 2 figs. 3, 4

†**Eobatrachus agilis* (YPM 1862) (Q9), pl. 1 figs. 1, 3, 5; pl. 2 fig. 1

Kermack, K. A., and F. Mussett

1958 The jaw articulation of the Docodonta and the classification of Mesozoic mammals. *Proc. Roy. Soc. Lond.* (B), *149,* 204–15.

† *Docodon striatus* (YPM 11823), pl. 5 fig. 2

Lull, R. S.

1910 The armor of *Stegosaurus*. *Amer. Jour. Sci.* (4), *29,* 201–10.

Stegosaurus ungulatus (YPM 1853) (Q12)

1910 *Stegosaurus ungulatus* Marsh recently mounted at the Peabody Museum of Yale University. *Amer. Jour. Sci.* (4), *30,* 361–77.

† *Stegosaurus ungulatus* (YPM 1853) (Q12), pl. 2

† *Stegosaurus ungulatus* (YPM 1858) (Q11), pl. 2

1921 The Cretaceous armored dinosaur, *Nodosaurus textilis*. *Amer. Jour. Sci.*
     (5), *1*, 98–126.

   † *Nodosaurus textilis* (YPM 1815) (Cretaceous Q) figs. 1–7; pls. 1–4

1930 Skeleton of *Camarasaurus lentus* recently mounted at Yale. *Amer. Jour.*
     Sci. (5), *19*, 1–5.

   † *Camarasaurus lentus* (YPM 1910) (Q13W), figs. 1, 2

Marsh, O. C.

   1877 Notice of new dinosaurian reptiles from the Jurassic Formation. *Amer.*
        Jour. Sci. (3), *14*, 514–16.

      * *Apatosaurus grandis* (YPM 1901) (YPM 1900) (Q1)

   1878 Notice of new dinosaurian reptiles. *Amer. Jour. Sci.* (3), *15*, 241–44.

      * *Allosaurus lucaris* (YPM 1931) (Q3)

     †*Creosaurus atrox (YPM 1890) (Q1)

      * *Laosaurus celer* (YPM 1874) (Q9?)

      * *Laosaurus gracilis* (YPM 1875) (Q9?)

      * *Morosaurus impar* (YPM 1900) (Q1)

   1878 Fossil mammal from the Jurassic of the Rocky Mountains. *Amer. Jour.*
        Sci. (3), *15*, 459.

     †**Dryolestes priscus* (YPM 11820 (Q?), fig. 1

   1878 New pterodactyl from the Jurassic of the Rocky Mountains. *Amer. Jour.*
        Sci. (3), *16*, 233–34.

      * *Pterodactylus montanus* (YPM 2020) (Q5)

   1878 Principal characters of American Jurassic dinosaurs Part I. *Amer. Jour.*
        Sci. (3), *16*, 411–16.

      † *Diplodocus longus* (YPM 4675) (Q1), pl. 8 fig. 4

     †*Laosaurus altus (YPM 1876) (Q5), pls. 9, 10 fig. 2

      † *Morosaurus grandis* (YPM 1901) (Q1), pls. 6, 7

      † *Morosaurus grandis* (YPM 1905) (Q1), pls. 5, 7, 10 fig. 3

     †**Morosaurus robustus* (YPM 1902) (Q1), pl. 8 figs. 1, 2

   1879 A new order of extinct reptiles (Sauranodonta) from the Jurassic Forma-
        tion of the Rocky Mountains. *Amer. Jour. Sci.* (3), *17*, 85–86.

      * *Sauranodon natans* (YPM 1952) (SQ2?)

   1879 Principal characters of American Jurassic dinosaurs Part II. *Amer. Jour.*
        Sci. (3), *17*, 86–92.

      † *Allosaurus fragilis* (YPM 1894) (Q4), pl. 8 fig. 2

      † *Allosaurus fragilis* (YPM 1932) (Q1?), pl. 10 figs. 3, 4

      † *Creosaurus atrox* (YPM 1890) (Q1), pl. 10 figs. 1, 2

Marsh, O. C. (*cont'd*)

    † *Morosaurus grandis* (YPM 1905) (Q1), pl. 1 figs. 3, 4, 7

    † *Morosaurus grandis* (YPM 1900) (Q1), pl. 5

1879 Additional characters of the Sauropoda. *Amer. Jour. Sci.* (3), *17*, 181–82.

    Morosaurus grandis (YPM 1905) (Q1)

1879 Notice of a new Jurassic mammal. *Amer. Jour. Sci.* (3), *18*, 60–61.

    * *Stylacodon gracilis* (YPM 11883)

1879 Additional remains of Jurassic mammals. *Amer. Jour. Sci.* (3), *18*, 215–16.

    * *Dryolestes vorax* (YPM 11818)

    †**Tinodon bellus* (YPM 11843), fig. 1

1879 Notice of new Jurassic mammals. *Amer. Jour. Sci.* (3), *18*, 396–98.

    †**Ctenacodon serratus* (YPM 11833), fig. 1

    * *Dryolestes arcuatus* (YPM 11822)

    * *Tinodon lepidus* (YPM 11845)

    * *Tinodon robustus* (YPM 11846)

1879 Notice of new Jurassic reptiles. *Amer. Jour. Sci.* (3), *18*, 501–05.

    * *Brontosaurus excelsus* (YPM 1980) (Q10)

    * *Camptonotus amplus* (YPM 1879) (Q1A)

    †**Camptonotus dispar* (YPM 1877) (Q13E), pl. 3

    † *Camptonotus dispar* (YPM 1878) (Q13E), pl. 3

    * *Coelurus fragilis* (YPM 1991) (Q13E)

    * *Stegosaurus ungulatus* (YPM 1853) (Q12)

1880 The limbs of *Sauranodon,* with notice of a new species. *Amer. Jour. Sci.* (3), *19*, 169–71.

    * *Sauranodon discus* (YPM 1955) (SQ4?)

    Sauranodon natans (YPM 1952) (SQ2?)

1880 Principal characters of American Jurassic dinosaurs Part III. *Amer. Jour. Sci.* (3), *19*, 253–59.

    † *"Stegosaurus armatus"* (YPM 4677) [=*Diplodocus*] (Q8), pl. 6 fig. 5

    † *Stegosaurus ungulatus* (YPM 1853) (Q12), pl. 6 figs. 1–3; pl. 7; pl. 8 figs. 2, 4; pl. 9; pl. 10 figs. 1–3; pl. 11

    † *Stegosaurus ungulatus* (YPM 1854) (Q13E), pl. 8 figs. 1, 3; pl. 10 fig. 4

1880 The sternum in dinosaurian reptiles. *Amer. Jour. Sci.,* *19*, 395–96.

    † *Brontosaurus excelsus* (YPM 1980) (Q10), pl. 18

1880 Notice of Jurassic mammals representing two new orders. *Amer. Jour. Sci.* (3), *20*, 235–39.

    †**Ctenacodon serratus* (YPM 13668), fig. 2

†*_Diplocynodon victor_ (YPM 11826), fig. 1

* _Dryolestes obtusus_ (YPM 11819A)

* _Stylacodon validus_ (YPM 11884)

* _Tinodon ferox_ (YPM 606)

* _Triconodon bisulcus_ (YPM 11851)

1881 Principal characters of American Jurassic dinosaurs Part IV: Spinal cord, pelvis and limbs of _Stegosaurus. Amer. Jour. Sci._ (3), _21,_ 167–70.

* _Stegosaurus affinis_ (YPM uncatalogued) (Q13W)

† _Stegosaurus ungulatus_ (YPM 1853) (Q12), pl. 6 figs. 1, 2; pl. 7 fig. 2; pl. 8

† _Stegosaurus ungulatus_ (YPM 1858) (Q11), pl. 6 figs. 3–5; pl. 7 fig. 1; pl. 8

† _Stegosaurus ungulatus_ (YPM 1854) (Q13E), pl. 8

1881 A new order of extinct Jurassic reptiles (Coeluria). _Amer. Jour. Sci._ (3), _21,_ 339–40.

† _Coelurus fragilis_ (YPM 1991) (Q13E), pl. 10 fig. 2

† _Coelurus fragilis_ (YPM 1992) (Q9), pl. 10 fig. 3

† _Coelurus fragilis_ (YPM 1993) (Q13E), pl. 10 fig. 1

1881 Discovery of a fossil bird in the Jurassic of Wyoming. _Amer. Jour. Sci._ (3), _21,_ 341–42.

* _Laopteryx priscus_ (YPM 1800) (Q9)

1881 Principal characters of American Jurassic dinosaurs Part V. _Amer. Jour. Sci._ (3), _21,_ 417–23.

* _Brontosaurus amplus_ (YPM 1981) (Q11)

† _Brontosaurus excelsus_ (YPM 1980) (Q10), pls. 12–18

* _Diracodon laticeps_ (YPM 1885) (Q13W)

1881 Notice of new Jurassic mammals. _Amer. Jour. Sci._ (3), _21,_ 511–13.

* _Allodon laticeps_ (YPM 11761)

* _Ctenacodon nanus_ (YPM 11832)

* _Docodon striatus_ (YPM 11823)

* _Dryolestes gracilis_ (YPM 11821)

1883 Principal characters of American Jurassic dinosaurs Part VI: Restorations of _Brontosaurus. Amer. Jour. Sci._ (3), _26,_ 81–85.

† _Brontosaurus excelsus_ (YPM 1980) (Q10), pl. 1

1884 Principal characters of American Jurassic dinosaurs Part VII: Diplodocidae, a new family of the Sauropoda. _Amer. Jour. Sci._ (3), 27, 160–68.

† _Diplodocus lacustris_ (YPM 4677) (Q8), pl. 4 fig. 3

† _Diplodocus longus_ (YPM 4675) (Q1), pl. 4 fig. 7

Marsh, O. C. (*cont'd*)

1884   Principal characters of American Jurassic dinosaurs Part VIII: The order
Theropoda. *Amer. Jour. Sci.* (3), *27,* 329–40.

†**Coelurus agilis* (YPM 2010) (Q13E), pl. 11 fig. 3
†   *Coelurus fragilis* (YPM 1993) (Q13E), pl. 13 fig. 1
†   *Coelurus fragilis* (YPM 1991) (Q13E), pl. 13 fig. 2
†   *Coelurus fragilis* (YPM 1992) (Q9), pl. 13 fig. 3
†   *Creosaurus atrox* (YPM 1890) (Q1), pl. 9 fig. 3, pl. 14 figs. 1, 2
†   *Creosaurus atrox* (YPM 1932) (Q1?), pl. 14 figs. 3, 4

1884   A new order of extinct Jurassic reptiles. *Amer. Jour. Sci.* (3), *27,* 341.

†**Macelognathus vagans* (YPM 1415) (Q9), fig. 1

1887   American Jurassic mammals. *Amer. Jour. Sci.* (3), *33,* 326–48.

†**Allodon fortis* (YPM 11760), pl. 7 figs. 7–15
†   *Allodon laticeps* (YPM 11761), pl. 7 figs. 1–6
†**Asthenodon segnis* (USNM 2862), pl. 9 figs. 6, 7
†**Ctenacodon potens* (YPM 11834), pl. 8 figs. 2, 3, 7–9
†   *Ctenacodon serratus* (YPM 11833), pl. 8 figs. 1, 4–6
†   *Diplocynodon victor* (YPM 11826), pl. 10 fig. 3
†   *Docodon striatus* (YPM 11823), pl. 10 fig. 2
†   *Dryolestes priscus* (YPM 11820) (Q?), pl. 9 fig. 2
†   *Dryolestes vorax* (USNM 2727), pl. 9 figs. 3, 4
*   *Enneodon affinus* (USNM 2129)
†**Enneodon crassus* (USNM 2130), pl. 10 fig. 4
†**Laodon venustus* (USNM 2142), pl. 9 fig. 5
†**Menacodon rarus* (USNM 2131), pl. 10 figs. 5, 6
†**Paurodon valens* (USNM 2143), pl. 10 figs. 7, 8
†**Priacodon ferox* (YPM 606), pl. 10 fig. 9
†   *Stylacodon gracilis* (YPM 11883), pl. 9 fig. 1
†   *Tinodon bellus* (YPM 11843), pl. 10 fig. 1

1887   Principal characters of American Jurassic dinosaurs Part IX: The skull
and dermal armor of *Stegosaurus. Amer. Jour. Sci.* (3), *34,* 413–17.

†   *Diracodon laticeps* (USNM 4288) (Q13W), pl. 9
*   *Stegosaurus duplex* (YPM 1858) (Q11)
†**Stegosaurus sulcatus* (USNM 4937) (Q13 Middle), pl. 8 figs. 4–6
†   *Stegosaurus ungulatus* (YPM 1853) (Q12), pls. 7, 8 figs. 1–3

1889   Notice of new American dinosaurs. *Amer. Jour. Sci.* (3), *37,* 331–36.

†**Morosaurus lentus* (YPM 1910) (Q13W), fig. 2

1889   Notice of gigantic horned Dinosauria from the Cretaceous. *Amer. Jour.
Sci.* (3), *38,* 173–75.

* *Nodosaurus textilis* (YPM 1815) (Cretaceous Quarry)

1890 Notice of some extinct Testudinata. *Amer. Jour. Sci.* (3), *40,* 177–79.

    † *Glyptops ornatus* (YPM 1357) (Q9), pl. 7 figs. 1, 2

1891 Restoration of *Brontosaurus. Amer. Jour. Sci.* (3), *41,* 341–42.

    † *Brontosaurus excelsus* (YPM 1980) (Q10), pl. 16

1891 Restoration of *Stegosaurus. Amer. Jour. Sci.* (3), *42,* 179–81.

    † *Stegosaurus ungulatus* (YPM 1853) (Q12), (YPM 1858) (Q11), (YPM 1854) (Q13E), pl. 9

1892 Notes on Mesozoic vertebrate fossils. *Amer. Jour. Sci.* (3), *44,* 171–76.

    † *Camptosaurus dispar* (YPM 1877, 1878) (Q13E), pl. 5 figs. 2, 3

    † *Laosaurus altus* (YPM 1876) (Q5), pl. 5 fig. 1

    † *Stegosaurus ungulatus* (YPM 1938) (Q9), pl. 4 fig. 1

    † *Stegosaurus ungulatus* (YPM 1853) (Q12), (YPM 1858) (Q11), (YPM 1854) (Q13E), pl. 4 figs. 2, 3

1894 Restoration of *Camptosaurus. Amer. Jour. Sci.* (3), *47,* 245–46.

    † *Camptosaurus dispar* (YPM 1877, 1878) (Q13E), pl. 6

1894 The typical Ornithopoda of the American Jurassic. *Amer. Jour. Sci.* (3), *48,* 85–90.

    † *Camptosaurus dispar* (YPM 1877) (Q13E), pl. 5 fig. 2 (scapula, coracoid)

    † *Camptosaurus dispar* (YPM 1878) (Q13E), pl. 5 fig. 2, pl. 7 fig. 3

    † *Camptosaurus dispar* (YPM 1877a) (Q13E), pl. 6 fig. 2

    †**Camptosaurus medius* (YPM 1880) (Q13W), pl. 4

    †**Camptosaurus nanus* (USNM 2110) (Q13 Middle), pl. 5 fig. 3

    † *Dryosaurus altus* (YPM 4860) (Q5), pl. 7 fig. 2

    †**Laosaurus consors* (YPM 1882) (Q7), pl. 5 fig. 4; pl. 7 fig. 1

1896 Dinosaurs of North America. *16th Ann. Report, U.S. Geol. Survey,* 1894–95 Part II, 133–415.

    Quarry 1

    † *Creosaurus atrox* (YPM 1890), pl. 12 figs. 1–3

    † *Creosaurus atrox* (YPM 1932), pl. 12 figs. 5, 6 (quarry doubtful)

    † *Diplodocus longus* (YPM 4675), pl. 26 fig. 6; pl. 39 fig. 5

    † *Morosaurus grandis* (YPM 1900), pl. 31 figs. 7, 8

    † *Morosaurus grandis* (YPM 1901), figs. 30–33; pl. 32 figs. 4–6; pl. 34 figs. 1, 2; pl. 38; pl. 39 figs. 3, 4

    † *Morosaurus grandis* (YPM 1905), pl. 29 fig. 2; pl. 30 figs. 2, 3; pl. 31 figs. 1–6; pl. 35 fig. 3; pl. 38

    †**Pleurocoelus montanus* (YPM 1908), figs. 35–41

Marsh, O. C. (*cont'd*)

 Quarry 3
 † *Morosaurus grandis* (YPM 4861), pl. 34 figs. 5–7

 Quarry 4
 † *Creosaurus atrox* (YPM 1894), pl. 12 fig. 4; pl. 13 fig. 5

 Quarry 5
 † *"Brontosaurus excelsus"* (YPM 4741), pl. 20 fig. 1
 † *Dryosaurus altus* (YPM 1876), pl. 55 fig. 4
 † *Dryosaurus altus* (YPM 4860) pl. 79 fig. 2; pl. 80 fig. 2

 Quarry 7
 † *Laosaurus consors* (YPM 1882), pl. 55 fig. 3; pl. 57; pl. 79 fig. 1

 Quarry 8
 † *"Coelurus fragilis"* (YPM 1933), pl. 7 fig. 1
 † *Diplodocus longus* (YPM 4677), pl. 26 fig. 2

 Quarry 9
 † *"Brontosaurus excelsus"* (USNM 5383), figs. 21–23
 † *Coelurus fragilis* (YPM 1992), pl. 7 fig. 4
 † *Stegosaurus ungulatus* (YPM 1938), pl. 46 fig. 1; pl. 78 fig. 3

 Quarry 10
 † *Brontosaurus excelsus* (YPM 1980), figs. 12, 16; pl. 20 figs. 3, 4; pls. 21–24; pl. 39 fig. 1; pl. 42

 Quarry 11
 † *Brontosaurus amplus* (YPM 1981), figs. 17–20, 29
 † *Stegosaurus ungulatus* (YPM 1858), pl. 46 figs. 2–5; pl. 48 fig. 2; pl. 52; pl. 79 fig. 6

 Quarry 12
 † *Stegosaurus ungulatus* (YPM 1853), pl. 44 figs. 3, 4; pl. 45; pl. 46 fig. 1; pl. 47 figs. 1–3, 5, 6; pl. 48 fig. 1; pl. 49 figs. 1–4; pl. 50 figs. 1, 2; pl. 52; pl. 77 fig. 1; pl. 80 fig. 5

 Quarry 13
 † *"Brontosaurus excelsus"* (YPM 1911) (13E), figs. 9–11; pl. 20 fig. 2
 † *Camptosaurus dispar* (YPM 1877) (13E), pl. 54 figs. 1, 2, 4; pl. 56
 † *Camptosaurus dispar* (YPM 1878) (13E), pl. 54 figs. 1, 2; pl. 56; pl. 79 fig. 3; pl. 81 fig. 1

† *Camptosaurus dispar* (YPM 1877a) (13E), pl. 54 fig. 3

† *Camptosaurus medius* (YPM 1880) (13W), pl. 53; pl. 78 fig. 1; pl. 80
fig. 1

† *Camptosaurus nanus* (USNM 2210) (13 Middle), pl. 55 fig. 2

† *Coelurus agilis* (YPM 2010) (13E), pl. 10 figs. 3, 4

† *Coelurus fragilis* (YPM 1993) (13E), pl. 7 fig. 2

† *Coelurus fragilis* (YPM 1991) (13E), pl. 7 fig. 3

† *Diracodon laticeps* (USNM 4288), pl. 51

† *Morosaurus lentus* (YPM 1910) (13W), figs. 34, 63; pl. 32 figs. 1–3;
pl. 33; pl. 34 figs. 3, 4; pl. 35 fig. 4; pl. 36 fig. 1; pl. 37 figs. 3–5

† *Stegosaurus stenops* (YPM 1856), pl. 48 fig. 3; pl. 81 fig. 3

† *Stegosaurus sulcatus* (USNM 4937) (13 Middle), pl. 50 figs. 4–6

† *Stegosaurus ungulatus* (YPM 1854) (13E), pl. 48 fig. 1; pl. 59 fig. 2

Quarry 14

†*Allosaurus ferox (YPM 1893), pl. 13 figs. 2–4

Cretaceous Quarry

† *Nodosaurus textilis* (YPM 1815), pl. 75 fig. 5

Matthew, W. D.

1905 The mounted skeleton of *Brontosaurus. Amer. Museum Jour.,* 5, 62–70.
Brontosaurus (AMNH 222) [=*Apatosaurus*].

1908 *Allosaurus,* a carnivorous dinosaur and its prey. *Amer. Museum Jour.,*
8, 3–5.
Allosaurus fragilis (AMNH 5753) (Cope Q3)

Osborn, H. F.

1898 Additional characters of the great herbivorous dinosaur *Camarasaurus.
Bull. Amer. Museum Nat. Hist.,* 10, 219–33.

   † *Brontosaurus excelsus* (YPM 1980) (Q10), figs. 6, 7c, 8

   † *"Camarasaurus"* (AMNH 222), figs. 2–5 [=*Apatosaurus*]

1899 A skeleton of *Diplodocus. Mem. Amer. Museum Nat. Hist., 1,* Part 5,
189–214.

   † *Diplodocus longus* (AMNH 223), figs. 1–5

1904 Manus, sacrum, and caudals of Sauropoda. *Bull. Amer. Museum Nat.
Hist., 29,* 181–90.

   † *Brontosaurus* (AMNH 222) [=*Apatosaurus*] fig. 6

1912 Crania of *Tyrannosaurus* and *Allosaurus. Mem. Amer. Museum Nat.
Hist.,* n.s. *1,* 1–30.

   † *Allosaurus fragilis* (AMNH 5753) (Cope Q3), figs. 9–11

Osborn, H. F., and W. Granger

1901 Fore and hind limbs of Sauropoda from the Bone Cabin Quarry. *Bull. Amer. Museum Nat. Hist., 14,* 199–208.

† *Brontosaurus* (AMNH 222), fig. 1c

Simpson, G. G.

1925 Mesozoic Mammalia I: American triconodonts. *Amer. Jour. Sci.* (5), *10,* 145–65, 334–58.

†**Aploconodon comoënsis* (USNM 2791), fig. 10

†**Phascolodon gidleyi* (USNM 2703), fig. 8

† *Priacodon ferox* (YPM 606), fig. 5

† *Priacodon ?ferox* (YPM 13626), figs. 13–16

†**Priacodon grandaevus* (YPM 10349), fig. 19

† *Priacodon grandaevus* (USNM 2698), fig. 20

†*Priacodon lulli (YPM 13625), fig. 17

† *Priacodon lulli* (YPM 10359), fig. 18

† *Priacodon robustus* (YPM 11846), fig. 6

† *Priacodon robustus* (YPM 10343), fig. 7

† *Triconodon bisulcus* (YPM 11851), fig. 1

† *Triconodon bisulcus* (YPM 10345), fig. 3

† *Triconodon bisulcus* (YPM 10340), fig. 4

   Triconodon bisulcus (YPM 13636)

† *Triconodon ?bisulcus* (YPM 10344), fig. 11

† *Triconodon ?bisulcus* (USNM 2699), fig. 12

   Triconodon sp. (YPM 13632)

   Triconodon sp. (YPM 13628)

1925 Mesozoic Mammalia II: *Tinodon and its allies. Amer. Jour. Sci.* (5), *10,* 451–70.

†**Amphidon aequicrurius* (YPM 13639), figs. 8, 9

†**Amphidon superstes* (YPM 13638), figs. 6, 7

† *Tinodon bellus* (YPM 11843), figs. 1, 2

† *Tinodon bellus* (YPM 13644), fig. 3

† *Tinodon lepidus* (YPM 11845), fig. 4

† *Tinodon lepidus* (USNM 2131), fig. 5

1926 American terrestrial Rhynchocephalia. *Amer. Jour. Sci.* (5), *12,* 12–16.

†**Theretairus antiquus* (YPM 13764) (Q9), fig. 1

1927 Mesozoic Mammalia VI: Genera of Morrison Pantotheres. *Amer. Jour. Sci.* (5), *13,* 409–16.

**Archeotrigon brevimaxillus* (USNM 2793)

Dicrocynodon victor (YPM 11826)

Docodon striatus (YPM 11823)

Dryolestes priscus (YPM 11820) (Q?)

Dryolestes priscus (YPM 10646)

Ennacodon crassus (USNM 2130)

*Euthlastus cordiformis (YPM 13755)

*Herpetairus arcuatus (YPM 11822)

*Laolestes eminens (YPM 13719)

*Malthacolestes osborni (YPM 13751)

*Melanodon oweni (YPM 10663)

*Miccylotyrans minimus (USNM 2754)

Paurodon valens (USNM 2143)

*Pelicopsis dubius (YPM 13754)

*Tanaodon agilis (YPM 13649)

1929 American Mesozoic Mammalia. *Mem. Peabody Museum, Yale Univ., 3,* Part I, 1–235.

† *Amblotherium debilis* (YPM 11821), pl. 12 fig. 1

† *Amblotherium debilis* (YPM 13728), pl. 12 fig. 2

† *Amblotherium debilis* (YPM 13730), pl. 12 fig. 3

Amblotherium debilis (YPM 13734)

Amblotherium debilis (USNM 2726)

† *Amblotherium gracilis* (YPM 11883), pl. 11 fig. 3

† *Amblotherium gracilis* (USNM 2142) (type of *Laodon venustus*), pl. 27 fig. 8

† *Amblotherium gracilis* (USNM 2693), pl. 27 figs. 6, 7

† *Amblotherium gracilis* (YPM 13732), pl. 11 fig. 2

Amblotherium gracilis (YPM 13731)

Amblotherium gracilis (YPM 13733)

† *Amphidon superstes* (YPM 13638), figs. 17, 20; pl. 25 figs. 3, 4

† *Aploconodon comoënsis* (USNM 2791), pl. 22 fig. 3

† *Archaeotrigon brevimaxillus* (USNM 2793), pl. 27 figs. 4, 5

Archaeotrigon brevimaxillus (YPM 13648)

† *Archaeotrigon distagmus* (YPM 13641), pl. 7 fig. 1

† *Archaeotrigon* sp. (YPM 13640), pl. 7 fig. 2

Archaeotrigon sp. (YPM 13642)

† *Ctenacodon laticeps* (YPM 11761), fig. 6

† *Ctenacodon laticeps* (YPM 11761), pl. 2, fig. 3; pl. 3 figs. 1–3

Ctenacodon laticeps (USNM 2681)

Ctenacodon laticeps (USNM 2682)

Simpson, G. G. (*cont'd*)

† *Ctenacodon nanus* (YPM 11832), pl. 2 fig. 2

† *Ctenacodon scindens* (YPM 10366), pl. 1 fig. 2

† *Ctenacodon scindens* (AMNH 28063), pl. 27 fig. 1

† *Ctenacodon serratus* (YPM 11833), pl. 2 fig. 1

† *Ctenacodon serratus* (YPM 13668), pl. 1 fig. 1

Ctenacodon serratus (USNM 2688)

† *Ctenacodon* sp. (YPM 13666), pl. 1 fig. 3

Docodon affinis (USNM 2129)

† *Docodon crassus* (USNM 2130), pl. 30 fig. 4

† *Docodon striatus* (YPM 11823), pl. 16 fig. 3; pl. 17 fig. 1; pl. 29 fig. 5

† *Docodon superus* (YPM 10647), fig. 40; pl. 19 figs. 2, 3; pl. 20, fig. 1

† *Docodon superus* (YPM 13769), pl. 20 fig. 3

† *Docodon superus* (YPM 13770), pl. 20 fig. 2; pl. 21 figs. 1, 2

† *Docodon superus* (USNM 2715), pl. 31 figs. 1–3

† *Docodon victor* (YPM 11826), pl. 17 figs. 2, 3; pl. 30 figs. 1, 2

† *Docodon* sp. (YPM 13767), fig. 39

† *Docodon* sp. (YPM 10649), pl. 18 figs. 1, 2

† *Docodon* sp. (YPM 13734), pl. 18 fig. 3

† *Docodon* sp. (YPM 13737), pl. 19 fig. 1

† *Docodon* sp. (USNM 2707), pl. 30 fig. 3

† *Dryolestes priscus* (YPM 11820) (Q?), fig. 20

† *Dryolestes priscus* (USNM 2722), pl. 28 fig. 1

† *Dryolestes priscus* (YPM 11884) (type of *Stylacodon validus*), pl. 7 fig. 3

† *Dryolestes priscus* (YPM 10646), pl. 8 fig. 1; pl. 28 fig. 2

† *Eurylambda aequicrurius* (YPM 13639), pl. 25 fig. 5; pl. 26 fig. 1

† *Euthlastus cordiformis* (YPM 13755), fig. 32; pl. 16 fig. 1

† *Herpetairus* or *Melanodon* sp. (YPM 11819a) (type of *Dryolestes obtusus*), pl. 13 fig. 2

† *Herpetairus arcuatus* (YPM 11822), fig. 28; pl. 13 fig. 1

Herpetairus arcuatus (YPM 13740)

Herpetairus arcuatus (YPM 13739)

Herpetairus arcuatus (YPM 13742)

*?*Herpetairus humilis* (YPM 13745)

Herpetairus sp. (YPM 11819)

Herpetairus sp. (YPM 10656b)

† *Laolestes eminens* (YPM 10661), pl. 10 fig. 3

† *Laolestes eminens* (YPM 13719), pl. 8 fig. 2; pl. 28 fig. 3

† *Laolestes eminens* (YPM 13726), pl. 10 fig. 2

† *Laolestes eminens* (YPM 10662), pl. 9 figs. 2, 3; pl. 10 fig. 1

† *Laolestes eminens* (YPM 13720), pl. 9 fig. 1

† *Laolestes eminens* (USNM 2731), pl. 29 fig. 2

† *Laolestes eminens* (AMNH 3001), pl. 29 fig. 3

Laolestes eminens (USNM 2727)

† *Laolestes eminens* (YPM 13725), pl. 8 fig. 3

†**Laolestes grandis* (YPM 13727), pl. 11 fig. 1

† *Laolestes* sp. (USNM 2862), pl. 29, fig. 3

† *Malthacolestes osborni* (YPM 13751), fig. 34; pl. 15 fig. 3

† *Melanodon goodrichi* (YPM 13738), pl. 15 fig. 2

† *Melanodon goodrichi* (YPM 13748), pl. 15 fig. 1

† *Melanodon* (cf.) *goodrichi* (YPM 13749), pl. 15 fig. 1

† *Melanodon oweni* (YPM 10663), fig. 30; pl. 13 fig. 3; pl. 14 figs. 1–3

† *Miccylotyrans minimus* (USNM 2754), fig. 33

† *Paurodon valens* (USNM 2143), fig. 20; pl. 27 fig. 2

† *Pelicopsis dubius* (YPM 13754), fig. 35; pl. 16 fig. 2

† *Phascolodon gidleyi* (USNM 2703), pl. 22 figs. 1, 2

† *Priacodon ferox* (YPM 606), pl. 23 fig. 1

† *Priacodon ferox* (YPM 13626), pl. 24 figs. 1, 2

† *Priacodon grandaevus* (YPM 10349), pl. 24 fig. 3

† *Priacodon grandaevus* (USNM 2698), pl. 25 fig. 2

† *Priacodon lulli* (YPM 13625), pl. 24 fig. 4

† *Priacodon lulli* (YPM 10359), pl. 25 fig. 1

† *Priacodon robustus* (YPM 11846), fig. 20; pl. 22 figs. 9, 10

† *Priacodon robustus* (YPM 10343), pl. 22 fig. 8

† *Psalodon fortis* (YPM 11760), pl. 5 fig. 3

† *Psalodon marshi* (YPM 13672), pl. 4 fig. 1

Psalodon marshi (USNM 2684)

Psalodon marshi (USNM 2687)

Psalodon marshi (USNM 2690)

† *Psalodon marshi* (YPM 13669), pl. 4 fig. 2

Psalodon marshi (USNM 2679)

† *Psalodon potens* (YPM 11834), fig. 6

† *Psalodon potens* (YPM 10363), pl. 4 fig. 3

Psalodon potens (USNM 2680)

Psalodon potens (AMNH 3003)

† *Psalodon potens* (YPM 11834), pl. 5 figs. 1, 2

† *Tathiodon agilis* (YPM 13649), pl. 6 figs. 1–3

Simpson, G. G. (*cont'd*)

 † *Tinodon bellus* (YPM 11843), fig. 20; pl. 26 fig. 5
 Tinodon bellus (YPM 13644)
 † *Tinodon lepidus* (YPM 11845), pl. 26 fig. 4
 † *Tinodon lepidus* (USNM 2131) (type of *Menacodon rarus*), pl. 26 figs. 2, 3
 † *Trioracodon bisulcus* (YPM 10345), pl. 22 fig. 7
 † *Trioracodon bisulcus* (YPM 10344), pl. 23 fig. 4
 † *Trioracodon bisulcus* (USNM 2699), pl. 23 figs. 2, 3
 † *Trioracodon bisulcus* (YPM 11851), pl. 23 figs. 4, 5
 † *Trioracodon bisulcus* (YPM 10340), pl. 22 fig. 6

Vandebroek, G.

 1960/61 The comparative anatomy of the teeth of lower and nonspecialized mammals. International Colloquium on the Evolution of Lower and Nonspecialized Mammals. *Köninklijke Vlaamse Academie voor Wetenschappen Letteren en Schone Kunsten van België,* Brussells, 320 pp.
 Amblotherium gracilis (YPM 11883)
 † *Amblotherium* sp. (USNM 2764), fig. 28
 † *Archaeotrigon* sp. (YPM 13640), fig. 24
 † *Docodon crassus* (USNM 2130), fig. 29
 † *Docodon victor* (YPM 11826), fig. 30
 † *Docodon victor* (USNM 2707), pl. 9
 † *Docodon* sp. (YPM 14618), pl. 6
 † *Docodon* sp. (USNM 2715), pls. 7, 9
 † *Docodon* sp. (YPM 13767), pl. 8
 † *Docodon* sp. (YPM 13737), pl. 9
 † *Dryolestes priscus* (YPM 11884), fig. 25
 Dryolestes priscus (YPM 10646)
 Herpetairus arcuatus (YPM 13739)
 † *Laolestes eminens* (YPM 10662), fig. 27
 Laolestes eminens (YPM 13725)
 Malthacolestes osborni (YPM 13751)
 Melanodon oweni (YPM 10663)

White, T. E.

 1958 Braincase of *Camarasaurus lentus* (Marsh). *Jour. Paleont., 32,* 477–94.
 Camarasaurus grandis (YPM 1905, 1901) (Q1)
 Camarasaurus lentus (YPM 1910) (Q13W)
 Camarasaurus robustus (YPM 1902) (Q1)

REFERENCES

PUBLISHED SOURCES

COPE, E. D. On a gigantic saurian from the Dakota epoch of Colorado. *Paleont.*
1877   *Bull.* No. 25, pp. 5–10 (*Camarasaurus supremus*).

LOOMIS, F. B. On Jurassic stratigraphy in southeastern Wyoming. *Bull. Amer.*
1901   *Museum Nat. Hist., 14,* 189–97.

MARSH, O. C. Notice of a new and gigantic dinosaur. *Amer. Jour. Sci.* (3) *14,*
1877   87–88 (*Titanosaurus montanus*).

————— New order of extinct Reptilia (Stegosauria) from the Jurassic of
1877   the Rocky Mountains. *Amer. Jour. Sci.* (3) *14,* 513–14 (*Stegosaurus armatus*).

————— Notice of new dinosaurian reptiles from the Jurassic Formation.
1877   *Amer. Jour. Sci.* (3) *14,* 514–16 (*Morosaurus grandis, Apatosaurus ajax*).

————— Notice of new dinosaurian reptiles. *Amer. Jour. Sci.* (3) *15,* 241–44
1878   (*Atlantosaurus immanis*).

————— Principal characters of American Jurassic dinosaurs. Part I. *Amer.*
1878   *Jour. Sci.* (3) *16,* 411–16 (*Diplodocus longus, Morosaurus robustus*).

————— Principal characters of American Jurassic dinosaurs. Part II. *Amer.*
1879   *Jour. Sci.* (3) *17,* 86–92 (*Apatosaurus laticollis*).

————— Notice of new Jurassic reptiles. *Amer. Jour. Sci.* (3) *18,* 501–05
1879   (*Brontosaurus excelsus, Stegosaurus ungulatus*).

————— Principal characters of American Jurassic dinosaurs. Part V. *Amer.*
1881   *Jour. Sci.* (3) *21,* 417–23 (*Brontosaurus amplus*).

————— Principal characters of American Jurassic dinosaurs. Part VI. Restoration of *Brontosaurus. Amer. Jour. Sci.* (3) *26,* 81–85.
1883

————— Principal characters of American Jurassic dinosaurs. Part IX. The
1887   skull and dermal armor of *Stegosaurus. Amer. Jour. Sci.* (3) *34,* 413–17 (*Stegosaurus stenops, S. sulcatus, S. duplex*).

————— Notice of new American dinosaurs. *Amer. Jour. Sci.* (3) *37,* 331–36
1889   (*Morosaurus lentus*).

————— Dinosaurs of North America, *U.S. Geol. Survey, 16th Annual Report,* Part II, pp. 133–415.
1896

SCHUCHERT, C., AND C. M. LEVENE. *O. C. Marsh, Pioneer in Paleontology.*
1940   Yale University Press, New Haven, 541 pp.

Unpublished Correspondence[1,2]

Ashley, E. G. (1880–83)

Beck, William (1884–87)

Brown, Fred (1880–89)

Carlin, William E. ("Edwards") (1877–78)

"Edwards" (William Edward Carlin) (1877–78)

"Harlow" (William Harlow Reed) (1877–78)

Kellum, A. B. (1884–87)

Kennedy, E. (1880–85)

Kenney, John L. (1882–84)

Kessler, Henry (1882–93)

Lakes, Arthur (1877–80)

Phelps, William E. (1883)

Reed, William H. ("Harlow") (1877–83)

Williston, Frank H. (1878–80)

Williston, Samuel W. (1877–78)

1. Correspondence from these men to Marsh is preserved among the memorabilia of the Peabody Museum.

2. Dates listed after collectors' names indicate the years each actively collected for Marsh, either at Como Bluff or elsewhere.

INDEX